FORMAL LANGUAGES
AND THEIR RELATION TO AUTOMATA

FORMAL LANGUAGES
AND THEIR RELATION TO AUTOMATA

JOHN E. HOPCROFT
Cornell University, Ithaca, New York

JEFFREY D. ULLMAN
Bell Telephone Laboratories, Murray Hill, New Jersey

ADDISON-WESLEY PUBLISHING COMPANY
Reading, Massachusetts · Menlo Park, California · London · Don Mills, Ontario

This book is in the
**ADDISON-WESLEY SERIES
IN COMPUTER SCIENCE AND INFORMATION PROCESSING**

Consulting Editors
MICHAEL A. HARRISON
RICHARD S. VARGA

PREFACE

The study of formal languages constitutes an important subarea of computer science. This area sprang to life around 1956 when Noam Chomsky gave a mathematical model of a grammar in connection with his study of natural languages. Shortly afterwards, the concept of a grammar was found to be of great importance to the programmer when the syntax of the programming language ALGOL was defined by a context-free grammar. This development led naturally to syntax-directed compiling and the concept of a compiler compiler. Since then a considerable flurry of activity has taken place, the results of which have related formal languages and automata theory to such an extent that it is impossible to treat the areas separately. By now, no serious study of computer science would be complete without a knowledge of the techniques and results from language and automata theory.

This book presents the theory of formal languages as a coherent theory and makes explicit its relationship to automata. The book begins with an explanation of the notion of a finite description of a language. The fundamental descriptive device—the grammar—is explained, as well as its three major subclasses—regular, context-free, and context-sensitive grammars. The context-free grammars are treated in detail, and such topics as normal forms, derivation trees, and ambiguity are covered. Four types of automata equivalent to the four types of grammars are described. These automata are the finite automaton, the pushdown automaton, the linear bounded automaton, and the Turing machine. The Turing machine is covered in detail, and unsolvability of the halting problem shown. The book concludes with certain advanced topics in language theory—closure properties, computational complexity, deterministic pushdown automata, $LR(k)$ grammars, stack automata, and decidability.

The emphasis is on ideas and ease of understanding rather than undue formalism. In some cases the details of long and tedious proofs are omitted. However, in all cases sufficient intuitive explanation is given so that the reader may easily provide the rigorous proof if desired.

The book is intended primarily as a textbook for a first or second year graduate course in formal languages. It is self-contained and presupposes only the normal level of maturity expected of a beginning graduate student.

Although not essential, it has been found that a course in finite state machines or Turing machines is useful preparation. The book is not intended as a research monogram on formal languages, although it covers many of the known results, and much of the material presented previously existed only in journals of mathematics and computer science. The chapters are provided with a guide to references on the material covered and related topics. The problems are an integral part of the text and their difficulty ranges from almost trivial to extremely difficult.

The material for this book is based upon class notes for courses in language theory taught by the authors at Princeton, Columbia, and Cornell. The authors would like to thank the many people who offered their suggestions and criticism. In particular, we would like to thank A. V. Aho, S. Amoroso, A. Korenjak, and M. Harrison. Thanks are also due to Bell Telephone Laboratories, and Princeton and Cornell Universities for providing the facilities for the preparation of the work.

J. E. H.
J. D. U.

CONTENTS

vii

CHAPTER 1

LANGUAGES AND THEIR REPRESENTATIONS

1.1 ALPHABETS AND LANGUAGES

What is the theory of languages? To answer this question we first ask: What is a language? Webster defines a language as "the body of words and methods of combining words used and understood by a considerable community." However, this definition is not sufficiently precise for building a mathematical theory of languages. Thus we shall define a formal language abstractly as a mathematical system. This formality will enable us to make rigorous statements about formal languages and to develop a body of knowledge which can then be applied to those languages which are suitably modeled. With these ideas in mind, we make the following definitions.

An *alphabet* or *vocabulary* is any finite set of symbols. Although a noncountably infinite number of symbols exists, we shall consider only a countably infinite† subset from which all finite sets will be drawn. This subset will include digits, the Latin and Greek letters both upper and lower case (possibly with combinations of subscripts, superscripts, underscores, etc.), and special symbols such as $\#$, $\cent$, and so on. Any countable number of additional symbols that the reader finds convenient may be added. Some examples of alphabets are the Latin alphabet, $\{A, B, C, \ldots, Z\}$, the Greek alphabet, $\{\alpha, \beta, \gamma, \ldots, \omega\}$, and the binary alphabet, $\{0, 1\}$.

A *sentence* over an alphabet is any string of finite length composed of symbols from the alphabet. Synonyms for sentence are *string* and *word*. The empty sentence, ϵ, is the sentence consisting of no symbols. If V is an alphabet, then V^* denotes the set of all sentences composed of symbols of V, including the empty sentence. We use V^+ to denote the set $V^* - \{\epsilon\}$. Thus, if $V = \{0, 1\}$, then $V^* = \{\epsilon, 0, 1, 00, 01, 10, 11, 000, \ldots\}$ and $V^+ = \{0, 1, 00, \ldots\}$.

A *language* is any set of sentences over an alphabet. Most languages of interest will contain an infinite number of sentences. Three important questions are raised.

First, how do we represent (i.e., specify the sentences of) a language? If the language contains only a finite number of sentences, the answer is easy.

---

† A set is countably infinite if it is in one-to-one correspondence with the integers (i.e., if it makes sense to talk about the ith element of the set).

One simply lists the finite set of sentences. On the other hand, if the language is infinite, we are faced with the problem of finding a finite representation for the language. This finite representation will itself usually be a string of symbols over some alphabet, together with some understood interpretation which associates a particular representation with a given language.

Second, does there exist a finite representation for every language? One would suspect that the answer is no. We shall see that the set of all sentences over an alphabet is countably infinite. A language is any subset of the set of all such sentences. It is a well-known fact of set theory that the set of all subsets of a countably infinite set is not countably infinite. Although we have not defined what constitutes a finite representation, we intuitively feel that any meaningful definition of a finite representation will result only in a countable number of finite representations, since one should be able to write down any such representation as some string of symbols. Thus, there are many more languages than finite representations.

Third, we might ask what can be said about the structure of those classes of languages for which there exist finite representations. Much of this book will be devoted to presenting various systems of representing and characterizing these classes of languages.

1.2 PROCEDURES AND ALGORITHMS

Before discussing the idea of a finite representation we informally introduce the concepts of a procedure and an algorithm. A _procedure_ is a finite sequence of instructions that can be mechanically carried out, such as a computer program.

We are somewhat vague in our definition of a procedure. We give a formal definition in Chapter 6 in terms of Turing machines. For the time being, if we cannot determine whether or not a step can be mechanically carried out, then we reduce the step to a sequence of simpler steps which we can determine can be carried out. For example, we might object to the step "Find the smallest integer, x, satisfying such and such a condition," unless it was obvious how to find the smallest x. Even if one knows that such a smallest x must exist, it may not be possible to find the x by mechanical means.

An example of a procedure which determines if an integer i, greater than one, is prime is given in Fig. 1.1. A second example of a procedure is given in Fig. 1.2; this procedure determines, for an integer i, whether there exists a perfect number† greater than i.

---

† A perfect number is an integer which is equal to the sum of all its divisors except itself. Thus 6 is a perfect number since $1 + 2 + 3 = 6$. 12 is not perfect since its divisors are 1, 2, 3, 4, and 6, which sum to 16.

Note that the first procedure will terminate for all values of i, since either a value of j will be reached which divides i, or j will eventually become equal to or greater than i. In either case the procedure terminates and tells us whether i is prime. A procedure which always terminates is called an *algorithm*. Thus we refer to the procedure of Fig. 1.1 as an algorithm for determining if an integer greater than one is prime.

Instructions:

1. Set $j = 2$.
2. If $j \geqq i$, then halt. i is prime.
3. If i/j is an integer, then halt. i is not prime.
4. Set $j = j + 1$.
5. Go back to Instruction 2.

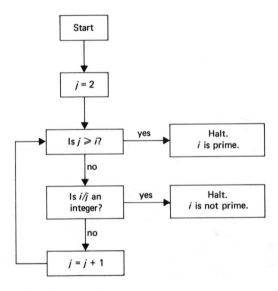

Fig. 1.1. A procedure for determining whether an integer greater than one is prime.

The second procedure need not always terminate. If there are only a finite number of perfect numbers,† then the procedure will not stop for any integer larger than the largest perfect number. Rather the procedure will keep testing larger and larger k, looking for another perfect number. In other words, if i is such that there is a perfect number greater than i, the procedure will find it. However, if no such perfect number exists, the procedure will run forever. As long as the procedure continues to run, we have

---

† The question of whether or not there are an infinity of perfect numbers is an unsolved problem of number theory.

Instructions:

1.   Set $k = i$.
2.   Set $k = k + 1$.
3.   Set sum $= 0$.
4.   Set $j = 1$.
5.   If $j < k$, then go to Instruction 8.
6.   If sum $\neq k$, then go to Instruction 2.
7.   Halt. k is a perfect number greater than i.
8.   If k/j is not an integer, then go to Instruction 10.
9.   Set sum $=$ sum $+ j$.
10. Set $j = j + 1$.
11. Go to Instruction 5.

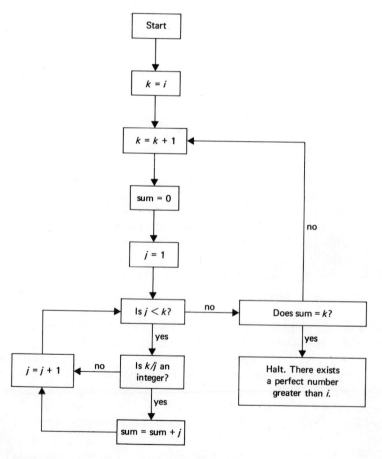

Fig. 1.2. A procedure for determining if there is a perfect number greater than i.

no way of knowing if it will eventually halt. Thus we may say that the procedure determines if there exists a perfect number greater than a given integer in the sense that, if such a perfect number exists, the procedure will eventually supply an affirmative answer. If no such perfect number exists, the procedure will supply no answer at all, since at no time do we know if the procedure might halt at some later time.

1.3 REPRESENTATIONS OF LANGUAGES

Let us now return to the problem of finite representations for languages. One way to represent a language is to give an algorithm which determines if a sentence is in the language or not. A more general way is to give a procedure which halts with the answer "yes" for sentences in the language and either does not terminate or else halts with the answer "no" for sentences not in the language. Such a procedure or algorithm is said to *recognize* the language. In Chapter 7 we see that there are languages we can recognize by a procedure, but not by any algorithm.

These above methods represent languages from a recognition point of view. We can also represent languages from a generative point of view. That is, we can give a procedure which systematically generates successive sentences of the language in some order.

If we can recognize the sentences of a language over alphabet V with either an algorithm or a procedure, then we can generate the language, since we can systematically generate all sentences in V^*, test each sentence to see if it is in the language, and output in a list only those sentences in the language. One must be careful in doing so. For if we generate the sentences in order and use a procedure which does not always halt for testing the sentences, we never get beyond the first sentence for which the procedure does not halt. The way to get around this problem is to organize the testing in such a manner that the procedure never continues to test one sentence forever. This organization requires that we introduce several constructions.

Assume that there are p symbols in V. We can think of the sentences of V^* as numbers represented in base p, plus the empty sentence ϵ. We can number the sentences in order of increasing length and in "numerical" order for sentences of the same length. In Fig. 1.3 we have the enumeration of the sentences of $\{a, b, c\}^*$. We have implicitly assumed that a, b, and c correspond to 0, 1, and 2, respectively. (This argument shows that the set of sentences over an alphabet is countable, as we have claimed.)

Let P be a procedure for testing a sentence to see if the sentence is in a language L. We assume that P can be broken down into discrete steps so that it makes sense to talk about the ith step in the procedure for any given sentence. Before giving a procedure to enumerate the sentences of L, we first give a procedure to enumerate pairs of positive integers.

1	ϵ
2	a
3	b
4	c
5	aa
6	ab
7	ac
8	ba
9	bb
⋮	⋮

		1	2	y 3	4	5
	1	1	3	6	10	15
	2	2	5	9	14	
x	3	4	8	13	.	
	4	7	12		.	
	5	11			.	

$$z(x, y)$$

Fig. 1.3. The enumeration of sentences in $\{a, b, c\}^*$.

Fig. 1.4. Mapping of ordered pairs of integers onto the integers.

We can map all ordered pairs of positive integers (x, y) onto the set of positive integers as shown in Fig. 1.4 by the formula

$$z = \frac{(x + y - 1)(x + y - 2)}{2} + y.$$

We can enumerate ordered pairs of integers according to the assigned value of z. Thus the first few pairs are $(1, 1)$, $(2, 1)$, $(1, 2)$, $(3, 1)$, $(2, 2)$, ... Given any pair of integers (i, j), it will eventually appear in the list. In fact, it will be the $\dfrac{(i + j - 1)(i + j - 2)}{2} + j$th pair enumerated. This technique of enumerating ordered pairs will be used throughout the book.

We can now give a procedure for enumerating the strings of L. Enumerate ordered pairs of integers. When the pair (i, j) is enumerated, generate the ith sentence in V^* and apply the first j steps of procedure P to the sentence. Whenever it is determined that a generated sentence is in L, add that sentence to the list of members of L. If word i is in L, it will be so determined by P in j steps, for some finite j. When (i, j) is enumerated, word i will be generated. It is easy to see that this procedure will indeed enumerate all sentences in L.

If we have a procedure for generating the sentences of a language, then we can construct a procedure for recognizing the sentences of the language, but not necessarily an algorithm. To determine if a sentence x is in L, simply enumerate the sentences of L and compare x with each sentence. If x is generated, the procedure halts, having recognized x as being in L. Of course, if x is not in L, the procedure will never terminate.

A language whose sentences can be generated by a procedure is said to be _recursively enumerable_. Alternatively, a language is said to be recursively enumerable if there is a procedure for recognizing the sentences of the language. A language is said to be _recursive_ if there exists an algorithm for recognizing the language. As we shall see in Chapter 7, the class of recursive languages is a proper subset of the class of recursively enumerable languages. Furthermore, there are languages which are not even recursively enumerable.

That is, there are languages for which we cannot even effectively list the sentences of the language.

Returning to the original question, "What is language theory?," we can say that language theory is the study of sets of strings of symbols, their representations, structures, and properties. Beyond this, we shall leave the question to be answered by the remaining chapters.

PROBLEMS

1.1 The function

$$J(x, y) = \frac{(x + y - 1)(x + y - 2)}{2} + y$$

maps ordered pairs of integers onto the integers. Find the inverse functions K and L with the property that $K(J(x, y)) = x$ and $L(J(x, y)) = y$.

1.2 Let $\hat{J}(w, x, y) = J(w, J(x, y))$. What triple is assigned the number 1000?

1.3 Describe a simple procedure for enumerating the sentences of a recursive language.

1.4 Prove that if a language and its complement are both recursively enumerable, then the language is recursive.

1.5 Prove that if there exists a procedure for enumerating a set of integers in a monotonic order, then the set is recursive in the sense that there is an algorithm to determine if an integer is in the set.

1.6 Show that all finite sets are recursive.

CHAPTER 2

GRAMMARS

2.1 MOTIVATION

There is one class of generating systems of primary interest to us—systems known as grammars. The concept of a grammar was originally formalized by linguists in their study of natural languages. Linguists were concerned not only with defining precisely what is or is not a valid sentence of a language, but also with providing structural descriptions of the sentences. One of their goals was to develop a formal grammar capable of describing English.

It was hoped that if, for example, one had a formal grammar to describe the English language, one could use the computer in ways that require it to "understand" English. Such a use might be language translation or the computer solution of word problems.

To date, this goal is for the most part unrealized. We still do not have a definitive grammar for English, and there is even disagreement as to what types of formal grammar are capable of describing English. However, in describing computer languages, better results have been achieved. For

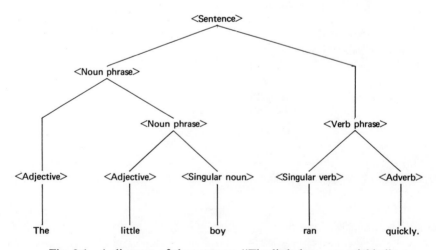

Fig. 2.1. A diagram of the sentence "The little boy ran quickly."

example, the Backus Normal Form used to describe ALGOL is a "context-free grammar," a type of grammar with which we shall deal.

We are all familiar with the idea of diagramming or parsing an English sentence. For example, the sentence "The little boy ran quickly" is parsed by noting that the sentence consists of the noun phrase "The little boy" followed by the verb phrase "ran quickly." The noun phrase is then broken down into the singular noun "boy" modified by the two adjectives "The" and "little." The verb phrase is broken down into the singular verb "ran" modified by the adverb "quickly." This sentence structure is indicated in the diagram of Fig. 2.1. We recognize the sentence structure as being grammatically correct. If we had a complete set of rules for parsing all English sentences, then we would have a technique for determining whether or not a sentence is grammatically correct. However, such a set does not exist. Part of the reason for this stems from the fact that there are no clear rules for determining precisely what constitutes a sentence.

The rules we applied to parsing the above sentence can be written in the following form:

$$\langle\text{sentence}\rangle \rightarrow \langle\text{noun phrase}\rangle \langle\text{verb phrase}\rangle$$
$$\langle\text{noun phrase}\rangle \rightarrow \langle\text{adjective}\rangle \langle\text{noun phrase}\rangle$$
$$\langle\text{noun phrase}\rangle \rightarrow \langle\text{adjective}\rangle \langle\text{singular noun}\rangle$$
$$\langle\text{verb phrase}\rangle \rightarrow \langle\text{singular verb}\rangle \langle\text{adverb}\rangle$$
$$\langle\text{adjective}\rangle \rightarrow \text{The}$$
$$\langle\text{adjective}\rangle \rightarrow \text{little}$$
$$\langle\text{singular noun}\rangle \rightarrow \text{boy}$$
$$\langle\text{singular verb}\rangle \rightarrow \text{ran}$$
$$\langle\text{adverb}\rangle \rightarrow \text{quickly}$$

The arrow in the above rules indicates that the item to the left of the arrow can generate the items to the right of the arrow. Note that we have enclosed the names of the parts of the sentence such as noun, verb, verb phrase, etc., in brackets to avoid confusion with the English words and phrases "noun," "verb," "verb phrase," etc.

One should note that we cannot only test sentences for their grammatical correctness, but can also generate grammatically correct sentences by starting with the quantity ⟨sentence⟩ and replacing ⟨sentence⟩ by ⟨noun phrase⟩ followed by ⟨verb phrase⟩. Next we select one of the two rules for ⟨noun phrase⟩ and apply it, and so on, until no further application of the rules is possible. In this way any one of an infinite number of sentences can be derived—that is, any sentence consisting of a string of occurrences of "the" and "little" followed by "boy ran quickly" such as "little the the boy ran quickly" can be generated. Most of the sentences do not make sense but, nevertheless, are grammatically correct in a broad sense.

2.2 THE FORMAL NOTION OF A GRAMMAR

Let us formalize the partial grammar for English which was mentioned in Section 2.1. Four concepts were present. First, there were certain syntactic categories—⟨singular noun⟩, ⟨verb phrase⟩, ⟨sentence⟩, etc., from which strings of words could be derived. The objects corresponding to syntactic categories we call "nonterminals" or "variables." Second, there were the words themselves. The objects which play the role of words we shall call "terminals."

The third concept is the relation that exists between various strings of variables and terminals. These relationships we call "productions." Examples of productions are ⟨noun phrase⟩ → ⟨adjective⟩ ⟨noun phrase⟩ or ⟨singular noun⟩ ⟨singular predicate⟩ → ⟨singular noun⟩ ⟨adverb⟩ ⟨singular verb⟩. Finally, one nonterminal is distinguished, in that it generates exactly those strings of terminals that are deemed in the language. In our example, ⟨sentence⟩ is distinguished. We call the distinguished nonterminal the "sentence" or "start" symbol.

Formally, we denote a *grammar* G by (V_N, V_T, P, S). The symbols V_N, V_T, P, and S are, respectively, the *variables*, *terminals*, *productions*, and *start symbol*. V_N, V_T, and P are finite sets. We assume that V_N and V_T contain no elements in common; that is,

$$V_N \cap V_T = \varphi\dagger.$$

We conventionally denote $V_N \cup V_T$ by V.

The set of productions P consists of expressions of the form $\alpha \to \beta$, where α is a string in V^+ and β is a string in V^*. Finally, S is always a symbol in V_N.

Customarily, we shall use capital Latin-alphabet letters for variables. Lower case letters at the beginning of the Latin alphabet are used for terminals. Strings of terminals are denoted by lower case letters near the end of the Latin alphabet, and strings of variables and terminals are denoted by lower case Greek letters.

We have presented a grammar, $G = (V_N, V_T, P, S)$, but have not yet defined the language it generates. To do so, we need the relations $\underset{G}{\Rightarrow}$ and $\underset{G}{\overset{*}{\Rightarrow}}$ between strings in V^*. Specifically, if $\alpha \to \beta$ is a production of P and γ and δ are any strings in V^*, then $\gamma\alpha\delta \underset{G}{\Rightarrow} \gamma\beta\delta\ddagger$. We say that the production $\alpha \to \beta$ is applied to the string $\gamma\alpha\delta$ to obtain $\gamma\beta\delta$. Thus $\underset{G}{\Rightarrow}$ relates two strings exactly when the second is obtained from the first by the application of a single production.

---

† φ denotes the empty set.

‡ Say $\gamma\alpha\delta$ *directly derives* $\gamma\beta\delta$ in grammar G.

Suppose that $\alpha_1, \alpha_2, \ldots, \alpha_m$ are strings in V^*, and $\alpha_1 \underset{G}{\Rightarrow} \alpha_2$, $\alpha_2 \underset{G}{\Rightarrow} \alpha_3$, $\ldots, \alpha_{m-1} \underset{G}{\Rightarrow} \alpha_m$. Then we say $\alpha_1 \underset{G}{\overset{*}{\Rightarrow}} \alpha_m$.† In simple terms, we say for two strings α and β that $\alpha \underset{G}{\overset{*}{\Rightarrow}} \beta$ if we can obtain β from α by application of some number of productions of P. By convention, $\alpha \underset{G}{\overset{*}{\Rightarrow}} \alpha$ for each string α.

We define the *language generated by G* [denoted $L(G)$] to be $\{w \mid w$ is in V_T^* and $S \underset{G}{\overset{*}{\Rightarrow}} w\}$.‡ That is, a string is in $L(G)$ if:

1. The string consists solely of terminals.
2. The string can be derived from S.

A string of terminals and nonterminals α is called a *sentential form* if $S \overset{*}{\Rightarrow} \alpha$. (Usually, if it is clear which grammar G is involved, we use $\Rightarrow$ for $\underset{G}{\Rightarrow}$ and $\overset{*}{\Rightarrow}$ for $\underset{G}{\overset{*}{\Rightarrow}}$.)

We define grammars G_1 and G_2 to be *equivalent* if $L(G_1) = L(G_2)$.

Example 2.1. Let us consider a grammar $G = (V_N, V_T, P, S)$, where $V_N = \{S\}$, $V_T = \{0, 1\}$, $P = \{S \rightarrow 0S1, S \rightarrow 01\}$. Here, S is the only variable, 0 and 1 are terminals. There are two productions, $S \rightarrow 0S1$ and $S \rightarrow 01$. By applying the first production $n - 1$ times, followed by an application of the second production, we have

$$S \Rightarrow 0S1 \Rightarrow 00S11 \Rightarrow 0^3 S1^3 \Rightarrow \cdots \Rightarrow 0^{n-1}S1^{n-1} \Rightarrow 0^n 1^n.§$$

Furthermore, these are the only strings in $L(G)$. After using the second production, we find that the number of S's in the sentential form decreases by one. Each time the first production is used, the number of S's remains the same. Thus, after using $S \rightarrow 01$, no S's remain in the resulting string. Since both productions have an S on the left, the only order in which the productions can be applied is $S \rightarrow 0S1$ some number of times followed by one application of $S \rightarrow 01$. Thus, $L(G) = \{0^n 1^n \mid n \geq 1\}$.

Example 2.1 was a simple example of a grammar. It was relatively easy to determine which words were derivable and which were not. In general, it may be exceedingly hard to determine what is generated by the grammar. Here is another, more difficult, example.

---

† Say α_1 *derives* α_m in grammar G.
‡ We shall often use the notation $L = \{x \mid \varphi(x)\}$, where $\varphi(x)$ is some statement about x, to define languages. It stands for "the set of all x such that $\varphi(x)$ is true." Sometimes, x itself will have some special form. For example, $\{ww \mid w$ is in $V^*\}$ is the set of words of V^* whose first half and second half are the same.
§ If w is any string, w^i will stand for w repeated i times. So $0^3 = 000$. Note: $w^0 = \epsilon$.

Example 2.2. Let $G = (V_N, V_T, P, S)$, $V_N = \{S, B, C\}$, $V_T = \{a, b, c\}$. P consists of the following productions:

1.	$S \rightarrow aSBC$	5.	$bB \rightarrow bb$
2.	$S \rightarrow aBC$	6.	$bC \rightarrow bc$
3.	$CB \rightarrow BC$	7.	$cC \rightarrow cc$
4.	$aB \rightarrow ab$		

The language $L(G)$ contains the word $a^n b^n c^n$ for each $n \geq 1$, since we can use production (1) $n - 1$ times to get $S \xrightarrow{*} a^{n-1}S(BC)^{n-1}$. Then, we use production (2) to get $S \xrightarrow{*} a^n(BC)^n$. Production (3) enables us to arrange the B's and C's so that all B's precede all C's. For example, if $n = 3$,

$$aaaBCBCBC \Rightarrow aaaBBCCBC \Rightarrow aaaBBCBCC \Rightarrow aaaBBBCCC.$$

Thus, $S \xrightarrow{*} a^n B^n C^n$.

Next we use production (4) once to get $S \xrightarrow{*} a^n b B^{n-1} C^n$. Then use production (5) $n - 1$ times to get $S \xrightarrow{*} a^n b^n C^n$. Finally, use production (6) once and production (7) $n - 1$ times to get $S \xrightarrow{*} a^n b^n c^n$.

Now, let us show that the words $a^n b^n c^n$ for $n \geq 1$ are the only terminal strings in $L(G)$. In any derivation beginning with S, until we use production (2), we cannot use (4), (5), (6), or (7), for each of productions (4) through (7) requires a terminal immediately to the left of a B or C. Until production (2) is used, all strings derived consist of a's followed by an S, followed by B's and C's.

After (2) is used, the string consists of n a's, for some $n \geq 1$, followed by n B's and n C's in some order. Now no S's appear in the string, so productions (1) and (2) may no longer be used. Note that the form of the string is all terminals followed by all variables. After applying any of productions (3) through (7), we see that the string will still have that property. Note that (4) through (7) are only applicable at the boundary between terminals and variables. Each has the effect of converting one B to b or one C to c. Production (3) causes B's to migrate to the left, and C's to the right.

Suppose that a C is converted to c before all B's are converted to b's. Then the string can be written as $a^n b^i c\alpha$, where $i < n$ and α is a string of B's and C's, but not all C's. Now, only productions (3) and (7) may be applied; (7) at the interface between terminals and variables, and (3) among the variables. We may use (3) to reorder the B's and C's of α, but not to remove any B's. Production (7) can convert C's to c's at the interface, but eventually, a B will be the leftmost variable. There is no production that can change the B, so this string can never result in a string with no variables.

We conclude that all B's must be converted to b's at the interface between terminals and variables before any C's are converted to c's. Thus, from a^n followed by n B's and n C's in any order, $a^n b^n c^n$ is the only derivable terminal string. Therefore, $L(G) = \{a^n b^n c^n \mid n \geq 1\}$.

2.3 THE TYPES OF GRAMMARS

$\alpha \rightarrow \beta$ no restrictions

We call the type of grammar we have defined a *type 0 grammar*. Certain restrictions can be made on the nature of the productions of a grammar to give three other types of grammars, sometimes called types 1, 2, and 3.

Let $G = (V_N, V_T, P, S)$ be a grammar. Suppose that for every production $\alpha \rightarrow \beta$ in P, $|\beta| \geq |\alpha|$.† Then the grammar G is *type 1* or *context sensitive*. We shall use the latter name more often than the former.

$2 \Rightarrow 1$

As an example, consider the grammar discussed in Example 2.2. Each of the seven productions of the grammar has at least as many symbols on the right as on the left. So, this grammar is context sensitive. Likewise the grammar in Example 2.1 is also context sensitive.

Some authors require that the productions of a context-sensitive grammar be of the form $\alpha_1 A \alpha_2 \rightarrow \alpha_1 \beta \alpha_2$, with α_1, α_2 and β in V^*, $\beta \neq \epsilon$ and A in V_N. It can be shown that this restriction does not change the class of languages generated. However, it does motivate the name context sensitive since the production $\alpha_1 A \alpha_2 \rightarrow \alpha_1 \beta \alpha_2$ allows A to be replaced by β whenever A appears in the context of α_1 and α_2.

Let $G = (V_N, V_T, P, S)$. Suppose that for every production $\alpha \rightarrow \beta$ in P,

1. α is a single variable.   2. β is any string other than ϵ.

Then the grammar is called *type 2* or *context free*. Note that a production of the form $A \rightarrow \beta$ allows the variable A to be replaced by the string β independent of the context in which the A appears. Hence the name context free.

Example 2.3. Let us consider an interesting context-free grammar. It is $G = (V_N, V_T, P, S)$, where $V_N = \{S, A, B\}$, $V_T = \{a, b\}$ and P consists of the following.

$$
\begin{array}{ll}
S \rightarrow aB & A \rightarrow bAA \\
S \rightarrow bA & B \rightarrow b \\
A \rightarrow a & B \rightarrow bS \\
A \rightarrow aS & B \rightarrow aBB
\end{array}
$$

The grammar G is context free since for each production, the left-hand side is a single variable and the right-hand side is a nonempty string of terminals and variables.

The language $L(G)$ is the set of all words in V_T^+ consisting of an equal number of a's and b's. We shall prove this statement by induction on the length of a word.

Inductive Hypothesis. For w in V_T^+,

1. $S \overset{*}{\Rightarrow} w$ if and only if w consists of an equal number of a's and b's.

2. $A \overset{*}{\Rightarrow} w$ if and only if w has one more a than it has b's.

3. $B \overset{*}{\Rightarrow} w$ if and only if w has one more b than it has a's.

---

† We use $|x|$ to stand for the length, or number of symbols in the string x.

The inductive hypothesis is certainly true if $|w| = 1$, since $A \xrightarrow{*} a$, $B \xrightarrow{*} b$, and no terminal string of length one is derivable from S. Also, no strings of length one, other than a and b are derivable from A and B, respectively.

Suppose that the inductive hypothesis is true for all w of length $k - 1$ or less. We shall show that it is true for $|w| = k$. First, if $S \xrightarrow{*} w$, then the derivation must begin with either $S \to aB$ or $S \to bA$. In the first case, w is of the form aw_1, where $|w_1| = k - 1$ and $B \xrightarrow{*} w_1$. By the inductive hypothesis, the number of b's in w_1 is one more than the number of a's, so w consists of an equal number of a's and b's. A similar argument prevails if the derivation begins with $S \to bA$.

We must now prove the "only if" of part (1), that is, if $|w| = k$ and w consists of an equal number of a's and b's, then $S \xrightarrow{*} w$. Either the first symbol of w is a or it is b. Assume that $w = aw_1$. Now $|w_1| = k - 1$, and w_1 has one more b than a. By the inductive hypothesis, $B \xrightarrow{*} w_1$. But then $S \Rightarrow aB \xrightarrow{*} aw_1 = w$. A similar argument prevails if the first symbol of w is b.

Our task is not done. To complete the proof, we must show parts (2) and (3) of the inductive hypothesis for w of length k. These parts are proved in a manner similar to our method of proof for part (1). They will be left to the reader.

Let $G = (V_N, V_T, P, S)$ be a grammar. Suppose that every production in P is of the form $A \to aB$ or $A \to a$, where A and B are variables and a is a terminal. Then G is called a _type 3_ or _regular_ grammar. In Chapter 3, we shall introduce the finite state machine and see that the languages generated by type 3 grammars are precisely the sets accepted by finite-state machines.

Example 2.4. Consider the grammar $G = (\{S, A, B\}, \{0, 1\}, P, S)$, where P consists of the following:

$$
\begin{array}{ll}
^1 S \to 0A & ^6 B \to 1B \\
^2 S \to 1B & ^7 B \to 1 \\
^3 A \to 0A & ^8 B \to 0 \\
^4 A \to 0S & ^9 S \to 0 \\
^5 A \to 1B &
\end{array}
$$

Clearly G is a regular grammar. We shall not describe $L(G)$, but rather leave it to the reader to determine what is generated and prove his conclusion.

It should be clear that every regular grammar is context free; every context-free grammar is context sensitive; every context-sensitive grammar is type 0. We shall call a language that can be generated by a type 0 grammar a *type 0 language*. A language generated by a context-sensitive, context-free, or regular grammar is a *context-sensitive, context-free*, or *regular language*, respectively.

We shall abbreviate context-sensitive, context-free, and regular grammar by csg, cfg, and rg,† respectively. Context-sensitive and context-free languages are abbreviated csl and cfl, respectively. In line with current practice, a type 3 or regular language will often be called a *regular set*. A type 0 language is abbreviated r.e. set, for *recursively enumerable set*. It shall be seen later that the languages generated by type 0 grammars correspond, intuitively to the languages which can be enumerated by finitely described procedures.

2.4 THE EMPTY SENTENCE

We might note that, as defined here, ϵ can be in no csl, cfl, or regular set. Recalling that our motivation for thinking of grammars was to find finite descriptions for languages, we would have to agree that if L had a finite description, $L_1 = L \cup \{\epsilon\}$ would likewise have a finite description. We could add "ϵ is also in L_1" to the description of L to get a finite description of L_1.

We shall extend our definition of csg, cfg, and rg to allow productions of the form $S \rightarrow \epsilon$, where S is the start symbol, provided that S does not appear on the right-hand side of any production. In this case, it is clear that the production $S \rightarrow \epsilon$ can only be used as the first step in a derivation. We shall use the following lemma.

> **Lemma 2.1.** If $G = (V_N, V_T, P, S)$ is a context-sensitive grammar, then there is another csg G_1 generating the same language as G, for which the start symbol of G_1 does not appear on the right of any production of G_1. Also, if G is a cfg, then such a cfg G_1 can be found. If G is an rg, then such an rg G_1 can be found.

Proof. Let S_1 be a symbol not in V_N or V_T. Let $G_1 = (V_N \cup \{S_1\}, V_T, P_1, S_1)$. P_1 consists of all the productions of P, plus all productions of the form $S_1 \rightarrow \alpha$ where $S \rightarrow \alpha$ is a production of P. Note that S_1 is not a symbol of V_N or V_T, so it does not appear on the right of any production of P_1.

We claim that $L(G) = L(G_1)$. For suppose that $S \overset{*}{\underset{G}{\Rightarrow}} w$. Let the first production used be $S \rightarrow \alpha$. Then we can write $S \underset{G}{\Rightarrow} \alpha \overset{*}{\underset{G}{\Rightarrow}} w$. By definition of P_1, $S_1 \rightarrow \alpha$ is in P_1, so $S_1 \underset{G_1}{\Rightarrow} \alpha$. Also, since P_1 contains all productions of P, $\alpha \overset{*}{\underset{G_1}{\Rightarrow}} w$. Thus $S_1 \overset{*}{\underset{G_1}{\Rightarrow}} w$. We can conclude that $L(G) \subseteq L(G_1)$.

---

† In most cases, we shall abbreviate the names of commonly used devices without periods to conform to current convention.

If we show that $L(G_1) \subseteq L(G)$, we prove that $L(G) = L(G_1)$. Suppose that $S_1 \overset{*}{\underset{G_1}{\Rightarrow}} w$. The first production used is $S_1 \rightarrow \alpha$, for some α. Then, $S \rightarrow \alpha$ is a production of P, so $S \underset{G}{\Rightarrow} \alpha$. Now, $\alpha \overset{*}{\underset{G_1}{\Rightarrow}} w$, but α cannot have S_1 among its symbols. Since S_1 does not appear on the right of any production of P_1, no sentential form in the derivation $\alpha \overset{*}{\underset{G_1}{\Rightarrow}} w$ can involve S_1. Thus the derivation is also a derivation in grammar G; that is, $\alpha \overset{*}{\underset{G}{\Rightarrow}} w$. We conclude that $S \overset{*}{\underset{G}{\Rightarrow}} w$, and $L(G) = L(G_1)$.

It is easy to see that if G is a csg, cfg, or rg, G_1 will be likewise.

Theorem 2.1. If L is context sensitive, context free, or regular, then $L \cup \{\epsilon\}$ and $L - \{\epsilon\}$ are csl's, cfl's, or regular sets, respectively.

Proof. Given a csg, we can find by Lemma 2.1 an equivalent csg G, whose start symbol does not appear on the right of any production. Let $G = (V_N, V_T, P, S)$. Define $G_1 = (V_N, V_T, P_1, S)$, where P_1 is P plus the production $S \rightarrow \epsilon$. Note that S does not appear on the right of any production of P_1. Thus $S \rightarrow \epsilon$ cannot be used, except as the first and only production in a derivation. Any derivation of G_1 not involving $S \rightarrow \epsilon$ is a derivation in G, so $L(G_1) = L(G) \cup \{\epsilon\}$.

If the csg $G = (V_N, V_T, P, S)$ generates L, and ϵ is in L, then P must contain the production $S \rightarrow \epsilon$. Also S does not appear on the right of any production in P. Form grammar $G_1 = (V_N, V_T, P_1, S)$ where P_1 is $P - \{S \rightarrow \epsilon\}$. Since $S \rightarrow \epsilon$ cannot be used in the derivation of any word but ϵ, $L(G_1) = L - \{\epsilon\}$.

If L is context free or regular, the proof is analogous.

Example 2.5. Consider the grammar G of Example 2.2. We can find a grammar $G_1 = (\{S, S_1, B, C\}, \{a, b, c\}, P_1, S_1)$ generating $L(G)$ by defining P_1 to have the seven productions of P (see Example 2.2) plus the productions $S_1 \rightarrow aSBC$ and $S_1 \rightarrow aBC$. $L(G_1) = L(G) = \{a^n b^n c^n | n \geq 1\}$. We can add ϵ to $L(G_1)$ by defining grammar $G_2 = (\{S, S_1, B, C\}, \{a, b, c\}, P_2, S_1)$, where $P_2 = P_1 \cup \{S_1 \rightarrow \epsilon\}$. Then

$$L(G_2) = L(G_1) \cup \{\epsilon\} = \{a^n b^n c^n | n \geq 0\}.$$

2.5   RECURSIVENESS OF CONTEXT-SENSITIVE GRAMMARS

We say that a grammar G is *recursive* if there is an algorithm which will determine for any word w, whether w is generated by G. To say that a grammar is recursive is a stronger statement than to say that there is a procedure for enumerating sentences in the language generated by the grammar.†

---

† There is, of course, always such a procedure for any grammar.

Let $G = (V_N, V_T, P, S)$ be a csg. The sentence ϵ is in $L(G)$ if and only if P contains the production $S \to \epsilon$. Thus we have a test to see if ϵ is in $L(G)$. By removing $S \to \epsilon$ from P if it is there, we can form a new csg

$$G_1 = (V_N, V_T, P_1, S)$$

generating $L(G) - \{\epsilon\}$. Every production of P_1 satisfies the original restriction on a csg. That is, the right-hand side is at least as long as the left-hand side. As a consequence, in every derivation in G_1, the successive sentential forms are nondecreasing in length.

Let $V = V_N \cup V_T$ have k symbols. Suppose that $w \neq \epsilon$, and that there is a derivation $S \overset{*}{\underset{G_1}{\Rightarrow}} w$. Let this derivation be $S \Rightarrow \alpha_1 \Rightarrow \alpha_2 \cdots \Rightarrow \alpha_m$, where $\alpha_m = w$. We have observed that $|\alpha_1| \leq |\alpha_2| \leq \cdots \leq |\alpha_m|$. Suppose that $\alpha_i, \alpha_{i+1}, \ldots, \alpha_{i+j}$ are all of the same length, say length p. Also, suppose that $j \geq k^p$. Then two of $\alpha_i, \alpha_{i+1}, \ldots, \alpha_{i+j}$ must be the same, for there are only k^p strings of length p in V^*. In this case, we can omit at least one step in the derivation. For, let $\alpha_r = \alpha_s$, where $r < s$. Then $S \Rightarrow \alpha_1 \Rightarrow \cdots \Rightarrow \alpha_r \Rightarrow \alpha_{s+1} \Rightarrow \cdots \Rightarrow \alpha_m = w$ is a shorter derivation of w in grammar G_1.

Intuitively, then, if there is a derivation of w, there is one which is "not too long." We shall give an algorithm in the next theorem which essentially incorporates this idea.

Theorem 2.2. If $G = (V_N, V_T, P, S)$ is a context-sensitive grammar, then G is recursive.

Proof. In the preceding paragraphs we saw that one could determine by inspection if ϵ was in $L(G)$ and then remove $S \to \epsilon$ from the productions if ϵ was there. We assume that P does not contain $S \to \epsilon$ and let w be a string in V_T^+. Suppose that $|w| = n$. Define the set T_m as the set of strings α in V^+, of length at most n, such that $S \overset{*}{\Rightarrow} \alpha$ by a derivation of at most m steps. Clearly, $T_0 = \{S\}$.

It is easy to see that we can calculate T_m from T_{m-1} by seeing what strings of length less than or equal to n can be derived from strings in T_{m-1} by a single application of a production. Formally,

$$T_m = T_{m-1} \cup \{\alpha| \text{ for some } \beta \text{ in } T_{m-1}, \beta \Rightarrow \alpha \text{ and } |\alpha| \leq n\}.$$

Also, if $S \overset{*}{\Rightarrow} \alpha$, and $|\alpha| \leq n$, then α will be in T_m for some m; if S does not derive α, or $|\alpha| > n$, then α will not be in T_m for any m.

It should also be evident that $T_m \supseteq T_{m-1}$ for all $m \geq 1$. Since T_m depends only on T_{m-1}, if $T_m = T_{m-1}$, then $T_m = T_{m+1} = T_{m+2} = \cdots$. Our algorithm will be to calculate $T_1, T_2, T_3, \ldots$ until for some m, $T_m = T_{m-1}$. If w is not in T_m, then it is not in $L(G)$, because for $j > m$, $T_j = T_m$. Of course, if w is in T_m, then $S \overset{*}{\Rightarrow} w$.

We have now to show that for some m $T_m = T_{m-1}$. Recall that for each $i \geq 1$, $T_i \supseteq T_{i-1}$. If $T_i \neq T_{i-1}$, then the number of elements in T_i is at least one greater than the number in T_{i-1}. But, let V have k elements. Then the number of strings in V^+ of length less than or equal to n is $k + k^2 + \cdots + k^n$, which is less than or equal to $(k + 1)^{n+1}$. These are the only strings that may be in any T_i. Thus $T_m = T_{m-1}$ for some $m \leq (k + 1)^{n+1}$. Our procedure, which is to calculate T_i for all $i \geq 1$ until two equal sets are found, is thus guaranteed to halt. Therefore, it is an algorithm.

It should need no mention that the algorithm of Theorem 2.2 also applies to context-free and regular grammars.

Example 2.6. Consider the grammar G of Example 2.2, with productions:

$$
\begin{array}{ll}
1.\ S \rightarrow aSBC & 5.\ bB \rightarrow bb \\
2.\ S \rightarrow aBC & 6.\ bC \rightarrow bc \\
3.\ CB \rightarrow BC & 7.\ cC \rightarrow cc \\
4.\ aB \rightarrow ab &
\end{array}
$$

We determine if $w = abac$ is in $L(G)$, using the algorithm of Theorem 2.2.

$$
\begin{aligned}
T_0 &= \{S\}. \\
T_1 &= \{S, aSBC, aBC\}.
\end{aligned}
$$

The first of these strings is in T_0, the second comes from S by application of production (1), the third, by application of (2).

$$T_2 = \{S, aSBC, aBC, abC\}.$$

The first three sentences of T_2 come from T_1, the fourth comes from aBC by application of (4). Note that although $aaSBCBC$ and $aaBCBC$ can be derived from $aSBC$ by productions (1) and (2), they are not in T_2, since their lengths are greater than $|w|$, which is 4. Similarly,

$$T_3 = \{S, aSBC, aBC, abC, abc\}.$$

We can easily see that $T_4 = T_3$. Since $abac$ is not in T_3, it is not in $L(G)$.

2.6 DERIVATION TREES FOR CONTEXT-FREE GRAMMARS

We now consider a visual method of describing any derivation in a context-free grammar. A *tree* is a finite set of *nodes* connected by directed *edges*, which satisfy the following three conditions (if an edge is directed from node 1 to node 2, we say the edge *leaves* node 1 and *enters* node 2):

1. There is exactly one node which no edge enters. This node is called the *root*.
2. For each node in the tree there exists a sequence of directed edges from the root to the node. Thus the tree is connected.

3. Exactly one edge enters every node except the root. As a consequence, there are no loops in the tree.

The set of all nodes n, such that there is an edge leaving a given node m and entering n, is called the set of *direct descendants* of m. A node n is called a *descendant* of node m if there is a sequence of nodes $n_1, n_2, \ldots, n_k$ such that $n_k = n$, $n_1 = m$, and for each i, n_{i+1} is a direct descendant of n_i. We shall, by convention, say a node is a descendant of itself.

For each node in the tree, we can order its direct descendants. Let n_1 and n_2 be direct descendants of node n, with n_1 appearing earlier in the ordering than n_2. Then we say that n_1 and all the descendants of n_1 are to the *left of* n_2 and all the descendants of n_2. Note that every node is a descendant of the root. If n_1 and n_2 are nodes, and neither is a descendant of the other, then they must both be descendants of some node. (This may not be obvious, but a little thought should suffice to make it clear.) Thus, one of n_1 and n_2 is to the left of the other.

Let $G = (V_N, V_T, P, S)$ be a cfg. A tree is a *derivation tree for G* if:

1. Every node has a *label*, which is a symbol of V.
2. The label of the root is S.
3. If a node n has at least one descendant other than itself, and has label A, then A must be in V_N.
4. If nodes $n_1, n_2, \ldots, n_k$ are the direct descendants of node n, in order from the left, with labels $A_1, A_2, \ldots, A_k$, respectively, then

$$A \to A_1 A_2 \ldots A_k$$

must be a production in P.

These ideas may be confusing, but an example should clarify things.

Example 2.7. Consider the grammar $G = (\{S, A\}, \{a, b\}, P, S)$, where P consists of:

$$\begin{array}{ll} S \to aAS & S \to a \\ A \to SbA & A \to ba \\ A \to SS & \end{array}$$

We draw a tree, just this once with circles instead of points for the nodes. The nodes will be numbered for reference. The labels will be adjacent to the nodes. Edges are assumed to be directed downwards. See Fig. 2.2.

Some general comments will illustrate the definitions we have made. The label of node 1 is S. Node 1 is the root of the tree. Nodes 2, 3, and 4 are the direct descendants of node 1. Node 2 is to the left of nodes 3 and 4. Node 3 is to the left of node 4. Node 10 is a descendant of node 3, although not a direct descendant. Node 5 is to the left of node 10. Node 11 is to the left of node 4, for surely node 3 is to the left of node 4, and 11 is a descendant of node 3.

The nodes with direct descendants are 1, 3, 4, 5, and 7. Node 1 has label S, and its direct descendants, from the left, have labels a, A, and S. Note that $S \rightarrow aAS$ is a production. Likewise, node 3 has label A, and the labels of its direct descendants are S, b, and A from the left. $A \rightarrow SbA$ is also a production. Nodes 4 and 5 each have label S. Their only direct descendants each have label a, and $S \rightarrow a$ is a production. Lastly, node 7 has label A and its direct descendants, from the left, have labels b and a. $A \rightarrow ba$ is also a production. Thus, the conditions that Fig. 2.2 represent a derivation tree for G have been met.

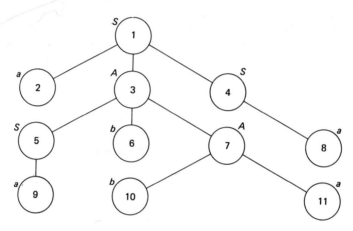

Fig. 2.2. Example of a derivation tree.

We shall see that a derivation tree is a very natural description of the derivation of a particular sentential form of the grammar G. Some of the nodes in any tree have no descendants. These nodes we shall call *leaves*. Given any two leaves, one is to the left of the other, and it is easy to tell which is which. Simply backtrack along the edges of the tree, toward the root, from each of the two leaves, until the first node of which both leaves are descendants is found.

If we read the labels of the leaves from left to right, we have a sentential form. We call this string the *result* of the derivation tree. Later, we shall see that if α is the result of some derivation tree for grammar $G = (V_N, V_T, P, S)$, then $S \overset{*}{\underset{G}{\Rightarrow}} \alpha$.

We need one additional concept, that of a *subtree*. A subtree of a derivation tree is a particular node of the tree together with all its descendants, the edges connecting them, and their labels. It looks just like a derivation tree, except that the label of the root may not be the start symbol of the grammar.

Example 2.8. Let us consider the grammar and derivation tree of Example 2.7. The derivation tree of Fig. 2.2 is reproduced without numbered nodes as Fig. 2.3(a). The result of the tree in Fig. 2.3(a) is *aabbaa*. Referring to Fig. 2.2 again, we see that the leaves are the nodes numbered 2, 9, 6, 10, 11, and 8, in that order, from the left. These nodes have labels *a, a, b, b, a, a,* respectively. Note that in this case all leaves had terminals for labels, but there is no reason why this should always be so. Note that $S \overset{*}{\underset{G}{\Rightarrow}} aabbaa$ by the derivation

$$S \Rightarrow aAS \Rightarrow aSbAS \Rightarrow aabAS \Rightarrow aabbaS \Rightarrow aabbaa.$$

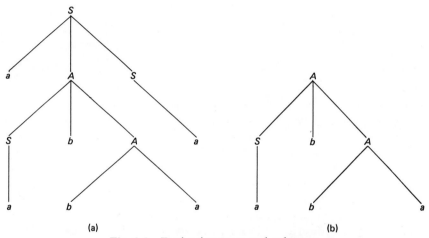

Fig. 2.3. Derivation trees and subtrees.

In part (b) of Fig. 2.3 is a subtree of the tree illustrated in part (a). It is node 3 of Fig. 2.2, together with its descendants. The result of the subtree is *abba*. The label of the root of the subtree is A, and $A \overset{*}{\Rightarrow} abba$. The derivation in this case is:

$$A \Rightarrow SbA \Rightarrow abA \Rightarrow abba.$$

We shall now prove a useful theorem about derivation trees for context-free grammars and, since every regular grammar is context free, for regular grammars also.

Theorem 2.3. Let $G = (V_N, V_T, P, S)$ be a context-free grammar. Then, for $\alpha \neq \epsilon$, $S \overset{*}{\Rightarrow} \alpha$ if and only if there is a derivation tree in grammar G with result α.

Proof. We shall find it easier to prove something in excess of the theorem. What we shall prove is that if we define G_A to be the grammar (V_N, V_T, P, A) (i.e., G with the variable A chosen as the start symbol), then for any A in

V_N, $A \xRightarrow{*} \alpha$ if and only if there is a tree in grammar G_A with α as the result.†
Note that for all grammars mentioned, the productions are the same. There-
fore $A \xRightarrow[G_A]{*} \alpha$ is equivalent to saying $A \xRightarrow[G_B]{*} \alpha$, for any B in V_N. Also, since
$G_S = G$, it is the same as saying $A \xRightarrow[G]{*} \alpha$.

Suppose, first, that α is the result of a derivation tree for grammar G_A.
We prove, by induction on the number of nodes in the tree that are not leaves,
that $A \xRightarrow[G_A]{*} \alpha$. If there is only one node that is not a leaf of the tree, the tree

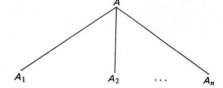

Fig. 2.4. Tree with one nonleaf.

must look like the one in Fig. 2.4. In that case, $A_1 A_2 \ldots A_n$ must be α, and
$A \rightarrow \alpha$ must be a production of P by definition of a derivation tree.

Now, suppose that the result is true for trees with up to $k - 1$ nodes
which are not leaves. Also, suppose that α is the result of a tree with root
labeled A, and suppose that that tree has k nodes which are not leaves,
$k > 1$. Consider the direct descendants of the root. These could not all be
leaves. Let the labels of the direct descendants be $A_1, A_2, \ldots, A_n$ in order
from the left. Number these nodes $1, 2, \ldots, n$. Then, surely, $S \rightarrow A_1 A_2 \ldots A_n$
is a production in P. Note that n may be any integer greater than or equal
to one in the argument that follows.

If the node i is not a leaf, it is the root of a subtree. Also, A_i must be a
variable. The subtree is a tree in grammar G_{A_i}, and has some result α_i. If
node i is a leaf, let $A_i = \alpha_i$. It is easy to see that if $j < i$, node j and all of
its descendants are to the left of node i and all of its descendants. Thus
$\alpha = \alpha_1 \alpha_2 \ldots \alpha_n$. A subtree must have fewer nodes that are not leaves
than its tree does, unless the subtree is the entire tree. By the inductive
hypothesis, for each node i which is not a leaf, $A_i \xRightarrow[G_{A_i}]{*} \alpha_i$. Thus $A_i \xRightarrow[G_A]{*} \alpha_i$.
If $A_i = \alpha_i$, then surely $A_i \xRightarrow[G_A]{*} \alpha_i$. We can put all these partial derivations
together, to see that

$$A \xRightarrow[G_A]{} A_1 A_2 \ldots A_n \xRightarrow[G_A]{*} \alpha_1 A_2 \ldots A_n \xRightarrow[G_A]{*} \alpha_1 \alpha_2 A_3 \ldots A_n \xRightarrow[G_A]{*} \cdots \xRightarrow[G_A]{*} \alpha_1 \alpha_2 \ldots \alpha_n = \alpha.$$

Thus $A \xRightarrow[G_A]{*} \alpha$.

---

† The introduction of these grammars is necessary only because a tree in grammar
G always has a root labeled S.

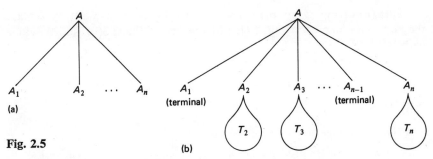

Fig. 2.5

Now, suppose that $A \overset{*}{\underset{G_A}{\Rightarrow}} \alpha$. We must show that there is a derivation tree with result α in grammar G_A. If $A \overset{*}{\underset{G_A}{\Rightarrow}} \alpha$ by a single step, then $A \rightarrow \alpha$ is a production in P, and there is a tree with result α, of the form shown in Fig. 2.4.

Now, assume that if $A \overset{*}{\underset{G_A}{\Rightarrow}} \alpha$ by a derivation of less than k steps, then there is a derivation tree in grammar G_A with result α. Suppose that $A \overset{*}{\underset{G_A}{\Rightarrow}} \alpha$ by a derivation of k steps. Let the first step be $A \Rightarrow A_1 A_2 \ldots A_n$. Now, it should be clear that any symbol in α must either be one of $A_1, A_2, \ldots, A_n$ or be derived from one of these. Also, that portion of α derived from A_i must lie to the left of the symbols derived from A_j, if $i < j$. Thus, we can write α as $\alpha_1 \alpha_2 \ldots \alpha_n$, where for each i between 1 and n, $A_i \overset{*}{\underset{G_A}{\Rightarrow}} \alpha_i$.

By the inductive hypothesis, there is a derivation tree for each variable A_i, in grammar G_{A_i}, with result α_i. Let this tree be T_i. We begin by constructing a derivation tree in grammar G_A with root labeled A, and n leaves labeled $A_1, A_2, \ldots, A_n$, and no other nodes. This tree is shown in Fig. 2.5(a). Each node with label A_i, where A_i is not a terminal, is replaced by the tree T_i. If A_i is a terminal, no replacement is made. An example appears in Fig. 2.5(b). In a straightforward manner, it can be shown that the result of this tree is α.

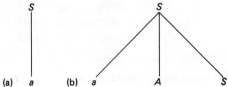

Fig. 2.6

Example 2.9. Consider the derivation $S \overset{*}{\Rightarrow} aabbaa$ of Example 2.8. The first step is $S \rightarrow aAS$. If we follow the derivation, we see that A eventually is replaced by SbA, then by abA, and finally, by $abba$. Part (b) of Fig. 2.3 is a derivation tree for this derivation. The only symbol derived from S in aAS is a. (This replacement is the last step.) Part (a) of Fig. 2.6 is a tree for the latter derivation.

Part (b) of Fig. 2.6 is the derivation tree for $S \Rightarrow aAS$. If we replace the node with label A in Fig. 2.6(b) by the tree of Fig. 2.3(b), and the node with label S in Fig. 2.6(b) with the tree of Fig. 2.6(a), we get the tree of Fig. 2.3(a), whose result is *aabbaa*.

PROBLEMS

2.1 Give a regular grammar generating

$L = \{w | w$ is in $\{0, 1\}^*$, and w does not contain two consecutive 1's$\}$.

2.2 Give a context-free grammar generating

$L = \{w | w$ is in $\{a, b\}^*$ and w consists of twice as many a's as b's$\}$.

2.3 Give a context-free grammar generating the FORTRAN arithmetic statements.

2.4 Give a context-sensitive grammar generating

$L = \{w | w$ in $\{a, b, c\}^*$, and w consists of equal numbers of a's, b's, and c's$\}$.

2.5 Give a context-sensitive grammar generating

$$L = \{ww | w \text{ is in } \{0, 1\}^*\}.$$

That is, L is all words in $\{0, 1\}^*$ whose first and last halves are equal.

2.6 Informally describe the words generated by the grammar G of Example 2.7.

2.7 Use the algorithm of Theorem 2.2 to determine if the following words are in $L(G)$, where G is as in Example 2.7.

a) *abaa*   b) *abbb*   c) *baaba*

2.8 If G is context free, can you improve upon the bound on m in Theorem 2.2? What if G is regular?

2.9 Consider the grammar G of Example 2.3. Draw a derivation tree in G for the following words.

a) *ababab*   b) *bbbaabaa*   c) *aabbaabb*

2.10 Let $G = (V_N, V_T, P, S)$, where $V_N = \{A, B, S\}$ and $V_T = \{0, 1\}$. P consists of the productions:

$$
\begin{array}{ll}
S \rightarrow 0AB & B \rightarrow 01 \\
1B \rightarrow 0 & A1 \rightarrow SB1 \\
B \rightarrow SA & A0 \rightarrow S0B
\end{array}
$$

Can you prove that $L(G)$ is empty?

2.11 In Fig. 2.7 is a derivation tree of some context-free grammar,

$$G = (V_N, V_T, P, S),$$

for which the productions and symbols are not known. What is the result of the tree? What symbols are necessarily in V_N? What symbols might be in V_T? Disregarding our convention that lower case italic letters denote terminals, do we find that b and c must be in V_T, or could they be in V_N? What productions must be in P? Is the word $bcbbcbb$ in $L(G)$?

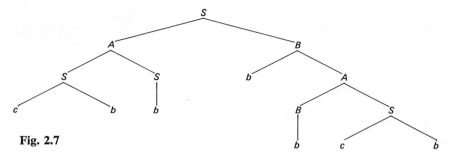

Fig. 2.7

2.12 Let G be a grammar where all productions are of the form $A \rightarrow xB$ and $A \rightarrow x$, where A and B are single variables and x is a string of terminals. Show that $L(G)$ can be generated by a regular grammar.

REFERENCES

Early works on generating systems are found in Chomsky [1956], Chomsky and Miller [1958], Chomsky [1959], and Bar-Hillel, Gaifman, and Shamir [1960]. The notation of grammar used here and the classification by type is due to Chomsky [1959].

For references on regular, context-free, recursively enumerable, and context-sensitive sets, check the references given at the end of Chapters 3, 4, 6, and 8, respectively. Two survey papers with additional references are Chomsky [1963] and Floyd [1964c].

CHAPTER 3

FINITE AUTOMATA
AND REGULAR GRAMMARS

3.1 THE FINITE AUTOMATON

In Chapter 2, we were introduced to a generating scheme—the grammar. Grammars are finite specifications for languages. In this chapter we shall see another method of finitely specifying infinite languages—the recognizer. We shall consider what is undoubtedly the simplest recognizer, called a finite automaton. The finite automaton (fa) cannot define all languages defined by grammars, but we shall show that the languages defined are exactly the type 3 languages. In later chapters, the reader will be introduced to recognizers for type 0, 1, and 2 languages. Here we shall define a finite automaton as a formal system, then give the physical meaning of the definition.

A *finite automaton* M over an alphabet Σ is a system $(K, \Sigma, \delta, q_0, F)$, where K is a finite, nonempty set of *states*, Σ is a finite *input alphabet*, δ is a mapping of $K \times \Sigma$ into K, q_0 in K is the *initial state*, and $F \subseteq K$ is the set of *final states*.

Our model in Fig. 3.1 represents a finite control which reads symbols from a linear input tape in a sequential manner from left to right. The set of states K consists of the states of the finite control. Initially, the finite control is in state q_0 and is scanning the leftmost symbol of a string of symbols in Σ which appear on the input tape. The interpretation of $\delta(q, a) = p$, for q and p in K and a in Σ, is that M, in state q and scanning the input symbol a, moves its input head one cell to the right and goes to state p.

The mapping δ is from $K \times \Sigma$ to K. We can extend δ to domain† $K \times \Sigma^*$ by defining a mapping $\hat{\delta}$ as follows:

$$\hat{\delta}(q, \epsilon) = q$$
$$\hat{\delta}(q, xa) = \delta(\hat{\delta}(q, x), a) \qquad \text{for each } x \text{ in } \Sigma^* \text{ and } a \text{ in } \Sigma.$$

Thus the interpretation of $\hat{\delta}(q, x) = p$ is that M, starting in state q with the string x written on the input tape, will be in state p when the input head moves right from the portion of the input tape containing x. Since δ and $\hat{\delta}$

---

† The *domain* of a mapping is the set of valid arguments for the mapping. The set of values which the mapping could take is called the *range*.

26

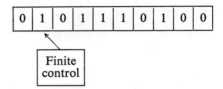

Fig. 3.1. A finite automaton.

agree wherever δ is defined, no confusion will arise if we fail to distinguish between δ and $\hat{\delta}$. Thus, for the remainder of the book, we shall use δ for both δ and $\hat{\delta}$.

A sentence x is said to be *accepted* by M if $\delta(q_0, x) = p$ for some p in F. The set of all x accepted by M is designated $T(M)$. That is,

$$T(M) = \{x \,|\, \delta(q, x) \text{ is in } F\}.$$

Any set of strings accepted by a finite automaton is said to be *regular*.

Example 3.1. The specifications for a finite automaton are given in Fig. 3.2(a). A *state diagram* for the automaton is shown in Fig. 3.2(b). The state diagram consists of a node for every state and a directed line from state q to state p with label a (in Σ) if the finite automaton, in state q, scanning the input symbol a, would go to state p. Final states, i.e., states in F, are indicated by a double circle. The initial state is marked by an arrow labeled start.

Consider the state diagram of Fig. 3.2(b). Suppose that 110101 is the input to M. Since $\delta(q_0, 1) = q_1$ and $\delta(q_1, 1) = q_0$, $\delta(q_0, 11) = q_0$. We might comment that thus, 11 is in $T(M)$, but we are interested in 110101. Now $\delta(q_0, 0) = q_2$, so $\delta(q_0, 110) = q_2$. Next $\delta(q_2, 1) = q_3$, so $\delta(q_0, 1101) = q_3$. Finally, $\delta(q_3, 0) = q_1$ and $\delta(q_1, 1) = q_0$, so $\delta(q_0, 110101) = q_0$, and thus 110101 is in $T(M)$. It is easily shown that $T(M)$ is the set of all sentences in $\{0, 1\}^*$ containing both an even number of 0's and an even number of 1's.

$M = (K, \Sigma, \delta, q_0, F)$
$\Sigma = \{0, 1\}$
$K = \{q_0, q_1, q_2, q_3\}$
$F = \{q_0\}$

$\delta(q_0, 0) = q_2 \qquad \delta(q_0, 1) = q_1$
$\delta(q_1, 0) = q_3 \qquad \delta(q_1, 1) = q_0$
$\delta(q_2, 0) = q_0 \qquad \delta(q_2, 1) = q_3$
$\delta(q_3, 0) = q_1 \qquad \delta(q_3, 1) = q_2$

(a)

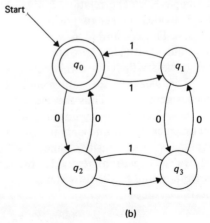

Fig. 3.2. A finite automaton accepting the set of strings with an even number of 0's and an even number of 1's. (a) A finite automaton. (b) State diagram of the finite automaton.

(b)

3.2 EQUIVALENCE RELATIONS AND FINITE AUTOMATA

A *binary relation* R on a set S is a set of pairs of elements in S. If (a, b) is in R, then we are accustomed to seeing this fact written as aRb.

Example 3.2. For a familiar example, consider the relation "less than" usually denoted by the symbol $<$ on the set of integers. In the formal sense, this relation is the set: $\{(i, j) \mid i$ is less than $j\}$. Thus $3 < 4, 2 < 17$, etc.

We are going to be concerned with some relations on sets of strings over a finite alphabet.

A binary relation R over a set S is said to be:

1. *reflexive* if for each s in S, sRs,
2. *symmetric* if for s and t in S, sRt implies tRs,
3. *transitive* if for s, t, and u in S, sRt and tRu imply sRu.

A relation which is reflexive, symmetric, and transitive is called an *equivalence relation*. An example of an equivalence relation over the set of positive integers is the relation E, given by: iEj if and only if $|i - j|$ is divisible by 3.

An important property of equivalence relations is that if R is an equivalence relation on the set S then we can divide S into k disjoint subsets, called *equivalence classes*, for some k between 1 and infinity, inclusive, such that aRb if and only if a and b are in the same subset.

The proof is simple. Define $[a]$ to be $\{b \mid aRb\}$. For any a and b in S, either $[a] = [b]$, or $[a]$ and $[b]$ are disjoint. Otherwise, let c be in $[a]$ and $[b]$, and d be in $[b]$ but not $[a]$. That is, aRc, bRc, and bRd, but not aRd. By symmetry, we have cRb. By transitivity, we can show cRd and aRd. The latter statement is a contradiction. The distinct sets that are $[a]$ for some a in S are the equivalence classes. Clearly, a and b are in the same set if and only if they are equivalent.

Example 3.3. The relation E given by iEj if and only if $|i - j|$ is divisible by 3 divides the set of positive integers into three classes $\{1, 4, 7, 10, \ldots\}$, $\{2, 5, 8, 11, \ldots\}$, and $\{3, 6, 9, 12, \ldots\}$. Any two elements from the same class are equivalent ($1E4$, $3E6$, etc.), and any two elements from different classes fail to satisfy the equivalence relation (not $7E9$, $1E5$, etc.).

The *index* of an equivalence relation is the number of equivalence classes generated. Thus the equivalence relation E has index 3.

Consider the finite automaton of Example 3.1. For x and y in $\{0, 1\}^*$, let (x, y) be in R if and only if $\delta(q_0, x) = \delta(q_0, y)$. The relation R is reflexive, symmetric, and transitive, since "$=$" has these properties, and thus, R is an equivalence relation. R divides the set $\{0, 1\}^*$ into four equivalence classes corresponding to the four states. In addition, if xRy, then $xz \, R \, yz$ for all z in $\{0, 1\}^*$, since

$$\delta(q_0, xz) = \delta(\delta(q_0, x), z) = \delta(\delta(q_0, y), z) = \delta(q_0, yz).$$

Such an equivalence relation is said to be *right invariant*. We see that every finite automaton induces a right invariant equivalence relation defined as R was defined, on its set of input strings. This result is formalized in the following theorem.

Theorem 3.1. The following three statements are equivalent:
1. The set $L \subseteq \Sigma^*$ is accepted by some finite automaton.
2. L is the union of some of the equivalence classes of a right invariant equivalence relation of finite index.
3. Let equivalence relation R be defined by: xRy if and only if for all z in Σ^*, xz is in L exactly when yz is in L. Then R is of finite index.

Proof. (1) $\Rightarrow$ (2). Assume that L is accepted by some fa $M = (K, \Sigma, \delta, q_0, F)$. Let R' be the equivalence relation $xR'y$ if and only if $\delta(q_0, x) = \delta(q_0, y)$. R' is right invariant since, for any z, if $\delta(q_0, x) = \delta(q_0, y)$, then

$$\delta(q_0, xz) = \delta(q_0, yz).$$

The index of R' is finite since the index is at most the number of states in K. Furthermore, L is the union of those equivalence classes which include an element x such that $\delta(q_0, x)$ is in F.

(2) $\Rightarrow$ (3). We show that any equivalence relation R' satisfying (2) is a refinement of R; that is, every equivalence class of R' is entirely contained in some equivalence class of R. Thus the index of R cannot be greater than the index of R' and so is finite. Assume that $xR'y$. Then since R' is right invariant, for each z in Σ^*, $xzR'yz$, and thus yz is in L if and only if xz is in L. Thus xRy, and hence, the equivalence class of x in R' is contained in the equivalence class of x in R. We conclude that each equivalence class of R' is contained within some equivalence class of R.

(3) $\Rightarrow$ (1). Assume that xRy. Then for each w and z in Σ^*, xwz is in L if and only if ywz is in L. Thus $xwRyw$, and R is right invariant. Now let K' be the finite set of equivalence classes of R and $[x]$ the element of K' containing x. Define $\delta'([x], a) = [xa]$. The definition is consistent, since R is right invariant. Let $q_0' = [\epsilon]$ and let $F' = \{[x] \mid x \in L\}$. The finite automaton $M' = (K', \Sigma, \delta', q_0', F')$ accepts L since $\delta'(q_0', x) = [x]$, and thus x is in $T(M')$ if and only if $[x]$ is in F'.

Theorem 3.2. The minimum state automaton accepting L is unique up to an isomorphism (i.e., a renaming of the states) and is given by M' of Theorem 3.1.

Proof. In the proof of Theorem 3.1 we saw that any fa $M = (K, \Sigma, \delta, q_0, F)$ accepting L defines an equivalence relation which is a refinement of R. Thus the number of states of M is greater than or equal to the number of states of M' of Theorem 3.1. If equality holds, then each of the states of M can be identified with one of the states of M'. That is, let q be a state of M. There must be some x in Σ^*, such that $\delta(q_0, x) = q$, otherwise q could be removed from K, and a smaller automaton found. Identify q with the state $\delta'(q_0', x)$, of M'. This identification will be consistent. If $\delta(q_0, x) = \delta(q_0, y) = q$, then, by Theorem 3.1, x and y are in the same equivalence class of R. Thus $\delta'(q_0', x) = \delta'(q_0', y)$.

3.3 NONDETERMINISTIC FINITE AUTOMATA

We now introduce the notion of a nondeterministic finite automaton. It will turn out that any set accepted by a nondeterministic finite automaton can also be accepted by a deterministic finite automaton.

However, the nondeterministic finite automaton is a useful concept in proving theorems. Also, the concept of a nondeterministic device is not an easy one to grasp. It is well to begin with a simple device. Later we deal with nondeterministic devices that are not equivalent to their deterministic counterparts. It is hoped that the study of nondeterministic finite automata will help in the understanding of those devices.

A *nondeterministic finite automaton* M is a system $(K, \Sigma, \delta, q_0, F)$, where K is a finite nonempty set of states, Σ the finite input alphabet, δ is a mapping of $K \times \Sigma$ into subsets of K, q_0 in K is the initial state, and $F \subseteq K$ is the set of final states.

The important difference between the deterministic and nondeterministic case is that $\delta(q, a)$ is a (possibly empty) set of states rather than a single state. The interpretation of $\delta(q, a) = \{p_1, p_2, \ldots, p_k\}$ is that M, in state q, scanning a on its input tape, moves its head one cell to the right and chooses any one of $p_1, p_2, \ldots, p_k$ as the next state.

The mapping δ can be extended to domain $K \times \Sigma^*$ by defining

$$\delta(q, \epsilon) = \{q\} \qquad \text{and} \qquad \delta(q, xa) = \bigcup_{p \text{ in } \delta(q,x)} \delta(p, a),$$

for each x in Σ^*, and a in Σ.

The mapping δ can be further extended to domain $2^K \times \Sigma^*$† by defining

$$\delta(\{p_1, p_2, \ldots, p_k\}, x) = \bigcup_{i=1}^{k} \delta(p_i, x).$$

A sentence x is *accepted* by M if there is a state p in both F and $\delta(q_0, x)$. The set of all x accepted by M is denoted $T(M)$.

Example 3.4. A nondeterministic fa which accepts the set of all sentences with either two consecutive 0's or two consecutive 1's is given in Fig. 3.3. The fa will make many choices upon reading an input string. Thus, suppose that 010110 is the input. After reading the first 0, M may stay in state q_0 or go to q_3. Next, with a 1 input, M can go nowhere from q_3, but from q_0 can

---

† 2^K, for any set K, denotes the *power set* or set of all subsets of K.

go to q_0 or q_1. Similarly, by the time the fourth input symbol is read, M can still be in only q_0 or q_1. When the fifth symbol, a 1, is read, M can go from q_1 to q_2 and from q_0 to q_0 or q_1. Thus M may be in state q_0, q_1, or q_2. Since there is a sequence of states leading to q_2, 01011 is accepted. Likewise, after the sixth symbol is read, M can be in state q_0, q_2, or q_3. Thus 010110 is also accepted.

$M = (\{q_0, q_1, q_2, q_3, q_4\},$
$\quad \{0, 1\}, \delta, q_0, \{q_2, q_4\})$

$\delta(q_0, 0) = \{q_0, q_3\};$
$\delta(q_1, 0) = \varphi;$
$\delta(q_2, 0) = \{q_2\};$
$\delta(q_3, 0) = \{q_4\};$
$\delta(q_4, 0) = \{q_4\};$

$\delta(q_0, 1) = \{q_0, q_1\}.$
$\delta(q_1, 1) = \{q_2\}.$
$\delta(q_2, 1) = \{q_2\}.$
$\delta(q_3, 1) = \varphi.$
$\delta(q_4, 1) = \{q_4\}.$

(a)

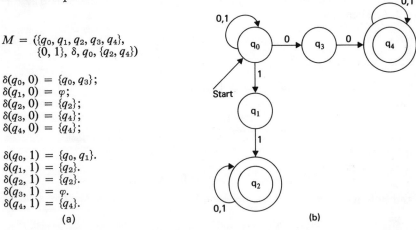

(b)

Fig. 3.3. A nondeterministic finite automaton which accepts the set of all sentences containing either two consecutive 0's or two consecutive 1's. (a) Specification. (b) State diagram.

Theorem 3.3. Let L be a set accepted by a nondeterministic finite automaton. Then there exists a deterministic finite automaton that accepts L.

Proof. Let $M = (K, \Sigma, \delta, q_0, F)$ be a nondeterministic fa accepting L. Define a deterministic fa, $M' = (K', \Sigma, \delta', q_0', F')$ as follows. The states of M' are all the subsets of the set of states of M. That is, $K' = 2^K$. M' will keep track of all the states M could be in at any given time. F' is the set of all states in K' containing a state of F. An element of K' will be denoted by $[q_1, q_2, \ldots, q_i]$, where $q_1, q_2, \ldots, q_i$ are in K. Note that $q_0' = [q_0]$.
    We define

$$\delta'([q_1, q_2, \ldots, q_i], a) = [p_1, p_2, \ldots, p_j]$$

if and only if

$$\delta(\{q_1, q_2, \ldots, q_i\}, a) = \{p_1, p_2, \ldots, p_j\}.$$

That is, δ' applied to an element Q of K' is computed by applying δ to each state of K represented by $Q = [q_1, q_2, \ldots, q_i]$. On applying δ to each of $q_1, q_2, \ldots, q_i$ and taking the union, we get some new set of states, $p_1, p_2, \ldots, p_j$. This new set of states has a representative, $[p_1, p_2, \ldots, p_j]$ in K', and that element is the value of $\delta'([q_1, q_2, \ldots, q_i], a)$.

It is easy to show by induction on the length of the input string x that

$$\delta'(q'_0, x) = [q_1, q_2, \ldots, q_i]$$

if and only if

$$\delta(q_0, x) = \{q_1, q_2, \ldots, q_i\}.$$

The result is trivial for $|x| = 0$, since $q'_0 = [q_0]$. Suppose that it is true for $|x| \leq l$. Then, for a in Σ,

$$\delta'(q'_0, xa) = \delta'(\delta'(q'_0, x), a).$$

By the inductive hypothesis,

$$\delta'(q'_0, x) = [p_1, p_2, \ldots, p_j]$$

if and only if

$$\delta(q_0, x) = \{p_1, p_2, \ldots, p_j\}.$$

But by definition,

$$\delta'([p_1, p_2, \ldots, p_j], a) = [r_1, r_2, \ldots, r_k]$$

if and only if

$$\delta(\{p_1, p_2, \ldots, p_j\}, a) = \{r_1, r_2, \ldots, r_k\}.$$

Thus,

$$\delta'(q'_0, xa) = [r_1, r_2, \ldots, r_k]$$

if and only if

$$\delta(q_0, xa) = \{r_1, r_2, \ldots, r_k\}.$$

To complete the proof, we have only to add that $\delta'(q'_0, x)$ is in F' exactly when $\delta(q_0, x)$ contains a state of K which is in F. Thus $T(M) = T(M')$.

Since the deterministic and nondeterministic finite automata accept the same sets, we shall not distinguish between them unless it becomes necessary, but shall simply refer to both as finite automata.

Example 3.5. Let $M = (\{q_0, q_1\}, \{0, 1\}, \delta, q_0, \{q_1\})$ be a nondeterministic fa, where:

$$\delta(q_0, 0) = \{q_0, q_1\} \qquad \delta(q_0, 1) = \{q_1\} \qquad \delta(q_1, 0) = \varphi \qquad \delta(q_1, 1) = \{q_0, q_1\}.$$

We can construct a deterministic fa, $M' = (K, \{0, 1\}, \delta', [q_0], F)$, accepting $T(M)$ as follows. K consists of all subsets of $\{q_0, q_1\}$. We denote the elements of K by $[q_0], [q_1], [q_0, q_1]$ and φ. Since $\delta(q_0, 0) = \{q_0, q_1\}$,

$$\delta'([q_0], 0) = [q_0, q_1].$$

Likewise,

$$\delta'([q_0], 1) = [q_1], \delta'([q_1], 0) = \varphi \qquad \text{and} \qquad \delta'([q_1], 1) = [q_0, q_1].$$

Naturally, $\delta'(\varphi, 0) = \delta'(\varphi, 1) = \varphi$. Lastly,

$$\delta'([q_0, q_1], 0) = [q_0, q_1],$$

since

$$\delta(\{q_0, q_1\}, 0) = \delta(q_0, 0) \cup \delta(q_1, 0) = \{q_0, q_1\} \cup \varphi = \{q_0, q_1\};$$

and

$$\delta'([q_0, q_1], 1) = [q_0, q_1],$$

since

$$\delta(\{q_0, q_1\}, 1) = \delta(q_0, 1) \cup \delta(q_1, 1) = \{q_1\} \cup \{q_0, q_1\} = \{q_0, q_1\}.$$

The set F of final states is $\{[q_1], [q_0, q_1]\}$.

3.4 FINITE AUTOMATA AND TYPE 3 LANGUAGES

We now turn to the relationship between the languages generated by type 3 grammars and the sets accepted by finite automata.

Theorem 3.4. Let $G = (V_N, V_T, P, S)$ be a type 3 grammar. Then there exists a finite automaton $M = (K, V_T, \delta, S, F)$ with $T(M) = L(G)$.

Proof. M will be a nondeterministic fa. The states of M are the variables of G, plus an additional state A, not in V_N. Thus, $K = V_N \cup \{A\}$. The initial state of M is S. If P contains the production $S \rightarrow \epsilon$, then $F = \{S, A\}$. Otherwise, $F = \{A\}$. Recall that S will not appear on the right of any production if $S \rightarrow \epsilon$ is in P. The state A is in $\delta(B, a)$ if $B \rightarrow a$ is in P. In addition, $\delta(B, a)$ contains all C such that $B \rightarrow aC$ is in P. $\delta(A, a) = \varphi$ for each a in V_T.

The fa M, when accepting a sentence x, simulates a derivation of x by the grammar G. We shall show that $T(M) = L(G)$. Let $x = a_1a_2\ldots a_n$ be in $L(G)$, $n \geq 1$. Then

$$S \Rightarrow a_1A_1 \Rightarrow \cdots \Rightarrow a_1a_2\ldots a_{n-1}A_{n-1} \Rightarrow a_1a_2\ldots a_{n-1}a_n$$

for some sequence of variables $A_1, A_2, \ldots, A_{n-1}$. From the definition of δ, we can see that $\delta(S, a_1)$ contains A_1, that $\delta(A_1, a_2)$ contains A_2, etc., and that $\delta(A_{n-1}, a_n)$ contains A. Thus x is in $T(M)$, since $\delta(S, x)$ contains A, and A is in F. If ϵ is in $L(G)$, then S is in F, so ϵ is in $T(M)$.

Likewise, if x is in $T(M)$, $|x| \geq 1$, then there exists a sequence of states $S, A_1, A_2, \ldots, A_{n-1}, A$ such that $\delta(S, a_1)$ contains A_1, $\delta(A_1, a_2)$ contains A_2, and so forth. Thus, P contains rules $S \rightarrow a_1A_1$, $A_1 \rightarrow a_2A_2, \ldots$ and $A_{n-1} \rightarrow a_n$. Therefore, $S \Rightarrow a_1A_1 \Rightarrow a_1a_2A_2 \Rightarrow \cdots \Rightarrow a_1a_2\ldots a_{n-1}A_{n-1} \Rightarrow a_1a_2\ldots a_n$ is a derivation in G and x is in $L(G)$. If ϵ is in $T(M)$, then S is in F, so $S \rightarrow \epsilon$ is a production in P, and ϵ is in $L(G)$.

Theorem 3.5. Given a finite automaton M, there exists a type 3 grammar G, such that $L(G) = T(M)$.

Proof. Without loss of generality let $M = (K, \Sigma, \delta, q_0, F)$ be a deterministic finite automaton. Define a type 3 grammar $G = (K, \Sigma, P, q_0)$ as follows.

1. $B \rightarrow aC$ is in P if $\delta(B, a) = C$.
2. $B \rightarrow a$ is in P if $\delta(B, a) = C$ and C is in F.

The proof that $q_0 \overset{*}{\underset{G}{\Rightarrow}} w$ if and only if $\delta(q_0, w)$ is in F, for $|w| \geq 1$, is similar to the proof of Theorem 3.4, and will be left to the reader. If q_0 is in F, then ϵ is in $T(M)$. In that case, $L(G) = T(M) - \{\epsilon\}$. By Theorem 2.1, we can obtain from G, a new type 3 grammar G_1, where

$$L(G_1) = L(G) \cup \{\epsilon\} = T(M).$$

If q_0 is not in F, then ϵ is not in $T(M)$, so $L(G) = T(M)$.

Example 3.6. Consider the following regular grammar, $G = (\{S, B\}, \{0, 1\}, P, S)$, where P consists of: $S \rightarrow 0B$, $B \rightarrow 0B$, $B \rightarrow 1S$, $B \rightarrow 0$.

We can construct a nondeterministic finite automaton $M = (\{S, B, A\}, \{0, 1\}, \delta, S, \{A\})$, where δ is given by:

1. $\delta(S, 0) = \{B\}$, since $S \rightarrow 0B$ is the only production in P with S on the left and 0 on the right.
2. $\delta(S, 1) = \varphi$, since no production has S on the left and 1 on the right.
3. $\delta(B, 0) = \{B, A\}$, since $B \rightarrow 0B$ and $B \rightarrow 0$ are in P.
4. $\delta(B, 1) = \{S\}$, since $B \rightarrow 1S$ is in P.
5. $\delta(A, 0) = \delta(A, 1) = \varphi$.

By Theorem 3.4, $T(M) = L(G)$, as one can easily verify.

We now use the construction of Theorem 3.3 to find a deterministic finite automaton M_1 equivalent to M. Then, we use the construction of Theorem 3.5 to find a grammar G_1, generating $L(G)$.

Let $M_1 = (K, \{0, 1\}, \delta', [S], F)$.

$$K = \{\varphi, [S], [A], [B], [A, S], [A, B], [B, S], [A, B, S]\}.$$

$$F = \{[A], [A, S], [A, B], [A, B, S]\}.$$

$$\delta'([S], 0) = [B] \qquad\qquad \delta'([S], 1) = \varphi$$
$$\delta'([B], 0) = [A, B] \qquad\qquad \delta'([B], 1) = [S]$$
$$\delta'([A, B], 0) = [A, B] \qquad\qquad \delta'([A, B], 1) = [S]$$
$$\delta'(\varphi, 0) = \delta'(\varphi, 1) = \varphi$$

There are other rules of δ'. However, no states other than φ, $[S]$, $[B]$, and $[A, B]$ will ever be entered by M_1, and the other states can be removed from K and F.

Now, let us construct grammar $G_1 = (K, \{0, 1\}, P_1, [S])$ from M_1. From $\delta'([S], 0) = [B]$ we get the production $[S] \rightarrow 0[B]$. From $\delta'([B], 0) = [A, B]$, we get $[B] \rightarrow 0[A, B]$ and, since $[A, B]$ is a final state of M_1, we place production $[B] \to 0$ in P_1, and so on. A complete list of the productions of P_1 is:

$$[S] \to 0[B] \qquad [S] \to 1\varphi$$
$$[B] \to 0[A, B] \qquad [B] \to 1[S] \qquad [B] \to 0$$
$$[A, B] \to 0[A, B] \qquad [A, B] \to 1[S] \qquad [A, B] \to 0$$
$$\varphi \to 0\varphi \qquad \varphi \to 1\varphi$$

The grammar G_1 is much more complicated than is G, but $L(G_1) = L(G)$. The reader can simplify grammar G_1 so that its equivalence to G is readily observable.

3.5 PROPERTIES OF TYPE 3 LANGUAGES

Since the class of languages generated by type 3 grammars is equivalent to the class of sets accepted by finite automata, we shall use both formulations in establishing the properties of the class of type 3 languages. First we intend to show that the type 3 languages form a Boolean algebra† of sets.

Lemma 3.1. The class of type 3 languages is closed under union.

Proof. Two proofs are possible. One involves the use of nondeterministic finite automata. We leave this proof to the reader. A proof using grammars is also easy, and is given here.

Let L_1 and L_2 be type 3 languages generated by type 3 grammars

$$G_1 = (V_N^{(1)}, V_T^{(1)}, P_1, S_1) \qquad \text{and} \qquad G_2 = (V_N^{(2)}, V_T^{(2)}, P_2, S_2),$$

respectively. By renaming symbols, if necessary, we can assume that $V_N^{(1)}$ and $V_N^{(2)}$ contain no symbols in common, and that S is in neither. We construct a new grammar,

$$G_3 = (V_N^{(1)} \cup V_N^{(2)} \cup \{S\}, V_T^{(1)} \cup V_T^{(2)}, P_3, S),$$

where P_3 consists of the productions of P_1 and P_2 except for $S_1 \to \epsilon$ or $S_2 \to \epsilon$, plus all productions of the form $S \to \alpha$ such that either $S_1 \to \alpha$ is in P_1 or $S_2 \to \alpha$ is in P_2.

It should be obvious that $S \underset{G_3}{\Rightarrow} \alpha$ if and only if $S_1 \underset{G_1}{\Rightarrow} \alpha$ or $S_2 \underset{G_2}{\Rightarrow} \alpha$. In the first case, only strings in alphabet $V_N^{(1)} \cup V_T^{(1)}$ can be derived from α. In the second case, only strings in $V_N^{(2)} \cup V_T^{(2)}$ can be derived from α. Formally, if $S_1 \underset{G_1}{\Rightarrow} \alpha$, then $\alpha \underset{G_3}{\overset{*}{\Rightarrow}} w$ if and only if $\alpha \underset{G_1}{\overset{*}{\Rightarrow}} w$, and if $S_2 \underset{G_2}{\Rightarrow} \alpha$, then $\alpha \underset{G_3}{\overset{*}{\Rightarrow}} w$ if and only if $\alpha \underset{G_2}{\overset{*}{\Rightarrow}} w$. Putting the above together, $S \underset{G_3}{\overset{*}{\Rightarrow}} w$ if and only if either $S_1 \underset{G_1}{\overset{*}{\Rightarrow}} w$ or $S_2 \underset{G_2}{\overset{*}{\Rightarrow}} w$. That is, $L(G_3) = L(G_1) \cup L(G_2)$.

---

† For our purposes a Boolean algebra of sets is a collection of sets closed under union, complement, and intersection. By the complement $\bar{L}$ of a language L, we mean $\Sigma^* - L$, for a finite set of symbols Σ, such that $L \subseteq \Sigma^*$.

Lemma 3.2. The class of sets accepted by finite automata (generated by type 3 grammars) is closed under complement.

Proof. Let $M_1 = (K, \Sigma_1, \delta_1, q_0, F)$ be a deterministic fa accepting a set S_1. Let Σ_2 be a finite alphabet containing Σ_1 and let d be a new state not in K. We construct M_2 to accept $\Sigma_2^* - S_1$. Let

$$M_2 = (K \cup \{d\}, \Sigma_2, \delta_2, q_0, (K - F) \cup \{d\}),$$

where $\delta_2(q, a) = \delta_1(q, a)$ for each q in K and a in Σ_1, $\delta_2(q, a) = d$ for each q in K and a in $\Sigma_2 - \Sigma_1$, and $\delta_2(d, a) = d$ for each a in Σ_2. Intuitively, M_2 is obtained by extending the input alphabet of M_1 to Σ_2, adding the "trap" state d and then interchanging final and nonfinal states. Clearly, M_2 accepts $\Sigma_2^* - S_1$.

Theorem 3.6. The class of sets accepted by finite automata forms a Boolean algebra.

Proof. Immediate from Lemmas 3.1 and 3.2 and the fact that

$$L_1 \cap L_2 = \overline{\overline{L_1} \cup \overline{L_2}}.$$

We now give some additional theorems which will culminate in the characterization of the type 3 languages.

Theorem 3.7. All finite sets are accepted by finite automata.

Proof. Consider the set containing only the sentence $x = a_1 a_2 \ldots a_n$. We can design a finite automaton M with $n + 2$ states $q_0, q_1, q_2, \ldots, q_n$, and p. The initial state is q_0, and q_n is the only final state. As M sees successive symbols of x, it moves to successively higher-numbered states. If M sees a symbol which is not the next symbol of x, M goes to state p which is a "trap state" with no exit. Formally,

$$\delta(q_{i-1}, a_i) = q_i, \qquad 1 \leq i \leq n,$$

$$\delta(q_{i-1}, a) = p, \qquad 1 \leq i \leq n, \qquad \text{if } a \neq a_i$$

and

$$\delta(q_n, a) = \delta(p, a) = p \qquad \text{for all } a.$$

The reader should be able to supply the steps necessary to show that M accepts the sentence x. The set containing only the empty sentence is accepted by $M = (\{q_0, p\}, \Sigma, \delta, q_0, \{q_0\})$ where $\delta(q_0, a) = \delta(p, a) = p$ for each a in Σ. The empty set is accepted by $M = (\{q_0\}, \Sigma, \delta, q_0, \varphi)$ where $\delta(q_0, a) = q_0$ for each a in Σ.

The theorem follows immediately from the closure of type 3 languages under union.

We now define the *product*† UV of two languages U and V by

$$UV = \{x|x = uv, u \text{ is in } U \text{ and } v \text{ is in } V\}.$$

That is, each string in the set UV is formed by concatenating a string in U with a string in V. As an example, if $U = \{01, 11\}$ and $V = \{1, 0, 101\}$, then the set UV is $\{011, 010, 01101, 111, 110, 11101\}$.

Theorem 3.8. The class of sets accepted by finite automata (generated by type 3 grammars) is closed under product.

Proof. Let $M_1 = (K_1, \Sigma_1, \delta_1, q_1, F_1)$ and $M_2 = (K_2, \Sigma_2, \delta_2, q_2, F_2)$ be deterministic finite automata accepting languages L_1 and L_2, respectively. Assume that K_1 and K_2 are disjoint. Furthermore, without loss of generality, we can assume that $\Sigma_1 = \Sigma_2 = \Sigma$. (Otherwise, we can add "dead" states to K_1 and K_2 as in the proof of Lemma 3.2.) We construct a nondeterministic finite automaton M_3, accepting $L_1 L_2$, which operates as follows. If the input string is x, M_3 behaves as M_1 until some initial portion (possibly ϵ) of x has been scanned. At this point, if M_1 would accept, M_3 guesses whether the end of the string from L_1 has been reached, or whether a longer initial portion is the string from L_1. In the former case, M_3 acts subsequently as M_2, and in the latter case, M_3 continues to behave as M_1.

Formally, let $M_3 = (K_1 \cup K_2, \Sigma, \delta_3, q_1, F)$. For each a in Σ let:

1. $\delta_3(q, a) = \{\delta_1(q, a)\}$ for each q in $K_1 - F_1$.
2. $\delta_3(q, a) = \{\delta_1(q, a), \delta_2(q_2, a)\}$ for each q in F_1.
3. $\delta_3(q, a) = \{\delta_2(q, a)\}$ for each q in K_2.

The purpose of Rule 1 is to allow M_3 to act like M_1 for some initial segment of the input (possibly ϵ). Rule 2 allows M_3 to continue the simulation of M_1 or to guess that a given symbol starts a word in L_2, provided that the previous symbol completed a word in L_1. Rule 3 allows only the simulation of M_2 after M_3 has guessed that the word from L_2 has been started.

If ϵ is not in L_2, then $F = F_2$. If ϵ is in L_2, then $F = F_1 \cup F_2$.

The *closure* of a language L, denoted by L^*, is the set consisting of the empty string and all finite-length strings formed by concatenating words in L. Thus, if $L = \{01, 11\}$, then $L^* = \{\epsilon, 01, 11, 0101, 0111, 1101, 1111, 010101, \ldots\}$. An alternative definition is $L^* = L^0 \cup L^1 \cup L^2 \cup \ldots$, where $L^0 = \{\epsilon\}$ and $L^i = L^{i-1}L$, for $i > 0$.

Theorem 3.9. The class of sets accepted by finite automata is closed under set closure.

---

† Also known as *concatenation* of sets.

Proof. Let $M = (K, \Sigma, \delta, q_0, F)$ be a finite automaton accepting L. We construct a nondeterministic finite automaton M', which behaves as M until an initial portion of a sentence x takes M to a final state. At this time, M' will guess whether or not this point corresponds to a point where a new string from L starts. Formally,

$$M' = (K \cup \{q_0'\}, \Sigma, \delta', \{q_0'\}, F \cup \{q_0'\}),$$

where q_0' is a new state, and

$$\begin{aligned}
\delta'(q_0', a) &= \{\delta(q_0, a), q_0\}, & &\text{if } \delta(q_0, a) \text{ is in } F, \\
&= \{\delta(q_0, a)\}, & &\text{otherwise.} \\
\delta'(q, a) &= \{\delta(q, a), q_0\}, & &\text{if } \delta(q, a) \text{ is in } F, \\
&= \{\delta(q, a)\}, & &\text{otherwise, for all } q \text{ in } K.
\end{aligned}$$

The purpose of the new initial state q_0' is to accept the empty string. If q_0 is not in F, we cannot simply make q_0 a final state since M may come back to q_0 for some input strings. Since the proof is somewhat more difficult than that of the previous theorems, we give a formal proof.

Assume that x is in L^*. Then either $x = \epsilon$, or $x = x_1 x_2 \ldots x_n$, where x_i is in L for all i between 1 and n. Clearly M' accepts ϵ. Now x_i in L implies $\delta(q_0, x_i)$ is in F. Thus $\delta'(q_0', x_i)$ and $\delta'(q_0, x_i)$ each contain q_0 and some p (possibly $p = q_0$) in F. Hence, $\delta'(q_0', x)$ contains some state in F, and x is in $T(M')$.

Now assume that $x = a_1 a_2 \ldots a_m$ is in $T(M')$. Then there exists some sequence of states $q_1, q_2, \ldots, q_m$ such that $\delta'(q_0', a_1)$ contains q_1, and $\delta'(q_i, a_{i+1})$ contains q_{i+1}, $1 \leq i < m$, and q_m is in F. Thus, for each i, either $q_{i+1} = q_0$ and $\delta(q_i, a_{i+1})$ is in F or $\delta(q_i, a_{i+1}) = q_{i+1}$. Thus x can be written as $x_1 x_2 \ldots x_n$, so that $\delta(q_0, x_i)$ is in F for $1 \leq i \leq n$, implying that x_i is in L.

Theorem 3.10. The class of sets accepted by finite automata is the smallest class containing all finite sets and closed under union, product, and closure.

Proof. That the class of sets accepted by finite automata contains the smallest class containing all finite sets and closed under union, product, and closure, is an immediate consequence of Lemma 3.1 and Theorems 3.7, 3.8, and 3.9. It remains to show that the smallest class containing all finite sets and closed under union, product, and closure contains the class of sets accepted by finite automata.

Let L_1 be a set accepted by some finite automaton,

$$M = (\{q_1, \ldots, q_n\}, \Sigma, \delta, q_1, F).$$

Let R_{ij}^k denote the set of all strings x such that $\delta(q_i, x) = q_j$, and if $\delta(q_i, y) = q_l$, for any y which is an initial segment of x other than x or ϵ, then $l \leq k$.

That is, R_{ij}^k is the set of all strings which take the finite automaton from state q_i to state q_j without going through any state q_l, $l > k$. Note that by "going through a state," we mean both entering and leaving. Thus i or j may be greater than k. We can define R_{ij}^k recursively:

$$R_{ij}^k = R_{ik}^{k-1}(R_{kk}^{k-1})^*R_{kj}^{k-1} \cup R_{ij}^{k-1}$$

$$R_{ij}^0 = \{a \,|\, \delta(q_i, a) = q_j\}.$$

Informally, the definition of R_{ij}^k above means that the inputs that cause M to go from q_i to q_j without passing through a state higher than q_k are either:

1. in R_{ij}^{k-1}, that is, they never reach a state as high as q_k.
2. composed of a string in R_{ik}^{k-1} (which takes M to q_k for the first time) followed by some number of strings in R_{kk}^{k-1} (which take M from q_k back to q_k without passing through q_k otherwise) followed by a string in R_{kj}^{k-1} (which takes M from state q_k to q_j).

We can show, by induction on k, that R_{ij}^k, $0 \leq k \leq l$, is, for all i and j, within the smallest class containing all finite sets and closed under union, complex product, and closure. The induction hypothesis is true for $l = 0$, since all R_{ij}^0 are finite sets. If true for all $k \leq l$, then it is true for $k = l + 1$ since we can express R_{ij}^{l+1} in terms of union, concatenation, and closure of various sets of the form R_{mn}^l, each of which is presumed to be in the smallest class of sets containing the finite sets and closed under union, concatenation, and closure. Now $L_1 = \bigcup_{q_j \text{ in } F} R_{1j}^n$. Thus L_1 is in the smallest class of sets containing the finite sets, and closed under union, concatenation, and closure.

As a result of Theorem 3.10, we know that any expression made up of finite subsets of Σ^* for some finite alphabet Σ, and a finite number of the operators $\cup$, $\cdot$† and $*$, with parentheses to determine the order of operations, denotes a set that is accepted by a finite automaton. Furthermore, every set accepted by some fa can be so expressed. This provides us with a good notation for describing regular sets. For example, $\{0, 1\}^*\{000\}\{0, 1\}^*$ denotes the set of all strings with three consecutive 0's, and $(\{0, 1\}\{0, 1\})^* \cup (\{0, 1\}\{0,1\}\{0, 1\})^*$ denotes the set of all strings whose length is divisible by two or three.

3.6 SOLVABLE PROBLEMS CONCERNING FINITE AUTOMATA

In this section we show that there are algorithms to answer many questions concerning finite automata and type 3 languages. In Chapter 14 we shall see that no such algorithms can possibly exist to answer some of these questions for the other types of languages discussed in Chapter 2.

---

† $S_1 \cdot S_2$ is the product $S_1 S_2$.

Theorem 3.11. The set of sentences accepted by a finite automaton with n states is:

1. nonempty if and only if the finite automaton accepts a sentence of length less than n.
2. infinite if and only if the automaton accepts a sentence of length l, $n \leq l < 2n$.

Thus, there is an algorithm to determine if a finite automaton accepts zero, a finite number, or an infinite number of sentences.

Proof. (1) The "if" portion is obvious. Suppose that a finite automaton $M = (K, \Sigma, \delta, q_0, F)$, with n states accepts some word. Let w be a word as short as any other word accepted. We might as well assume that $|w| \geq n$, else the result is proven for M. Since there are but n states, M must pass through the same state twice in accepting w. Formally, we can find q in K such that we can write $w = w_1 w_2 w_3$, with $w_2 \neq \epsilon$, $\delta(q_0, w_1) = q$, $\delta(q, w_2) = q$, and $\delta(q, w_3)$ in F. Then $w_1 w_3$ is in $T(M)$, since

$$\delta(q_0, w_1 w_3) = \delta(q_0, w_1 w_2 w_3).$$

But $|w_1 w_3| < |w|$, contradicting the assumption that w is as short as any word in $T(M)$.

(2) We leave most of this part to the reader. We merely observe that if w is in $T(M)$ and $n \leq |w| < 2n$, then we can write $w = w_1 w_2 w_3$, $w_2 \neq \epsilon$, and for all i, $w_1 w_2^i w_3$ is in $T(M)$. Next, if M accepts an infinity of words, and none is of length between n and $2n - 1$, then let w be of length at least $2n$, but as short as any word in $T(M)$ whose length is $\geq 2n$. Then, we can write $w = w_1 w_2 w_3$, with $1 \leq |w_2| \leq n$, and $w_1 w_3$ in $T(M)$, thus deriving a contradiction.

In part (1), the algorithm to decide if $T(M)$ is empty is: "See if any word of length up to n is in $T(M)$." Clearly there is such a procedure which is guaranteed to halt. In part (2), the algorithm to decide if $T(M)$ is infinite is: "See if any word of length between n and $2n - 1$ is in $T(M)$." Again, clearly there is such a procedure which is guaranteed to halt.

We now show that there is an algorithm to determine if two type 3 grammars generate the same language. As we shall see later, no such algorithm exists for type 0, 1, or 2 grammars.

Theorem 3.12. There is an algorithm to determine if two finite automata are equivalent (i.e., if they accept the same language).

Proof. Let M_1 and M_2 be fa, accepting L_1 and L_2, respectively. By Theorem 3.6, $(L_1 \cap \bar{L}_2) \cup (\bar{L}_1 \cap L_2)$ is accepted by some finite automaton, M_3. It is easy to see that M_3 accepts a word if and only if $L_1 \neq L_2$. Hence, by Theorem 3.11, there is an algorithm to determine if $L_1 = L_2$.

3.7 TWO-WAY FINITE AUTOMATA

We now turn our attention to finite automata that can move two ways on their input tapes. Our reason for studying these is twofold. First it is easier to introduce the concept of moving two ways on the input with finite automata than with more complicated automata. Second, we wish to introduce the concept of a finite table being stored in a finite control, a tool we shall find useful later on.

A *two-way finite automaton* M will be represented by a 5-tuple $(K, \Sigma, \delta, q_0, F)$, where K is a set of states, Σ is the set of input symbols, δ is a mapping from $K \times \Sigma$ to $K \times \{L, R, S\}$, q_0 in K is the initial state, and $F \subseteq K$ is the set of final states. The interpretation of $\delta(q, a) = (p, D)$, p in K and D in $\{L, R, S\}$ is that M, in state q, scanning the input symbol a, will move its input head one cell to the left, to the right, or not move its input head at all, depending on whether D equals L, R, or S, respectively. The state of M will also be changed to state p. Note that δ cannot be extended from $K \times \Sigma$ to $K \times \Sigma^*$ in the obvious manner, since one must keep track of the net change in input position.

We define a *configuration* of M to be a state and a number (q, i), where q is the present state of M and i is the location of the input head. That is, i is the number of cells the input head is from the left end of the input.

A two-way finite automaton will start in state q_0 with its input head scanning the leftmost cell on the input tape. Should M ever move off either end of x, M halts. An input word will be *accepted* by M if and only if M eventually moves off the right end of x at the same time it enters a final state.

M can reject a word x by:

1. moving off the left end of x.
2. moving off the right end of x in a nonfinal state.
3. looping.

Theorem 3.13. The class of sets accepted by two-way finite automata is the same as the class of sets accepted by one-way finite automata.

Proof. Let $M = (K, \Sigma, \delta, q_0, F)$ be a two-way finite automaton and $x = a_1 a_2 \ldots a_n$ be the input to M. We can associate with each initial segment of x, $a_1 a_2 \ldots a_i$, a mapping Δ_i of K to $K \cup \{R\}$. We say that Δ_i is *associated* with $a_1 a_2 \ldots a_i$. The interpretation of $\Delta_i(q) = p$, p in K, is that if M is started in state q, scanning the ith cell, M will eventually move right to the $i + 1$st cell. On the move which takes M to the $i + 1$st cell for the first time, M enters state p. Note that before reaching the $i + 1$st cell M may move its input head back and forth on cells 1 through i many times.

The interpretation of $\Delta_i(q) = R$ is that if M is started in state q scanning the ith cell, M will reject x without ever having moved right from the ith cell to the $i + 1$st cell. That is, M will either enter a loop or move off the input tape to the left.

The number of distinct mappings of K to $K \cup \{R\}$ is $(s + 1)^s$, where s is the number of elements in K. We can define a one-way finite automaton $M' = (K', \Sigma, \delta', q_0', F')$, whose states except one are ordered pairs $[q, \Delta]$ where q is in K and Δ is a mapping of K to $K \cup \{R\}$.† Also in K' is a "trap state" t, having the property that $\delta'(t, a) = t$ for all a in Σ. The interpretation of the state $[q, \Delta]$ is that the one-way fa M' will be in state $[q, \Delta]$ after reading an input x if and only if the two-way finite automaton M would be in state q the first time M moves right from string x and the mapping Δ is the mapping associated with the string x. Thus M' carries in its finite control a table which contains the information as to the eventual outcome if M moves left into x in any state.

We define the mapping δ' as follows.

$$\delta'([q_1, \Delta_1], a) = [q_2, \Delta_2]$$

exactly when we can compute q_2 and Δ_2 from q_1 and Δ_1 by:

1. $\Delta_2(p_1) = p$ if there exists a sequence of states $p_2, p_3, \ldots, p_n, p$, such that either

$$\delta(p_i, a) = (p_{i+1}, S)$$

or

$$\delta(p_i, a) = (p_i', L)$$

and

$$\Delta_1(p_i') = p_{i+1}$$

for all i, where $1 \leq i < n$. Finally, $\delta(p_n, a) = (p, R)$.
2. $\Delta_2(p_1) = R$ if there is no finite sequence satisfying (1). Note that if any sequence $p_1, p_2, \ldots, p_n, p$ satisfies (1), then there is a sequence satisfying (1) such that no state appears twice in the sequence.
3. $q_2 = \Delta_2(q_1)$. If $\Delta_2(q_1) = R$, however, there is no such q_2, therefore $\delta'([q_1, \Delta_1], a)$ is t, the trap state.

Informally, to compute $\Delta_2(p_1)$, assume that Δ_1 is associated with the first $j - 1$ symbols. We begin constructing a sequence of states $p_1, p_2, \ldots$ by adding to the sequence, each time M scans the jth cell, the state of M at that time. Hopefully, from one of these states, M will move to the right and enter some state p. Then we can end the sequence, since we have $\Delta_2(p_1) = p$. Suppose that we have constructed the sequence $p_1, p_2, \ldots, p_i$. Then the fa M will be in configuration (p_i, j), scanning an a on its input. Three cases arise:

1. $\delta(p_i, a) = (q, S)$. Here M will again scan cell j, this time in state q. So $p_{i+1} = q$.

---

† Do not confuse R in the range of Δ, which means reject, with R in the range of δ which means move right.

2. $\delta(p_i, a) = (q, R)$. Here, we have our answer. M has moved to cell $j + 1$ for the first time and entered state q. Thus, q has the role of p in the sequence, i.e., $\Delta_2(p_1) = q$.

3. $\delta(p_i, a) = (q, L)$. Here, M next moves left to cell $j - 1$. We consult Δ_1 to see what happens next. If $\Delta_1(q) = R$, then M will never again scan cell j, so it cannot scan $j + 1$ either. We therefore let $\Delta_2(p_1) = R$. If $\Delta_1(q) = q'$, then $p_{i+1} = q'$.

The above process will produce a value for $\Delta_2(p_1)$ in all cases, provided that the sequence $p_1, p_2, \ldots$ never repeats a state. If a state is repeated, M is in a loop and will never reach cell $j + 1$. In this case, $\Delta_2(p_1) = R$. We have now covered all contingencies. We leave it to the reader to see that if Δ_1 is the table associated with input x, then Δ_2 will be the table associated with xa.

If M' is to be a one-way finite automaton simulating M, we must let its initial state, q'_0, be $[q_0, \Delta_0]$, where Δ_0 is the table associated with ϵ, i.e., $\Delta_0(q) = R$ for all q. Also,

$$F' = \{[q, \Delta] \mid q \text{ is in } F\}.$$

We must now prove by induction on the length of input x that M' moves right in state $[q, \Delta]$ (for some Δ) from x if and only if M moves right from x in q. Thus M' accepts x if and only if M does. If x is of length 1, the result follows from the way $\delta'([q_0, \Delta_0], x)$ is constructed. That is, if and only if $\delta'([q_0, \Delta_0], x) = [q, \Delta]$, will M eventually move to the right from its first input symbol and enter state q at that time. Note $[q, \Delta]$ is accepting if and only if q is accepting for M.

Suppose that the result is true for $|x| < k$, and let xa be an input of length k. Then M will scan the final symbol, a, of xa for the first time in state q if and only if $\delta'([q_0, \Delta_0], x) = [q, \Delta_1]$ for some Δ_1. But then M will move to the right from xa and enter state p if and only if $\delta'([q, \Delta_1], a) = [p, \Delta_2]$, for the proper Δ_2. This follows from the construction of Δ_2 from Δ_1 just given. The acceptance of xa by M occurs if and only if p is in F. But then $[p, \Delta_2]$ is in F', so M' accepts xa.

Example 3.7. Consider the two-way finite automaton.

$$M = (\{q_0, q_1\}, \{a, b\}, \delta, q_0, \{q_1\})$$

where δ is defined by:

$$\delta(q_0, a) = (q_0, R) \quad \delta(q_0, b) = (q_1, S) \quad \delta(q_1, a) = (q_0, L) \quad \delta(q_1, b) = (q_0, L).$$

We can construct a one-way finite automaton $M' = (K, \{a, b\}, \delta', q'_0, F)$ equivalent to M. Here K is the set of objects of the form $[q, \Delta]$, where $q = q_0$ or q_1 and Δ is a map from $\{q_0, q_1\}$ to $\{q_0, q_1, R\}$, plus a trap state. There are nine possible values of Δ. The set of all $[q_1, \Delta]$ is F.

$$q'_0 = [q_0, \Delta_0], \quad \text{where } \Delta_0(q_0) = \Delta_0(q_1) = R.$$

Since M' has 19 states, we shall not construct δ' for all of these, but simply give one case. We compute

$$\delta'([q_0, \Delta_1], a) \qquad \text{and} \qquad \delta'([q_0, \Delta_1], b),$$

where $\Delta_1(q_0) = q_0$ and $\Delta_1(q_1) = q_1$. Let

$$\delta'([q_0, \Delta_1], a) = [q_a, \Delta_a] \qquad \text{and} \qquad \delta'([q_0, \Delta_1], b) = [q_b, \Delta_b].$$

To compute $\Delta_a(q_0)$, we note that $\delta(q_0, a) = (q_0, R)$. Thus M immediately moves to the right from a and enters state q_0. We have $\Delta_a(q_0) = q_0$. For $\Delta_a(q_1)$, we note that $\delta(q_1, a) = (q_0, L)$. Thus, we must consult $\Delta_1(q_0)$ to see if M will ever return to the symbol a. We have $\Delta_1(q_0) = q_0$, so M does return in state q_0. From a, in state q_0, M next moves to the right, remaining in q_0, since $\delta(q_0, a) = (q_0, R)$. Hence

$$\Delta_a(q_1) = q_0 \qquad \text{and} \qquad q_a = \Delta_a(q_0) = q_0.$$

To compute $\Delta_b(q_0)$, note that $\delta(q_0, b) = (q_1, S)$, so M would remain scanning the b, but in state q_1. Next, $\delta(q_1, b) = (q_0, L)$. Now, $\Delta_1(q_0) = q_0$, so M would return to a in state q_0, where it started. M is in a loop, so $\Delta_b(q_0) = R$. Likewise, $\Delta_b(q_1) = R$. But $\Delta_b(q_0) = R$, so $\delta'([q_0, \Delta_1], b)$ is the trap state.

PROBLEMS

3.1 Find a one-way, deterministic finite automaton accepting all strings in $\{0, 1\}^*$ such that every 0 has a 1 immediately to its right.

3.2 From the finite automaton of Problem 3.1, construct a type 3 grammar generating the language of that problem.

3.3 Give an example of a relation which is:

a) reflexive and symmetric, but not transitive.
b) symmetric and transitive, but not reflexive.
c) reflexive and transitive, but not symmetric.

3.4 Let

$$M = (\{q_0, q_1, q_2\}, \{a, b\}, \delta, q_0, \{q_2\})$$

be a nondeterministic finite automaton, with

$$\delta(q_0, a) = \{q_1, q_2\} \qquad \delta(q_1, a) = \{q_0, q_1\} \qquad \delta(q_2, a) = \{q_0, q_2\}$$
$$\delta(q_0, b) = \{q_0\} \qquad \delta(q_1, b) = \varphi \qquad \delta(q_2, b) = \{q_1\}.$$

Find a deterministic finite automaton accepting $T(M)$.

3.5 Complete the specification of the one-way finite automaton in Example 3.7.

3.6 Use the notion of a nondeterministic finite automaton to show that if L is a type 3 language, then

$$L^R = \{w \mid w \text{ reversed is in } L\}$$

is a type 3 language.

3.7 From Problem 3.6, show that grammars where all productions are of the form $A \to Bb$ or $A \to b$, A and B variables, b terminal, generate all and only the type 3 languages.

3.8 A nondeterministic two-way finite automaton is denoted by $M = (K, \Sigma, \delta, q_0, F)$ as the two-way deterministic finite automaton, except that $\delta(q, a)$, for q in K and a in Σ, is a subset of $K \times \{L, R, S\}$. Each (p, D) in $\delta(q, a)$ represents a possible move of M when the automaton is in state q scanning a on its input. If any sequence of choices of moves causes M to move off the right end of its input in an accepting state, M accepts. Show that only type 3 languages are accepted by nondeterministic, two-way finite automata.

3.9 Let L be a type 3 language. Let Init (L) be the set of words x, such that for some word y, xy is in L. Show that Init (L) is a type 3 language.

3.10 Let R be a type 3 language consisting only of words whose length is divisible by 3. Consider the language formed by taking the first third of each sentence in R. Is this language a type 3 language? What about the last third? Middle third? What about the language formed by concatenating the first and last third of each word in R?

3.11 Some people allow a two-way finite automaton to have an end marker, $\mathrm{\mathcal{c}}$, at the left end of each tape. This finite automaton is said to accept w if it moves off the right end of $\mathrm{\mathcal{c}}w$ while entering a final state. Show that under this definition, it is still only regular sets which are accepted.

REFERENCES

The notion of a finite state device is usually attributed to McCulloch and Pitts [1943]. The formalism we have used was suggested in Moore [1956] and is found in Rabin and Scott [1959].

Theorem 3.1 is from Nerode [1958] and was proven in a slightly weaker form by Myhill. The minimization of finite automata (Theorem 3.2) appeared originally in Huffman [1954] and Moore [1956]. Nondeterministic finite automata and Theorem 3.3 are from Rabin and Scott [1959]; Theorem 3.13 and two-way finite automata are found in Rabin and Scott [1959] and Shepherdson [1959]. Theorem 3.10 is from Kleene [1956]. The description of regular languages that follows Theorem 3.10 is known as a "regular expression," and is from Kleene [1956]. Many results concerning regular expressions can be found in Brzozowski [1962] and McNaughton and Yamada [1960]. The algorithms in Section 3.6 are from Moore [1956], and the results of Section 3.4 relating type 3 grammars and finite automata are from Chomsky and Miller [1958].

Many books have been written on the subject of finite automata. Among them are Gill [1962] and Ginsburg [1962]. Finite automata are also covered extensively by Harrison [1965], Booth [1967], and Minsky [1967].

CHAPTER 4

CONTEXT-FREE GRAMMARS

4.1 SIMPLIFICATION OF CONTEXT-FREE GRAMMARS

In this chapter we describe some of the basic simplifications of context-free grammars and prove several important normal-form theorems. One of these will be the *Chomsky Normal-Form Theorem*, which states that every context-free language is generated by a grammar for which all productions are of the form $A \to BC$ or $A \to b$.† Here A, B, and C are variables, and b is a terminal.

Another is the *Greibach Normal-Form Theorem*, which states that every context-free language is generated by a grammar for which all productions are of the form $A \to b\alpha$, where b is a terminal and α is a string of variables.

We also show that there exist algorithms to determine whether the language generated by a context-free grammar is empty, finite, or infinite. We define a property of certain context-free grammars, called the self-embedding property, and show that a context-free language is nonregular if and only if every type 2 grammar generating the language has the self-embedding property. Finally we consider certain special types of restricted context-free grammars such as sequential grammars and linear grammars.

The formal definition of a context-free grammar allows for certain structures which are in a sense "wasteful." For example, the vocabulary could include variables that can never be used in the derivation of a terminal string, or there might be a production of the form $A \to A$ for some variable, A. Thus we prove several theorems to show that every context-free language can be generated by a context-free grammar of a specified form. Furthermore, we show that algorithms exist which, for any context-free grammar, will find an equivalent context-free grammar in one of the specified forms. First, we prove a result which is quite important in its own right.

Theorem 4.1. There is an algorithm for determining if the language generated by a given context-free grammar is empty.

---

† Until Section 4.6, we shall revert to the original definition of a cfg and not allow ϵ to be in any cfl. The reader can easily supply the appropriate modification to include the case where $S \to \epsilon$ can be a production.

Proof. Let $G = (V_N, V_T, P, S)$ be a context-free grammar. Suppose that $S \overset{*}{\Rightarrow} w$ for some terminal string w. Consider a derivation tree of w in the grammar G. Suppose that there is a path in the tree with two nodes, n_1 and n_2, having the same label A, with n_1 higher on the path than n_2.† Here we can refer to Fig. 4.1. The subtree with root at n_1 represents the generation of a word w_1, such that $A \overset{*}{\Rightarrow} w_1$. The subtree with root at n_2 likewise represents the generation of a word w_2, such that $A \overset{*}{\Rightarrow} w_2$. (Note that w_2 must be a subword of w_1, perhaps all of w_1.)

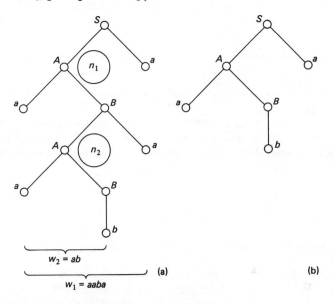

$G = (\{S,A,B\},\{a,b\},\{S{\rightarrow}Aa,A{\rightarrow}aB,B{\rightarrow}Aa,B{\rightarrow}b\},S)$.

Fig. 4.1. Obtaining the tree for the derivation of $w_3w_2w_4 = aba$ from the tree for the derivation of $w = aabaa$.

Now the word w can be written in the form $w_3w_1w_4$ where w_3 or w_4, or both, may be ϵ. If we replace the subtree of n_1 by that of n_2, we have a new word, $w_3w_2w_4$ (possibly the same word), such that $S \overset{*}{\Rightarrow} w_3w_2w_4$. In Fig. 4.1, $w_3 = \epsilon$ and $w_4 = a$. A tree for $S \overset{*}{\Rightarrow} w_3w_2w_4$ is shown in Fig. 4.1(b). However, we have eliminated at least one node, n_1, from the tree. If the new tree has a path with two identically labeled nodes, the process may be repeated with $w_3w_2w_4$ instead of w. In fact, the process may be repeated until

---

† A *path* is a connected sequence of directed edges. The *length* of a path is the number of edges in the path.

there are no paths in the tree with two nodes labeled identically. Since each iteration eliminates one or more nodes, the process must eventually terminate.

Now consider the tree which is ultimately produced. If there are m variables in the grammar G, then there can be no path of length greater than m, lest some variable would be repeated in this path. We conclude that if G generates any word at all, then there is a derivation of a word whose tree contains no path of length greater than m. Thus the following algorithm will determine if $L(G)$ is empty.

Form a collection of trees corresponding to derivations in G as follows. Start the collection with the tree containing the single node labeled S. Repeatedly add to the collection any tree that can be obtained from a tree already in the collection by application of a single production and that:

1. is not already in the collection, and
2. does not have any path of length greater than m.

Since there are a finite number of trees corresponding to derivations with no path length greater than m, the process must eventually terminate. Now $L(G)$ is nonempty if and only if at least one of the trees in the collection corresponds to the derivation of a terminal string.

The existence of an algorithm to determine whether a given cfl is empty is very important. We shall use this fact extensively in simplifying context-free grammars. As we shall see later, for more complex types of grammars, such as the context-sensitive grammars, no such algorithm exists.

Theorem 4.2. Given any context-free grammar $G = (V_N, V_T, P, S)$, generating a nonempty language, it is possible to find an equivalent grammar G_1, such that for every variable A of G_1 there is a terminal string w, such that $A \xrightarrow{*} w$.

Proof. For each variable A in V_N, consider the grammar $G_A = (V_N, V_T, P, A)$. If the language $L(G_A)$ is empty, then we can remove A from V_N, and we can remove all productions involving A, either on the right or left, from P.

After deleting from G all occurrences of variables A such that $L(G_A)$ is empty, we have a new grammar $G_1 = (V_N', V_T, P', S)$ where V_N' and P' are the remaining variables and productions. Clearly $L(G_1) \subseteq L(G)$, since a derivation in G_1 is a derivation in G. Suppose that there is a word w in $L(G)$ which is not in $L(G_1)$. Then some derivation of w must involve a sentential form $\alpha_1 A \alpha_2$, where A is in $V_N - V_N'$ and $S \underset{G}{\xrightarrow{*}} \alpha_1 A \alpha_2 \underset{G}{\xrightarrow{*}} w$. Then, however, there must be some w_1 in V_T^* such that $A \underset{G}{\xrightarrow{*}} w_1$, a fact that contradicts the requirement that A be in $V_N - V_N'$.

In addition to removing variables from which no terminal string can be derived, we can also remove variables which are useless in the sense that they can never appear in a derivation.

Theorem 4.3. Given any context-free grammar generating a nonempty cfl L, it is possible to find a grammar G, generating L, such that for each variable A there is a derivation

$$S \overset{*}{\Rightarrow} w_1 A w_3 \overset{*}{\Rightarrow} w_1 w_2 w_3,$$

where w_1, w_2, and w_3 are in V_T^*.

Proof. Let $G_1 = (V_N, V_T, P, S)$ be any grammar generating L that satisfies Theorem 4.2. If $S \overset{*}{\Rightarrow} \alpha_1 A \alpha_2$, α_1 and α_2 in V^*, then there exists a derivation $S \overset{*}{\Rightarrow} w_1 A w_2 \overset{*}{\Rightarrow} w_1 w_2 w_3$, since terminal strings can be derived from A and from all variables appearing in α_1 and α_2. We can effectively construct the set V_N' of all variables A, such that $S \overset{*}{\Rightarrow} \alpha_1 A \alpha_2$, as follows. Start by placing S in the set. Add to the set any variable which appears on the right-hand side of any production $A \rightarrow \alpha$, if A is in the set. The procedure stops when no new members can be added to the set.

Let $G_2 = (V_N', V_T, P', S)$ where P' is the set of productions remaining after removing all productions from P which have variables in $V_N - V_N'$ on either the left or right. Now $L(G) = L(G')$, as one can easily show, and G_2 satisfies the condition of the theorem.

Before the next theorem, let us introduce the concept of a *leftmost derivation*. We say that a derivation is leftmost if, at every step, the variable replaced has no variable to its left in the sentential form from which the replacement is made. That is, if $S \Rightarrow \alpha_1 \Rightarrow \alpha_2 \Rightarrow \cdots \Rightarrow \alpha_n$ is a leftmost derivation in some grammar $G = (V_N, V_T, P, S)$, then for $1 \leq i < n$, we can write α_i as $x_i A_i \beta_i$, where the string x_i is in the set V_T^*, β_i is an arbitrary string in V^*, A_i is a variable and $A_i \rightarrow \gamma_i$ is a production of P. Finally, $x_i \gamma_i \beta_i$ is α_{i+1}, and α_{i+1} was derived from α_i by replacing A_i by γ_i.

Lemma 4.1. Given a context-free grammar $G = (V_N, V_T, P, S)$, if $S \overset{*}{\underset{G}{\Rightarrow}} w$, then there is a leftmost derivation of w in G.

Proof. We prove by induction on the number of steps in the derivation that if A is any variable and $A \overset{*}{\underset{G}{\Rightarrow}} w$, w in V_T^*, then $A \overset{*}{\underset{G}{\Rightarrow}} w$ by a leftmost derivation. The statement is trivially true for one-step derivations. Suppose that it is true for derivations of k or fewer steps. Let $A \Rightarrow \alpha_1 \overset{*}{\Rightarrow} w$ be a $k + 1$ step derivation in G and suppose that $\alpha_1 = B_1 B_2 \ldots B_m$, where B_i is in V, $1 \leq i \leq m$. The first step of the derivation is clearly $A \Rightarrow B_1 B_2 \ldots B_m$. We can write w as $u_1 u_2 \ldots u_m$, where $B_i \overset{*}{\Rightarrow} u_i$, for $1 \leq i \leq m$. By the inductive hypothesis, there exist leftmost derivations of u_i from B_i, $1 \leq i \leq m$. Note that B_i may be a terminal, in which case $B_i = u_i$ and the derivation takes no steps. Thus the first step of the derivation of w is followed by a leftmost derivation of u_1 from B_1, yielding a leftmost derivation of $u_1B_2B_3\ldots B_m$ from A. Now u_1 is in V_T^*, so a leftmost derivation of u_2 from B_2 will not violate the definition of a leftmost derivation of w from A. In turn, we replace each B_i which is not a terminal by u_i according to a leftmost derivation. It is easy to see that the definition of a leftmost derivation for $A \overset{*}{\Rightarrow} w$ is never violated.

Theorem 4.4. Given a context-free grammar G, we can find an equivalent grammar G_1 with no productions of the form $A \to B$, where A and B are variables.

Proof. Let G be the grammar (V_N, V_T, P, S). Call the productions in P of the form $A \to B$, A and B in V_N, "type x" productions and all other productions "type y."

We construct a new set of productions P_1 from P by first including all type y productions of P. Then, suppose that $A \overset{*}{\underset{G}{\Rightarrow}} B$, for A and B in V_N. We add to P_1 all productions of the form $A \to \alpha$, where $B \to \alpha$ is a type y production of P.

Observe that we can easily test if $A \overset{*}{\underset{G}{\Rightarrow}} B$, since if

$$A \underset{G}{\Rightarrow} B_1 \underset{G}{\Rightarrow} B_2 \underset{G}{\Rightarrow} \cdots \Rightarrow B_m \underset{G}{\Rightarrow} B,$$

and some variable appears twice in the sequence, we can find a shorter sequence of type x productions which will result in $A \overset{*}{\underset{G}{\Rightarrow}} B$. Thus it is sufficient to consider only those sequences of type x productions whose length is less than the number of variables of G.

We now have a modified grammar, $G_1 = (V_N, V_T, P_1, S)$. Surely, if $A \to \alpha$ is a production of P_1, then $A \overset{*}{\underset{G}{\Rightarrow}} \alpha$. Thus if there is a derivation of w in G_1, then there is a derivation of w in G.

Now suppose that w is in $L(G)$ and consider a leftmost derivation of w in G, say $S = \alpha_0 \underset{G}{\Rightarrow} \alpha_1 \underset{G}{\Rightarrow} \cdots \underset{G}{\Rightarrow} \alpha_n = w$. If, for $0 \leq i < n$, $\alpha_i \underset{G}{\Rightarrow} \alpha_{i+1}$ by a type y production, then $\alpha_i \underset{G_1}{\Rightarrow} \alpha_{i+1}$. Suppose that $\alpha_i \underset{G}{\Rightarrow} \alpha_{i+1}$ by a type x production, but that $\alpha_{i-1} \underset{G}{\Rightarrow} \alpha_i$ by a type y production unless $i = 0$. Also, suppose that $\alpha_{i+1} \underset{G}{\Rightarrow} \alpha_{i+2} \underset{G}{\Rightarrow} \cdots \underset{G}{\Rightarrow} \alpha_j$ all by type x productions and $\alpha_j \underset{G}{\Rightarrow} \alpha_{j+1}$ by a type y production. Then $\alpha_i, \alpha_{i+1}, \ldots, \alpha_j$ are all of the same length, and since the derivation is leftmost, the symbol replaced in each of these must be at the same position. But then $\alpha_i \underset{G_1}{\Rightarrow} \alpha_{j+1}$ by one of the productions of $P_1 - P$. Hence $L(G_1) = L(G)$.

4.2 CHOMSKY NORMAL FORM

We now prove the first of two normal-form theorems. These each state that all context-free grammars are equivalent to grammars with restrictions on the forms of productions.

Theorem 4.5. (*Chomsky Normal Form.*) Any context-free language can be generated by a grammar in which all productions are of the form $A \to BC$ or $A \to a$. Here A, B, and C are variables and a is a terminal.

Proof. Let G be a context-free grammar. By Theorem 4.4, we can find an equivalent grammar, $G_1 = (V_N, V_T, P, S)$, such that P contains no productions of the form $A \to B$, where A and B are variables. Thus, if a production has a single symbol on the right, that symbol is a terminal, and the production is already in an acceptable form.

Now consider a production in P, of the form $A \to B_1 B_2 \ldots B_m$, where $m \geq 2$. Each terminal B_i is replaced by a new variable C_i, which appears on the right of no other production. We then create a new production $C_i \to B_i$ which is of allowable form, since B_i is a terminal. The production $A \to B_1 B_2 \ldots B_m$ is replaced by $A \to C_1 C_2 \ldots C_m$ where $C_i = B_i$ if B_i is a variable.

Let the new set of variables be V_N', and the new set of productions, P'. Consider the grammar $G_2 = (V_N', V_T, P', S)$.† If $\alpha \underset{G_1}{\Rightarrow} \beta$, then $\alpha \underset{G_2}{\overset{*}{\Rightarrow}} \beta$. Thus $L(G_1) \subseteq L(G_2)$. Now we show by induction on the number of steps in a derivation that if $A \underset{G_2}{\overset{*}{\Rightarrow}} w$, A in V_N and w in V_T^*, then $A \underset{G_1}{\overset{*}{\Rightarrow}} w$. The result is trivial for one-step derivations. Suppose that it is true for derivations of up to k steps. Let $A \underset{G_2}{\overset{*}{\Rightarrow}} w$ by a $k + 1$ step derivation. The first step must be of the form

$$A \Rightarrow C_1 C_2 \ldots C_m, \qquad m \geq 2.$$

We can write

$$w = w_1 w_2 \ldots w_m, \qquad \text{where } C_i \underset{G_2}{\overset{*}{\Rightarrow}} w_i, \quad 1 \leq i \leq m.$$

If C_i is in $V_N' - V_N$, then there is only one production of P' we may use, namely $C_i \to a_i$ for some a_i in V_T. In this case, $a_i = w_i$. By the construction of P', there is a production $A \to B_1 B_2 \ldots B_m$ of P where $B_i = C_i$ if C_i is in V_N and $B_i = a_i$ if C_i is in $V_N' - V_N$. For those C_i in V_N, we know that the derivation $C_i \underset{G_2}{\overset{*}{\Rightarrow}} w_i$ takes no more than k steps, so by the inductive hypothesis, $B_i \underset{G_1}{\overset{*}{\Rightarrow}} w_i$. Hence $A \underset{G_1}{\overset{*}{\Rightarrow}} w$.

---

† Note that G_2 is not yet in Chomsky normal form.

We have now proved the intermediate result that any context-free language can be generated by a grammar for which every production is either of the form $A \to a$ or $A \to B_1 B_2 \ldots B_m$, for $m \geq 2$. Here A and B_1, $B_2, \ldots, B_m$ are variables and a is a terminal.

Let us consider such a grammar $G_2 = (V'_N, V_T, P', S)$. We modify G_2 by adding some additional symbols to V'_N and replacing some productions of P'. For each production $A \to B_1 B_2 \ldots B_m$ of P' for $m \geq 3$ we create new variables $D_1, D_2, \ldots, D_{m-2}$ and replace $A \to B_1 B_2 \ldots B_m$ by the set of productions

$$\{A \to B_1 D_1, \; D_1 \to B_2 D_2, \ldots, \; D_{m-3} \to B_{m-2} D_{m-2}, \; D_{m-2} \to B_{m-1} B_m\}.$$

Let V''_N be the new nonterminal vocabulary and P'' the new set of productions. Let $G_3 = (V''_N, V_T, P'', S)$. It is clear that if $A \underset{G_2}{\overset{*}{\Rightarrow}} \beta$, then $A \underset{G_3}{\overset{*}{\Rightarrow}} \beta$ so $L(G_2) \subseteq L(G_3)$. But it is also true that $L(G_3) \subseteq L(G_2)$, as can be shown in essentially the same manner as it was shown that $L(G_2) \subseteq L(G_1)$. The proof will be left to the reader.

Example 4.1. Let us consider the grammar $(\{S, A, B\}, \{a, b\}, P, S)$ which has the productions:

$$
\begin{array}{ll}
S \to bA & S \to aB \\
A \to a & B \to b \\
A \to aS & B \to bS \\
A \to bAA & B \to aBB
\end{array}
$$

and find an equivalent grammar in Chomsky normal form.

First, the only productions already in proper form are $A \to a$ and $B \to b$. There are no productions of the form $C \to D$, where C and D are variables, so we may begin by replacing terminals on the right by variables, except in the case of the productions $A \to a$ and $B \to b$. $S \to bA$ is replaced by $S \to C_1 A$ and $C_1 \to b$. Similarly, $A \to aS$ is replaced by $A \to C_2 S$ and $C_2 \to a$. $A \to bAA$ is replaced by $A \to C_3 AA$ and $C_3 \to b$. $S \to aB$ is replaced by $S \to C_4 B$ and $C_4 \to a$. $B \to bS$ is replaced by $B \to C_5 S$ and $C_5 \to b$. $B \to aBB$ is replaced by $B \to C_6 BB$ and $C_6 \to a$.

In the next stage, the production $A \to C_3 AA$ is replaced by $A \to C_3 D_1$ and $D_1 \to AA$, and the production $B \to C_6 BB$ is replaced by $B \to C_6 D_2$ and $D_2 \to BB$. The productions for the grammar in Chomsky normal form are shown below.

$$
\begin{array}{llll}
S \to C_1 A & S \to C_4 B & C_1 \to b & C_4 \to a \\
A \to C_2 S & B \to C_5 S & C_2 \to a & C_5 \to b \\
A \to C_3 D_1 & B \to C_6 D_2 & C_3 \to b & C_6 \to a \\
D_1 \to AA & D_2 \to BB & A \to a & B \to b
\end{array}
$$

4.3 GREIBACH NORMAL FORM

We now develop a normal-form theorem which uses productions whose right-hand sides each start with a terminal symbol, perhaps followed by some variables. First we prove two lemmas which say we can modify the productions of a cfg in certain ways without affecting the language generated.

Lemma 4.2. Define an *A-production* to be a production with a variable A on the left. Let $G = (V_N, V_T, P, S)$ be a context-free grammar. Let $A \rightarrow \alpha_1 B \alpha_2$ be a production in P and $\{B \rightarrow \beta_1, B \rightarrow \beta_2, \ldots, B \rightarrow \beta_r\}$ be the set of all B-productions. Let $G_1 = (V_N, V_T, P_1, S)$ be obtained from G by deleting the production $A \rightarrow \alpha_1 B \alpha_2$ from P and adding the productions $A \rightarrow \alpha_1 \beta_1 \alpha_2, A \rightarrow \alpha_1 \beta_2 \alpha_2, \ldots, A \rightarrow \alpha_1 \beta_r \alpha_2$. Then $L(G) = L(G_1)$.

Proof. Obviously $L(G_1) \subseteq L(G)$, since if $A \rightarrow \alpha_1 \beta_i \alpha_2$ is used in a derivation of G_1, then

$$A \underset{G}{\Rightarrow} \alpha_1 B \alpha_2 \underset{G}{\Rightarrow} \alpha_1 \beta_i \alpha_2$$

can be used in G. To show that $L(G) \subseteq L(G_1)$, one simply notes that $A \rightarrow \alpha_1 B \alpha_2$ is the only production in G not in G_1. Whenever $A \rightarrow \alpha_1 B \alpha_2$ is used in a derivation by G, the variable B must be rewritten at some later step using a production of the form $B \rightarrow \beta_i$. These two steps can be replaced by the single step $A \underset{G}{\Rightarrow} \alpha_1 \beta_i \alpha_2$.

Lemma 4.3. Let $G = (V_N, V_T, P, S)$ be a context-free grammar. Let

$$\{A \rightarrow A\alpha_1, A \rightarrow A\alpha_2, \ldots, A \rightarrow A\alpha_r\}$$

be the set of A-productions for which A is the leftmost symbol of the right-hand side. Let

$$A \rightarrow \beta_1, A \rightarrow \beta_2, \ldots, A \rightarrow \beta_s$$

be the remaining productions with A on the left. Let $G_1 = (V_N \cup \{Z\}, V_T, P_1, S)$ be the cfg formed by adding the variable Z to V_N, and replacing all the A-productions by the productions:

$$(1) \quad \left. \begin{array}{l} A \rightarrow \beta_i, \\ A \rightarrow \beta_i Z, \end{array} \right\} \quad 1 \leq i \leq s \qquad (2) \quad \left. \begin{array}{l} Z \rightarrow \alpha_i, \\ Z \rightarrow \alpha_i Z, \end{array} \right\} \quad 1 \leq i \leq r.$$

Then $L(G_1) = L(G)$.

Proof. Before proving the lemma, we point out that the A-productions alone, by leftmost derivations, generate the regular set

$$\{\beta_1, \beta_2, \ldots, \beta_s\}\{\alpha_1, \alpha_2, \ldots, \alpha_r\}^*,$$

and this is precisely the set generated by the productions in G_1 with A or Z on the left.

Let x be in $L(G)$. From a leftmost derivation of x by G we can construct a derivation of x by G_1 as follows: Whenever there occurs in the leftmost derivation a sequence of steps

$$tA\gamma \underset{G}{\Rightarrow} tA\alpha_{j_1}\gamma \underset{G}{\Rightarrow} tA\alpha_{j_2}\alpha_{j_1}\gamma \underset{G}{\Rightarrow} \cdots \underset{G}{\Rightarrow} tA\alpha_{j_p}\cdots\alpha_{j_2}\alpha_{j_1}\gamma \underset{G}{\Rightarrow} t\beta_i\alpha_{j_p}\cdots\alpha_{j_2}\alpha_{j_1}\gamma,$$

replace the entire sequence by

$$tA\gamma \underset{G_1}{\Rightarrow} t\beta_iZ\gamma \underset{G_1}{\Rightarrow} t\beta_i\alpha_{j_p}Z\gamma \underset{G_1}{\Rightarrow} \cdots \underset{G_1}{\Rightarrow} t\beta_i\alpha_{j_p}\cdots\alpha_{j_2}Z\gamma \underset{G_1}{\Rightarrow} t\beta_i\alpha_{j_p}\cdots\alpha_{j_2}\alpha_{j_1}\gamma.$$

The resulting derivation is a derivation of x in G_1, although not a leftmost derivation. Thus $L(G) \subseteq L(G_1)$.

Now consider a leftmost derivation of x in G_1. Whenever a Z is introduced into the sentential form, reorder the derivation by immediately applying the productions that cause the Z to disappear. That is, for some instance of Z, a production $Z \to \alpha Z$ may be used. Then, in the leftmost derivation, α will derive a terminal string, and another production involving Z will be used. It should be clear that α could be left, temporarily, and the productions with Z on the left used immediately. Of course, the derivation will no longer be leftmost. Finally, a production $Z \to \beta$ will be used, where β has no Z. Then, the α's generated, as well as β, can be expanded normally. The result of the revised order of derivation will be the same as the original leftmost derivation.

Replace the resulting sequence of steps involving Z, namely:

$$tA\gamma \underset{G_1}{\Rightarrow} t\beta_iZ\gamma \underset{G_1}{\Rightarrow} t\beta_i\alpha_{j_p}Z\gamma \underset{G_1}{\Rightarrow} \cdots \underset{G_1}{\Rightarrow} t\beta_i\alpha_{j_p}\cdots\alpha_{j_2}Z\gamma \underset{G_1}{\Rightarrow} t\beta_i\alpha_{j_p}\cdots\alpha_{j_2}\alpha_{j_1}\gamma.$$

by

$$tA\gamma \underset{G}{\Rightarrow} tA\alpha_{j_1}\gamma \underset{G}{\Rightarrow} tA\alpha_{j_2}\alpha_{j_1}\gamma \underset{G}{\Rightarrow} \cdots \underset{G}{\Rightarrow} tA\alpha_{j_p}\cdots\alpha_{j_2}\alpha_{j_1}\gamma \underset{G}{\Rightarrow} t\beta_i\alpha_{j_p}\cdots\alpha_{j_2}\alpha_{j_1}\gamma.$$

The result is a derivation of x in G. Thus $L(G_1) \subseteq L(G)$.

Theorem 4.6. (*Greibach Normal Form.*) Every context-free language L can be generated by a grammar for which every production is of the form $A \to a\alpha$, where A is a variable, a is a terminal, and α is a (possibly empty) string of variables.

Proof. Let $G = (V_N, V_T, P, S)$ be a Chomsky normal-form grammar generating the cfl L. Assume that $V_N = \{A_1, A_2, \ldots, A_m\}$. The first step in the construction is to modify the productions so that if $A_i \to A_j\gamma$ is a production, then $j > i$. This will be done as follows, starting with A_1 and proceeding to A_m. Assume that the productions have been modified so that, for $1 \le i \le k$, $A_i \to A_j\gamma$ is a production only if $j > i$. We now modify the A_{k+1}-productions.

If $A_{k+1} \to A_j\gamma$ is a production, with $j < k + 1$, we generate a new set of productions by substituting for A_j the right-hand side of each A_j-production according to Lemma 4.2. By repeating the process $k - 1$ times at most, we obtain productions of the form $A_{k+1} \to A_l\gamma$, $l \geq k + 1$. The productions with $l = k + 1$ are then replaced according to Lemma 4.3, introducing a new variable Z_{k+1}.

By repeating the above process for each original variable, we have only productions of the forms:

1. $A_k \to A_l\gamma$, $l > k$
2. $A_k \to a\gamma$, a in V_T
3. $Z_k \to \gamma$, γ in $(V_N \cup \{Z_1, Z_2, \ldots, Z_m\})^*$.

Note that the leftmost symbol on the right-hand side of any production for A_m must be a terminal, since A_m is the highest-numbered variable. The leftmost symbol on the right-hand side of any production for A_{m-1} must be either A_m or a terminal symbol. When it is A_m, we can generate new productions by replacing A_m by the right-hand side of the productions for A_m according to Lemma 4.2. These productions must have right-hand sides that start with a terminal symbol. We then proceed to the productions for $A_{m-2}, \ldots, A_2, A_1$ until the right-hand side of each production for an A_i starts with a terminal symbol.

As the last step we examine the productions for the new variables, $Z_1, Z_2, \ldots, Z_m$. These productions start with either a terminal symbol or an original variable. Thus one more application of Lemma 4.2 for each Z_i production completes the construction.

Example 4.2. Convert to Greibach normal form, the grammar

$$G = (\{A_1, A_2, A_3\}, \{a, b\}, P, A_1),$$

where P consists of the following.

$$
\begin{array}{ll}
A_1 \to A_2A_3 & A_3 \to A_1A_2 \\
A_2 \to A_3A_1 & A_3 \to a \\
A_2 \to b &
\end{array}
$$

Step 1. Since the right-hand side of the productions for A_1 and A_2 start with terminals or higher-numbered variables, we begin with the production $A_3 \to A_1A_2$ and substitute the string A_2A_3 for A_1. Note that $A_1 \to A_2A_3$ is the only production with A_1 on the left.

The resulting set of productions is:

$$
\begin{array}{ll}
A_1 \to A_2A_3 & A_3 \to A_2A_3A_2 \\
A_2 \to A_3A_1 & A_3 \to a. \\
A_2 \to b &
\end{array}
$$

Since the right-hand side of the production $A_3 \to A_2A_3A_2$ begins with a lower-numbered variable, we substitute for the first occurrence of A_2 either

A_3A_1 or b. Thus $A_3 \rightarrow A_2A_3A_2$ is replaced by $A_3 \rightarrow A_3A_1A_3A_2$ and $A_3 \rightarrow bA_3A_2$. The new set is

$$
\begin{aligned}
A_1 &\rightarrow A_2A_3 & A_3 &\rightarrow A_3A_1A_3A_2 \\
A_2 &\rightarrow A_3A_1 & A_3 &\rightarrow bA_3A_2 \\
A_2 &\rightarrow b & A_3 &\rightarrow a
\end{aligned}
$$

We now apply Lemma 4.3 to the productions

$$A_3 \rightarrow A_3A_1A_3A_2, \quad A_3 \rightarrow bA_3A_2, \quad \text{and} \quad A_3 \rightarrow a.$$

Symbol Z_3 is introduced, and the production $A_3 \rightarrow A_3A_1A_3A_2$ is replaced by

$$A_3 \rightarrow bA_3A_2Z_3, \quad A_3 \rightarrow aZ_3, \quad Z_3 \rightarrow A_1A_3A_2, \quad \text{and} \quad Z_3 \rightarrow A_1A_3A_2Z_3.$$

The resulting set is

$$
\begin{aligned}
A_1 &\rightarrow A_2A_3 & A_3 &\rightarrow bA_3A_2Z_3 \\
A_2 &\rightarrow A_3A_1 & A_3 &\rightarrow aZ_3 \\
A_2 &\rightarrow b & Z_3 &\rightarrow A_1A_3A_2Z_3 \\
A_3 &\rightarrow bA_3A_2 & Z_3 &\rightarrow A_1A_3A_2. \\
A_3 &\rightarrow a
\end{aligned}
$$

Step 2. Now all the productions with A_3 on the left have right-hand sides that start with terminals. These are used to replace A_3 in the production $A_2 \rightarrow A_3A_1$ and then the productions with A_2 on the left are used to replace A_2 in the production $A_1 \rightarrow A_2A_3$. The result is the following.

$$
\begin{aligned}
A_3 &\rightarrow bA_3A_2 & A_3 &\rightarrow bA_3A_2Z_3 \\
A_3 &\rightarrow a & A_3 &\rightarrow aZ_3 \\[4pt]
A_2 &\rightarrow bA_3A_2A_1 & A_2 &\rightarrow bA_3A_2Z_3A_1 \\
A_2 &\rightarrow aA_1 & A_2 &\rightarrow aZ_3A_1 \\
A_2 &\rightarrow b \\[4pt]
A_1 &\rightarrow bA_3A_2A_1A_3 & A_1 &\rightarrow bA_3A_2Z_3A_1A_3 \\
A_1 &\rightarrow aA_1A_3 & A_1 &\rightarrow aZ_3A_1A_3 \\
A_1 &\rightarrow bA_3 \\[4pt]
Z_3 &\rightarrow A_1A_3A_2Z_3 & Z_3 &\rightarrow A_1A_3A_2
\end{aligned}
$$

Step 3. The two Z_3 productions are converted to proper form resulting in ten more productions. That is, the productions

$$Z_3 \rightarrow A_1A_3A_2 \quad \text{and} \quad Z_3 \rightarrow A_1A_3A_2Z_3$$

are altered by substituting the right-hand side of each of the five productions with A_1 on the left for the first occurrences of A_1. Thus, $Z_3 \rightarrow A_1A_3A_2$ becomes

$$Z_3 \rightarrow bA_3A_3A_2, \quad Z_3 \rightarrow bA_3A_2A_1A_3A_3A_2, \quad Z_3 \rightarrow aA_1A_3A_3A_2,$$
$$Z_3 \rightarrow bA_3A_2Z_3A_1A_3A_3A_2, \quad \text{and} \quad Z_3 \rightarrow aZ_3A_1A_3A_3A_2.$$

The other production for Z_3 is replaced similarly. The final set of productions is:

$A_3 \twoheadrightarrow bA_3A_2$ $\qquad\qquad$ $A_3 \twoheadrightarrow bA_3A_2Z_3$

$A_3 \twoheadrightarrow a$ $\qquad\qquad$ $A_3 \twoheadrightarrow aZ_3$

$A_2 \twoheadrightarrow bA_3A_2A_1$ $\qquad\qquad$ $A_2 \twoheadrightarrow bA_3A_2Z_3A_1$

$A_2 \twoheadrightarrow aA_1$ $\qquad\qquad$ $A_2 \twoheadrightarrow aZ_3A_1$

$A_2 \twoheadrightarrow b$

$A_1 \twoheadrightarrow bA_3A_2A_1A_3$ $\qquad\qquad$ $A_1 \twoheadrightarrow bA_3A_2Z_3A_1A_3$

$A_1 \twoheadrightarrow aA_1A_3$ $\qquad\qquad$ $A_1 \twoheadrightarrow aZ_3A_1A_3$

$A_1 \twoheadrightarrow bA_3$

$Z_3 \twoheadrightarrow bA_3A_3A_2$ $\qquad\qquad$ $Z_3 \twoheadrightarrow bA_3A_3A_2Z_3$

$Z_3 \twoheadrightarrow bA_3A_2A_1A_3A_3A_2$ $\qquad$ $Z_3 \twoheadrightarrow bA_3A_2A_1A_3A_3A_2Z_3$

$Z_3 \twoheadrightarrow aA_1A_3A_3A_2$ $\qquad\qquad$ $Z_3 \twoheadrightarrow aA_1A_3A_3A_2Z_3$

$Z_3 \twoheadrightarrow bA_3A_2Z_3A_1A_3A_3A_2$ $\qquad$ $Z_3 \twoheadrightarrow bA_3A_2Z_3A_1A_3A_3A_2Z_3$

$Z_3 \twoheadrightarrow aZ_3A_1A_3A_3A_2$ $\qquad\qquad$ $Z_3 \twoheadrightarrow aZ_3A_1A_3A_3A_2Z_3$

4.4 SOLVABILITY OF FINITENESS AND THE "*uvwxy* THEOREM"

In Theorem 4.2 we showed that we could eliminate from a grammar those variables generating no terminal strings. In fact, we can do more. We can test if a language generated by a given symbol is finite or infinite and eliminate those variables, other than the sentence symbol, from which only a finite number of terminal strings can be derived. In proving this result, we shall show two results (Theorems 4.7 and 4.8) quite interesting in their own right.

Theorem 4.7. Let L be any context-free language. There exist constants p and q depending only on L, such that if there is a word z in L, with $|z| > p$, then z may be written as $z = uvwxy$, where $|vwx| \leq q$ and v and x are not both ϵ, such that for each integer $i \geq 0$, uv^iwx^iy is in L.

Proof. Let $G = (V_N, V_T, P, S)$ be any Chomsky normal-form grammar for L. If G has k variables, then let $p = 2^{k-1}$ and let $q = 2^k$. It is easy to see that, for a Chomsky normal-form grammar, if a derivation tree has no path of length greater than j, then the terminal string derived is of length no greater than 2^{j-1}. The proof is left to the reader.

Hence, if z is in L and $|z| > p$, then the tree for any derivation of z by the grammar G contains a path of length greater than k. We consider a path P, of longest length, and observe that there must be two nodes, n_1 and n_2, satisfying the following conditions.

1. The nodes n_1 and n_2 both have the same label, say A.
2. Node n_1 is closer to the root than node n_2.
3. The portion of path P from n_1 to the leaf is of length at most $k + 1$.†

---

† Clearly, a path of longest length includes a leaf.

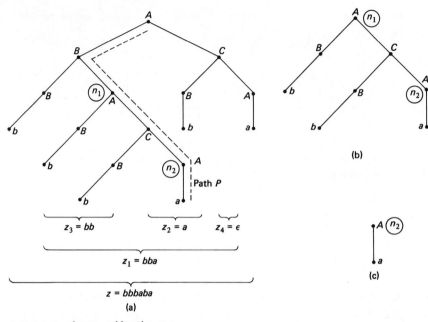

$z_1 = z_3z_2z_4$, where $z_3 = bb$ and $z_4 = \epsilon$.

$G = (\{A,B,C\},\{a,b\},\{A \to BC, B \to BA, C \to BA, A \to a, B \to b\},A)$

Fig. 4.2. Illustration of subtrees T_1 and T_2 of Theorem 4.7.   (a) Tree. (b) Subtree T_1.   (c) Subtree T_2.

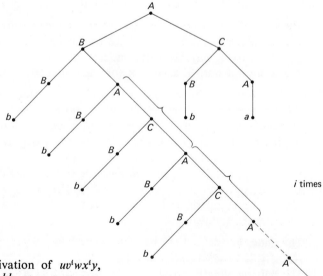

Fig. 4.3. The derivation of uv^iwx^iy, where $u = b$, $v = bb$, $w = a$, $x = \epsilon$, $y = ba$.

To see that n_1 and n_2 can always be found, just proceed up path P from the leaf, keeping track of the labels encountered. Of the first $k + 2$ nodes, only the leaf has a terminal label. The remaining $k + 1$ nodes cannot have distinct variable labels.

Now the subtree T_1 with root n_1 represents the derivation of a subword of length at most 2^k (and hence, of length less than or equal to q). This is true because there can be no path in T_1 of length greater than $k + 1$, since P was a path of longest length in the entire tree. Let z_1 be the result of the subtree T_1. If T_2 is the subtree generated by node n_2 and z_2 is the result of the subtree T_2, then we can write z_1 as $z_3 z_2 z_4$. Furthermore, z_3 and z_4 cannot both be ϵ, since the first production used in the derivation of z_1 must be of the form $A \rightarrow BC$ for some variables B and C. The subtree T_2 must be completely within either the subtree generated by B or the subtree generated by C. The above is illustrated in Fig. 4.2.

We now know that

$$A \underset{G}{\overset{*}{\Rightarrow}} z_3 A z_4 \underset{G}{\overset{*}{\Rightarrow}} z_3 z_2 z_4, \qquad \text{where } |z_3 z_2 z_4| \leqq q.$$

But it follows that $A \underset{G}{\overset{*}{\Rightarrow}} z_3^i z_2 z_4^i$ for each $i \geqq 0$. See Fig. 4.3. The string z can clearly be written as $u z_3 z_2 z_4 y$, for some u and y. We let $z_3 = v$, $z_2 = w$, and $z_4 = x$, to complete the proof.

Theorem 4.8. There is an algorithm to determine if a given context-free grammar G generates a finite or infinite number of words.

Proof. Let p and q be the constants defined in Theorem 4.7. Thus, if z is in $L(G)$ and $|z| > p$, then z can be written as $uvwxy$ where for each $i \geqq 0$, $uv^i wx^i y$ is in $L(G)$. Also $|v| + |x| > 0$. Hence if there is a word in $L(G)$ of length greater than or equal to p, then $L(G)$ is infinite.

Suppose that $L = L(G)$ is infinite. Then there are arbitrarily long words in $L(G)$ and, in particular, a word of length greater than $p + q$. This word may be written as

$$uvwxy, \quad \text{where } |vwx| \leqq q, \quad |v| + |x| > 0,$$

and $uv^i wx^i y$ is in L for all $i \geqq 0$. In particular, uwy is in L, and $|uwy| < |uvwxy|$. Also $|uwy| > p$. If $|uwy| > p + q$, we repeat the procedure until we eventually find a word in L of length l, $p < l \leqq p + q$. Thus L is infinite if and only if it contains a word of length l, $p < l \leqq p + q$.

Since we may test whether a given word is in a given context-free language (Theorem 2.2), we have merely to test all words of length between p and $p + q$ for membership in $L(G)$. If there is such a word, then L is clearly infinite; if not, then there are no words of length greater than p in L, so L is finite.

Theorem 4.9. Given a context-free grammar G_1, we can find an equivalent grammar G_2 for which, if A is a variable of G_2 other than the sentence symbol, there are an infinity of terminal strings derivable from A.

Proof. If $L(G_1)$ is finite, the theorem is trivial, so assume that $L(G_1)$ is infinite. If $G_1 = (V_N, V_T, P_1, S)$, then for each A in V_N, we know from Theorem 4.8 that by considering the context-free grammar $G_A = (V_N, V_T, P_1, A)$ we can determine whether there is an infinity of terminal strings w, such that $A \overset{*}{\underset{G_1}{\Rightarrow}} w$. Suppose that $A_1, A_2, \ldots, A_k$ are exactly the variables generating an infinity of terminal strings, and that $B_1, B_2, \ldots, B_m$ are exactly those generating a finite number of terminal strings. We create a new set of productions, P_2, from P_1 as follows.

Suppose that $C_0 \rightarrow C_1 C_2 \ldots C_r$ is a production of P_1; C_0 is among $A_1, A_2, \ldots, A_k$. Then every production of the form $C_0 \rightarrow u_1 u_2 \ldots u_r$ is in P_2, where for $1 \leq i \leq r$,

1. If C_i is terminal, $u_i = C_i$.
2. If C_i is among $A_1, A_2, \ldots, A_k$, then $u_i = C_i$.
3. If C_i is among $B_1, B_2, \ldots, B_m$, u_i is one of the finite number of terminal words such that $C_i \overset{*}{\underset{G_1}{\Rightarrow}} u_i$.

We know that P_2 contains no productions with any of $B_1, B_2, \ldots, B_m$ on the left. We consider the new grammar $G_2 = (V_N', V_T, P_2, S)$, where $V_N' = \{A_1, A_2, \ldots, A_k\}$. Note that S must be in V_N', since L is assumed to be infinite. Surely, if $\alpha \underset{G_2}{\Rightarrow} \beta$, then $\alpha \overset{*}{\underset{G_1}{\Rightarrow}} \beta$, so $L(G_2) \subseteq L(G_1)$.

As usual, to show that $L(G_1) \subseteq L(G_2)$, we prove by induction on the number of steps in the derivation that if

$$A_i \overset{*}{\underset{G_1}{\Rightarrow}} w, \qquad 1 \leq i \leq k,$$

where w is a terminal string, then $A_i \overset{*}{\underset{G_2}{\Rightarrow}} w$. The result is trivial for one-step derivations, so assume that it is true for up to j steps. Now suppose that in a derivation of $j + 1$ steps, the first production used is $A_i \rightarrow C_1 C_2 \ldots C_r$. We can write w as

$$w_1 w_2 \ldots w_r, \qquad \text{where } C_i \overset{*}{\underset{G_1}{\Rightarrow}} w_i, \quad 1 \leq i \leq r.$$

There is a production $A_i \rightarrow u_1 u_2 \ldots u_r$ in P_2, where $u_p = w_p$ if either C_p is a terminal or if C_p is among $B_1, B_2, \ldots, B_m$ and $u_p = C_p$ if C_p is among $A_1, A_2, \ldots, A_k$. The inductive step follows immediately.

Example 4.3. Consider the grammar $G = (\{S, A, B\}, \{a, b, c, d\}, \{S \rightarrow ASB, S \rightarrow AB, A \rightarrow a, A \rightarrow b, B \rightarrow c, B \rightarrow d\}, S)$. It is easy to see that A generates only the strings a and b and B generates only the strings c and d. However, S generates an infinity of strings. The only productions with S on the left are $S \to ASB$ and $S \to AB$. The production $S \to ASB$ is replaced by $S \to aSc$, $S \to aSd$, $S \to bSc$, and $S \to bSd$. Likewise, the production $S \to AB$ is replaced by $S \to ac$, $S \to ad$, $S \to bc$, and $S \to bd$. The new grammar is

$$G_2 = (\{S\}, \{a, b, c, d\}, P, S)$$

where

$$P = \{S \to aSc, S \to aSd, S \to bSc, S \to bSd, S \to ac,$$
$$S \to ad, S \to bc, S \to bd\}.$$

4.5 THE SELF-EMBEDDING PROPERTY

A context-free grammar G is said to be *self-embedding* if there is a variable A with the property that $A \overset{*}{\underset{G}{\Rightarrow}} \alpha_1 A \alpha_2$ where α_1 and α_2 are nonempty strings. The variable A is also said to be *self-embedding*. Note that it is the self-embedding property that gives rise to sentences of the form $uv^i w x^i y$. One gets the feeling that it is the self-embedding property that distinguishes a strictly context-free language from a regular set. One should note that simply because a grammar is self-embedding does not mean that the language generated is not regular. For example, the grammar

$$G = (\{S\}, \{a, b\}, P, S),$$

where

$$P = \{S \to aSa, S \to aS, S \to bS, S \to a, S \to b\}$$

generates a regular set. In fact, $L(G) = \{a, b\}^+$.

In this section we shall see that a context-free grammar that is not self-embedding generates a regular set. Consequently, a context-free language is nonregular if and only if all of its grammars are self-embedding.

Theorem 4.10. Let G be a non-self-embedding context-free grammar. Then $L(G)$ is a regular set.

Proof. In examining the constructions for the normal forms developed in this chapter, we note that each of the constructions has the property that if the original grammar was non-self-embedding, then the normal-form grammar was non-self-embedding. In particular this is true of the Greibach normal form. Thus, if G is non-self-embedding, we can find a grammar $G_1 = (V_N, V_T, P_1, S_1)$ in Greibach normal form, equivalent to G, which is non-self-embedding.† Moreover, by Theorem 4.2 a terminal string can be derived from each variable in V_N.

---

† Although the statement is not obvious, it is easy to prove. Clearly the application of Lemma 4.2 does not introduce self-embedding. In Lemma 4.3 one must show that Z is self-embedding only if A is self-embedding.

Consider a leftmost derivation in G_1. If G_1 has m variables, and l is the length of the longest right-hand side of any production, then no sentential form can have more than ml variables appearing in it. To see this, assume that more than ml variables appear in some sentential form α of a leftmost derivation. In the derivation tree for α, consider those nodes on the path from the root to the leftmost variable of α. In particular, consider those nodes where variables are introduced to the right of the path. Since the maximum number of variables coming directly from any node is $l - 1$, and since a variable to the right of the above path has not been rewritten, there must be at least $m + 1$ such nodes. Thus some variable A must appear twice among the labels of these nodes. Since we are considering only nodes where new variables are introduced to the right of the path, and since each production introduces a terminal as the leftmost character, the variable A must be self-embedding.

Now if there are at most ml variables in any sentential form, we can design a type 3 grammar $G_2 = (V_N', V_T, P_2, S)$, generating $L(G)$ as follows. The variables of G_2 correspond to strings of variables of G_1 of length less than or equal to ml. That is, $V_N' = \{[\alpha] \,|\, |\alpha| \leq ml$ and α in $V_N^+\}$. S is $[S_1]$. If $A \to b\alpha$ is in P_1, then for all variables of V_N' corresponding to strings starting with A we have $[A\beta] \to b[\alpha\beta]$ in P_2 provided that $|\alpha\beta| \leq ml$. It should be obvious from the construction that G_2 simulates all leftmost derivations in G_1, so $L(G_2) = L(G_1)$. Thus $L(G)$ is regular.

4.6 ε-RULES IN CONTEXT-FREE GRAMMARS

Earlier we showed that several restrictions can be placed on the productions of context-free grammars without limiting the class of languages that can be generated. Now we consider an extension of context-free grammars to include productions of the form $A \to \epsilon$ for any variable A. Such a production is called an *ε-rule*. Many descriptions of context-free languages allow these productions. We shall show that a language generated by a cfg with ε-rules is always a cfl.

The concepts concerning trees for context-free grammars carry over directly to these augmented grammars. One simply allows ϵ to be the label of a node. Clearly, that node must be a leaf.

Theorem 4.11. If L is a language generated by a grammar $G = (V_N, V_T, P, S)$ and every production in P is of the form $A \to \alpha$, where A is a variable and α is a string (possibly ϵ) in V^*, then L can be generated by a grammar in which every production is either of the form $A \to \alpha$, with A a variable and α in V^+, or $S \to \epsilon$, and further, S does not appear on the right of any production.

Proof. By a trivial extension of Lemma 2.1, we can assume that S does not appear on the right-hand side of any production in P. For any variable A

of G we can decide whether $A \xrightarrow[G]{*} \epsilon$. For if so, then there is a derivation whose tree has no path longer than the number of variables of G. (This argument was used in Theorem 4.1.)

Let $A_1, A_2, \ldots, A_k$ be those variables of V from which ϵ can be derived and $B_1, B_2, \ldots, B_m$ be those from which it cannot. We construct a new set of productions P_1 according to the following rules.

1. If $S \xrightarrow[G]{*} \epsilon$, then $S \rightarrow \epsilon$ is in P_1.
2. No other production of the form $A \rightarrow \epsilon$ appears in P_1.
3. If
$$A \rightarrow C_1 C_2 \ldots C_r, \qquad r \geq 1,$$
   is in P, then each production of the form $A \rightarrow \alpha_1 \alpha_2 \ldots \alpha_r$ is in P_1, where if C_i is in $V_T \cup \{B_1, B_2, \ldots, B_m\}$, then $C_i = \alpha_i$, and if C_i is in $\{A_1, A_2, \ldots, A_k\}$, then α_i may be C_i or ϵ. However, not all α_i's may be ϵ.

As usual, it should be clear that if $G_1 = (V_N, V_T, P_1, S)$, then $L(G_1) \subseteq L(G)$. We must show by induction on the number of steps in the derivation, that if $A \xrightarrow[G]{*} w$, $w \neq \epsilon$, then $A \xrightarrow[G_1]{*} w$, for A in V_N. For one step, the result is obvious, so assume that it is true for up to k steps. Suppose that $A \xrightarrow[G]{*} w$ by a $k + 1$-step derivation and suppose that $A \rightarrow C_1 C_2 \ldots C_r$ is the first production used. We can write w as $w_1 w_2 \ldots w_r$ where for $1 \leq i \leq r$, $C_i \xrightarrow[G]{*} w_i$. If $w_i \neq \epsilon$, then by induction we know that $C_i \xrightarrow[G_1]{*} w_i$. Now, there is a production of P_1 of the form $A \rightarrow \alpha_1 \alpha_2 \ldots \alpha_r$, where $\alpha_i = C_i$ if $w_i \neq \epsilon$ and $\alpha_i = \epsilon$ if $w_i = \epsilon$. Hence

$$A \xrightarrow[G_1]{*} w.$$

It follows immediately from Theorem 4.11 that the only difference between context-free grammars with productions of the form $A \rightarrow \epsilon$ and those with no such productions is that the former may include ϵ as a word in the language. From here on we call a context-free grammar with ϵ-rules simply a context-free grammar, knowing that an equivalent context-free grammar without ϵ productions (except for $S \rightarrow \epsilon$, possibly) can be found.

4.7 SPECIAL TYPES OF CONTEXT-FREE LANGUAGES AND GRAMMARS

At this point, we mention several restricted classes of context-free languages. If every production of a cfg is of the form $A \rightarrow uBv$ or $A \rightarrow u$, A and B variables, u and v terminal strings, then we say that the grammar is *linear*. A language that can be generated by a linear grammar is called a *linear language*. Not all context-free languages are linear languages. Observe that no string derivable in a linear grammar has more than one variable.

Example 4.4. The grammar

$$G = (\{S\}, \{0, 1\}, \{S \to 0S1, S \to \epsilon\}, S)$$

is a linear grammar which generates $\{0^n1^n | n \geq 0\}$.

A grammar $G = (V_N, V_T, P, S)$ is said to be *sequential* if the variables in V_N can be ordered $A_1, A_2, \ldots, A_k$ such that if $A_i \to \alpha$ is a production in P, then α contains no A_j with $j < i$. A language generated by a sequential grammar is called a *sequential language*.

Example 4.5. The grammar

$$G = (\{A_1, A_2\}, \{0, 1\}, \{A_1 \to A_2A_1, A_1 \to A_2, A_2 \to 0A_21, A_2 \to \epsilon\}, A_1)$$

is a sequential grammar which generates the language $\{0^n1^n | n \geq 0\}^*$.

If a context-free language L over an alphabet V_T is a subset of the language $w_1^* w_2^* \ldots w_k^*$† for some k, where w_i is in V_T^*, $1 \leq i \leq k$, then we say that L is a *bounded language*.

Example 4.6. The language

$$\{(ab)^n c^n (dd)^* | n \geq 1\}$$

is a bounded language. Here $k = 3$ and $w_1 = ab$, $w_2 = c$ and $w_3 = d$.

A context-free grammar $G = (V_N, V_T, P, S)$ is said to be *ambiguous* if there is a word in $L(G)$ with two or more distinct leftmost derivations. If every grammar generating a context-free language is ambiguous, we say that the language is *inherently ambiguous*.

There exist inherently ambiguous context-free languages. An example is the language $L = \{a^i b^j c^k | i = j \text{ or } j = k\}$. Essentially the reason that L is inherently ambiguous is that any context-free grammar generating L must generate those words for which $i = j$ by a process different from that used to generate those words for which $j = k$. It is impossible not to generate some of those words for which $i = j = k$ by both processes.

Example 4.7. Consider the grammar G of Example 4.1, which had productions $S \to bA$, $S \to aB$, $A \to a$, $B \to b$, $A \to aS$, $B \to bS$, $A \to bAA$, $B \to aBB$. The word *aabbab* has the following two leftmost derivations:

$$S \Rightarrow aB \Rightarrow aaBB \Rightarrow aabB \Rightarrow aabbS \Rightarrow aabbaB \Rightarrow aabbab$$
$$S \Rightarrow aB \Rightarrow aaBB \Rightarrow aabSB \Rightarrow aabbAB \Rightarrow aabbaB \Rightarrow aabbab.$$

Hence G is ambiguous. However, the language

$$L(G) = \{w | w \text{ consists of an equal number of } a\text{'s and } b\text{'s}\}$$

---

† Strictly speaking $w_1^* w_2^* \ldots w_k^*$ should be written $\{w_1\}^*\{w_2\}^*\ldots\{w_k\}^*$. No confusion should result.

is not inherently ambiguous. For example, $L(G)$ is generated by the unambiguous grammar

$$G_1 = (\{S, A, B\}, \{a, b\}, P, S),$$

where P consists of:

$$S \rightarrow aBS, \, S \rightarrow aB, \, S \rightarrow bAS, \, S \rightarrow bA, \, A \rightarrow bAA, \, A \rightarrow a, \, B \rightarrow aBB, \, B \rightarrow b.$$

PROBLEMS

4.1 Given a context-free grammar with m variables, for which the right side of no production is longer than l, provide an upper bound on the number of trees with no path longer than $m + 1$?

4.2 Give a simple algorithm to determine if the language generated by a cfg is empty. Note that if a grammar generates a nonempty language, at least one variable must have a production whose right-hand side contains only terminals.

4.3 Given two strings α_1 and α_2 and a context-free grammar G, give an algorithm to determine if $\alpha_1 \underset{G}{\overset{*}{\Rightarrow}} \alpha_2$.

4.4 Complete the proof of Theorem 4.5.

4.5 Consider the grammar

$$G = (\{S, T, L\}, \{a, b, +, -, \times, /, [,], \}, P, S),$$

where P consists of the productions:

$$
\begin{array}{lll}
S \rightarrow T + S & T \rightarrow L \times T & L \rightarrow [S] \\
S \rightarrow T - S & T \rightarrow L/T & L \rightarrow a \\
S \rightarrow T & T \rightarrow L & L \rightarrow b.
\end{array}
$$

Informally describe $L(G)$. Find a grammar in Chomsky normal form generating $L(G)$.

4.6 Consider the grammar $G = (\{A, B, C\}, \{0, 1\}, P, A)$, where P consists of the productions:

$$
\begin{array}{ll}
A \rightarrow 0A1 & B \rightarrow 1C0 \\
A \rightarrow 0AC & B \rightarrow AC \\
A \rightarrow 0 & C \rightarrow 1CB \\
A \rightarrow 1B0 & C \rightarrow AB
\end{array}
$$

Find an equivalent grammar G_1, such that if D is a variable of G_1, then $D \Rightarrow w$ for some terminal string w.

4.7 If G is a Chomsky normal-form grammar, where w is in $L(G)$, and there is a derivation of w using p steps, how long is w? Prove your answer.

4.8 Show how to put the productions of a Chomsky normal-form grammar into the form $A \rightarrow BC$, where $B \neq C$, and if $A \rightarrow \alpha_1 B \alpha_2$ and $A \rightarrow \gamma_1 B \gamma_2$ are productions then $\alpha_1 = \gamma_1$ and $\alpha_2 = \gamma_2$.

4.9 Several times we have modified the productions of a grammar and then proved that the resulting grammar was equivalent to the original, one such case being Lemma 4.3. Can you think of a general type of modification that will include most of the special cases? Prove that your modification results in an equivalent grammar.

4.10 Consider the grammar $G = (\{S\}, \{p, [,], \sim, \supset\}, P, S)$ where P is the set of productions:

$$S \to p \qquad S \to \sim S \qquad S \to [S \supset S].$$

Describe $L(G)$ informally. Find a Chomsky normal-form grammar for $L(G)$. Number the variables, giving S the highest number. Find a Greibach normal-form grammar for $L(G)$ from the Chomsky normal-form grammar you have obtained. Can you find a simpler Greibach normal-form grammar for $L(G)$?

4.11 Show that every context-free language can be generated by a grammar in which every production is of the form $A \to a$, $A \to aB$, or $A \to aBC$, where a is terminal, and A, B, and C are variables.

4.12 Show that every context-free language can be generated by a grammar in which every production is of the form $A \to a$ or $A \to a\alpha b$, where a and b are terminals and α is a string of variables.

4.13 Use Theorem 4.7 to show that $\{a^i | i \text{ a prime}\}$ is not a context-free language.

4.14 Show that $\{a^i | i \text{ is a perfect square}\}$ is not a context-free language.

4.15 Use Theorem 4.7 to show that $\{a^i b^i c^i | i \geq 1\}$ is not a context-free language.

4.16 Consider the grammar $G = (\{S, A, B\}, \{0, 1\}, P, S)$, where P consists of the following productions:

$$
\begin{array}{ll}
S \to AB & B \to 0A1 \\
A \to BSB & B \to \epsilon \\
A \to BB & B \to 0 \\
& A \to 1.
\end{array}
$$

Find an equivalent grammar for which S does not appear on the right of any production and $S \to \epsilon$ is the only production with ϵ on the right.

4.17 Find a cfl that cannot be generated by a linear grammar.

4.18 Find a cfl that is not a bounded language.

4.19 Find a cfl that is not a sequential language.

4.20 Show that the grammar G_1 of Example 4.7 is unambiguous.

4.21 Which of the following grammars are self-embedding? Find finite automata accepting those languages which have non-self-embedding grammars.

a) $G = (\{A, B, C\}, \{a, b\}, P, A)$, where P contains the productions

$$
\begin{array}{ll}
A \to CB & C \to AB \\
A \to b & C \to a \\
B \to CA &
\end{array}
$$

b) $G = (\{A, B, C\}, \{a, b\}, P, A)$, where P contains the productions

$$A \to CB \quad A \to Ca$$
$$C \to AB$$
$$B \to bC \quad C \to b$$

4.22 Show that every cfl over a one-symbol alphabet is regular.

REFERENCES

The original work on context-free languages appears in Chomsky [1956], Chomsky [1959], and Bar-Hillel, Perles, and Shamir [1961]. Theorems 4.1, 4.7 and 4.8 are from the latter paper. Theorem 4.5 appears in Chomsky [1959] and Theorem 4.6 in Greibach [1965]. A simple proof of the latter result can be found in Rosenkrantz [1967]. Theorem 4.10 is from Chomsky [1959]. Ginsburg [1966] is a good reference on the properties of context-free languages. For results on linear languages, see Greibach [1963], Gross [1964], Haines [1964], and Greibach [1966]. For sequential languages, see Ginsburg and Rice [1962], Ginsburg and Rose [1963(a) and (b)], and Shamir [1965]. For bounded languages, see Ginsburg and Spanier [1964]. Ambiguity and inherent ambiguity are treated more extensively in Chapter 14. For the application of context-free languages to the area of programming, see Samelson and Bauer [1960], Irons [1961], Floyd [1962(a) and (b)], [1963], and [1964(a) and (c)], and Lewis and Stearns [1966].

There are two interesting theorems concerning context-free languages which we have not covered. We have not, in fact, developed the notation even to state them formally, but they deserve mention. The first is Parikh's Theorem (Parikh [1961]) which essentially states that if L is a cfl contained in Σ^*, then for each w in L, the numbers of instances of each symbol of Σ found in w satisfy one of a finite number of nontrivial sets of simultaneous linear equations. For example, $\{a^n b^{n^2} | n \geq 1\}$ is not a context-free language, since the numbers of a's and b's in each word satisfy only quadratic equations.

The second theorem is the characterization of cfl's in terms of "Dyck languages." A Dyck language is a cfl generated by a grammar

$$G_k = (\{S\}, \{a_1, a_2, \ldots, a_k, b_1, b_2, \ldots, b_k\}, P, S),$$

where P consists of the productions $S \to SS$, $S \to \epsilon$, and $S \to a_i S b_i$ for $1 \leq i \leq k$. $L(G_k)$ can be thought of as being composed of strings of balanced parentheses of k types. The corresponding left and right parentheses for each i are a_i and b_i. The theorem states that every cfl can be expressed as a homomorphism (see Chapter 9) of the intersection of a Dyck language and a regular set. The theorem was first proved in Chomsky [1962]. Alternative proofs appear in Stanley [1965] and Ginsburg [1966].

CHAPTER 5

PUSHDOWN AUTOMATA

5.1 INFORMAL DESCRIPTION

We shall now consider a device which is quite important in the study of formal languages—the pushdown automaton. This device is essentially a finite automaton with control of both an input tape and a pushdown store. The pushdown store is a "first in–last out" list. That is, symbols may be entered or removed only at the top of the list. When a symbol is entered at the top, the symbol previously at the top becomes second from the top, the symbol previously second from the top becomes third, etc. Similarly, when a symbol is removed from the top of the list, the symbol previously second from the top becomes the top symbol, the symbol previously third from the top becomes second, and so on.

A familiar example of a pushdown store is the stack of plates on a spring which we often see in cafeterias. There is a spring below the plates with just enough strength so that only one plate appears above the level of the counter. When that top plate is removed, the load on the spring is lightened, and the plate directly below appears above the level of the counter. If a plate is then put on top of the stack, the pile is pushed down, and that plate appears above the counter. For our purposes, we make the assumption that the spring is arbitrarily long so that we may add as many plates as we desire.

Let us see how we can use the stack of plates, coupled with a finite control, to recognize a nonregular set. The set $L = \{wcw^R | w$ in $\{0, 1\}^*\}$† is a context-free language, generated by the grammar

$$G = (\{S\}, \{0, 1, c\}, \{S \to 0S0, S \to 1S1, S \to c\}, S)$$

It is not hard to show that L cannot be accepted by any finite automaton. To accept L, we shall make use of a finite control with two states, q_1 and q_2, and a pushdown store on which we place blue, green, and red plates. The device will operate by the following rules.

1. The machine starts with one red plate on the stack and with the finite control in state q_1.

---

† w^R denotes w reversed.

2. If the input to the device is 0 and the device is in state q_1, a blue plate is placed on the stack. If the input to the device is 1 and the device is in state q_1, a green plate is placed on the stack. In both cases the finite control remains in state q_1.

3. If the input is c and the device is in state q_1, it changes state to q_2 without adding or removing any plates.

4. If the input is 0 and the device is in state q_2 with a blue plate on top of the stack, the plate is removed. If the input is 1 and the device is in state q_2 with a green plate on top of the stack, the plate is removed. In both cases the finite control remains in state q_2.

5. If the device is in state q_2 and a red plate is on top of the stack, the plate is removed without waiting for the next input.

6. For all cases other than those described above, the device can make no move.

The preceding moves are summarized in Fig. 5.1.

We say that the device described above accepts an input string if, on processing the last symbol of the string, the stack of plates becomes completely empty. Note that, once the stack is completely empty, no further moves are possible.

Essentially, the device operates in the following way. In state q_1, the device makes an image of its input by placing a blue plate on top of the stack of plates each time a 0 appears in the input and a green plate each time a 1

| | | *INPUT* | | |
Top plate	*State*	*0*	*1*	*c*
Blue	q_1	Add blue plate; stay in state q_1.	Add green plate; stay in state q_1.	Go to state q_2.
	q_2	Remove top plate; stay in state q_2.	—	—
Green	q_1	Add blue plate; stay in state q_1.	Add green plate; stay in state q_1.	Go to state q_2.
	q_2	—	Remove top plate; stay in state q_2.	—
Red	q_1	Add blue plate; stay in state q_1.	Add green plate; stay in state q_1.	Go to state q_2.
	q_2	Without waiting for next input, remove top plate.	Without waiting for next input, remove top plate.	Without waiting for next input, remove top plate

Fig. 5.1. Finite control for pushdown machine accepting $\{wcw^R \mid w \text{ in } \{0, 1\}^*\}$.

appears in the input. When c is the input, the device transfers to state q_2. Next, the remaining input is compared with the stack by removing a blue plate from the top of stack each time the input symbol is a 0 and a green plate each time the input symbol is a 1. Should the top plate be of the wrong color, the device halts and no further processing of the input is possible. If all plates match the inputs, eventually the red plate at the bottom of the stack is exposed. The red plate is immediately removed and the device is said to accept the input string. All plates can be removed only in the case where the string that enters the device after the c is the reversal of what entered before the c.

5.2 DEFINITIONS

We shall now formalize the concept of a pushdown automaton (pda). The pda will have an input tape, a finite control, and a pushdown store. The pushdown store is a string of symbols in some alphabet. The leftmost symbol will be considered to be at the "top" of the store. The device will be nondeterministic, having some finite number of choices of moves in each situation. The moves will be of two types. In the first type of move, an input symbol is scanned. Depending on the input symbol, the top symbol on the pushdown store, and the state of the finite control, a number of choices are possible. Each choice consists of a next state for the finite control and a (possibly empty) string of symbols to replace the top pushdown store symbol. After selecting a choice, the input head is advanced one symbol.

The second type of move (called an ϵ-*move*) is similar to the first, except that the input symbol is not used, and the input head is not advanced after the move. This type of move allows the pda to manipulate the pushdown store without reading input symbols.

Finally, we must define the language accepted by a pushdown automaton. There are two natural ways to do this. The first, which we have already seen, is to define the language accepted to be the set of all inputs for which some sequence of moves causes the pushdown automaton to empty its pushdown store. This language is referred to as the language accepted by empty store.

The second way of defining the language accepted is similar to the way a finite automaton accepts tapes. That is, we could designate some states as final states and define the accepted language as the set of all inputs for which some choice of moves causes the pushdown automaton to enter a final state.

As we shall see, the two definitions of acceptance are equivalent in the sense that if a set can be accepted by empty store by some pda, it can be accepted by final state by some other pda, and vice-versa.

Acceptance by final state is the more common notion, but it is easier to prove the basic theorem of pushdown automata by using acceptance by empty store. The basic theorem is that a language is accepted by a pushdown automaton if and only if it is a context-free language.

A *pushdown automaton* M is a system $(K, \Sigma, \Gamma, \delta, q_0, Z_0, F)$ where

1. K is a finite set of *states*.
2. Σ is a finite alphabet called the *input alphabet*.
3. Γ is a finite alphabet, called the *pushdown alphabet*.
4. q_0 in K is the *initial state*.
5. Z_0 in Γ is a particular pushdown symbol called the *start symbol*. Z_0 initially appears on the pushdown store.
6. $F \subseteq K$ is the set of *final states*.
7. δ is a mapping from $K \times (\Sigma \cup \{\epsilon\}) \times \Gamma$ to finite subsets of $K \times \Gamma^*$.

We use lower-case letters near the front of the alphabet to denote input symbols and lower-case letters near the end of the alphabet to denote strings of input symbols. Capital letters usually denote pushdown symbols and Greek letters indicate strings of pushdown symbols.

The interpretation of

$$\delta(q, a, Z) = \{(p_1, \gamma_1), (p_2, \gamma_2), \ldots, (p_m, \gamma_m)\}$$

where q and p_i, $1 \leq i \leq m$, are in K, a is in Σ, Z is in Γ, and γ_i is in Γ^*, $1 \leq i \leq m$, is that the pda in state q, with input symbol a and Z the top symbol on the pushdown store, can, for any i, enter state p_i, replace Z by γ_i, and advance the input head one symbol. We adopt the convention that the leftmost symbol of γ_i will be placed highest on the store and the rightmost symbol lowest on the store.†

The interpretation of

$$\delta(q, \epsilon, Z) = \{(p_1, \gamma_1), (p_2, \gamma_2), \ldots, (p_m, \gamma_m)\}$$

is that the pda in state q, independent of the input symbol being scanned and with Z the top symbol on the pushdown store, can enter state p_i and replace Z by γ_i for any i, $1 \leq i \leq m$. In this case, the input head is not advanced.

Example 5.1. Figure 5.2 gives a formal pushdown automaton which accepts $\{wcw^R | w \text{ in } \{0, 1\}^*\}$ by empty store. Note that for a move in which the pda writes a symbol on the top of the store δ has a value (q, γ) where $|\gamma| = 2$. For example, $\delta(q_1, 0, R) = \{(q_1, BR)\}$. If γ were of length one, the pda would simply replace the top symbol by a new symbol and not increase the length of the pushdown store. This allows us to let γ equal ϵ for the case in which we wish to erase the top symbol, thereby shortening the pushdown store.

Note that the rule $\delta(q_2, \epsilon, R) = \{(q_2, \epsilon)\}$ means that the pda, in state q_2 with R the top pushdown symbol, can erase the R independent of the input symbol. In this case the input head is not advanced.

---

† This convention is opposite that used by some other writers. We prefer it since it simplifies notation in what follows.

$$M = (\{q_1, q_2\}, \{0, 1, c\}, \{R, B, G\}, \delta, q_1, R, \varphi)\dagger$$

$$\delta(q_1, 0, R) = \{(q_1, BR)\} \qquad \delta(q_1, 1, R) = \{(q_1, GR)\}$$
$$\delta(q_1, 0, B) = \{(q_1, BB)\} \qquad \delta(q_1, 1, B) = \{(q_1, GB)\}$$
$$\delta(q_1, 0, G) = \{(q_1, BG)\} \qquad \delta(q_1, 1, G) = \{(q_1, GG)\}$$
$$\delta(q_1, c, R) = \{(q_2, R)\}$$
$$\delta(q_1, c, B) = \{(q_2, B)\}$$
$$\delta(q_1, c, G) = \{(q_2, G)\}$$
$$\delta(q_2, 0, B) = \{(q_2, \epsilon)\} \qquad \delta(q_2, 1, G) = \{(q_2, \epsilon)\}$$
$$\delta(q_2, \epsilon, R) = \{(q_2, \epsilon)\}$$

Fig. 5.2. Formal pushdown automaton accepting $\{wcw^R | w$ in $\{0, 1\}^*\}$ by empty tape.

A *configuration* of a pda is a pair (q, γ) where q is a state in K and γ is a string of pushdown symbols. We say that a pda M is in configuration (q, γ) if M is in state q with γ on the pushdown store, the leftmost symbol of γ being the top symbol on the pushdown store. If a is in $\Sigma \cup \{\epsilon\}$, γ and β are in Γ^*, and Z is in Γ, and further, if the pair (p, β) is in $\delta(q, a, Z)$, then we write

$$a:(q, Z\gamma) \,\underset{M}{\vdash}\, (p, \beta\gamma).$$

The above means that according to the rules of the pda the input a may cause M to go from configuration $(q, Z\gamma)$ to configuration $(p, \beta\gamma)$.

If for $a_1, a_2, \ldots, a_n$, each in $\Sigma \cup \{\epsilon\}$, states $q_1, q_2, \ldots, q_{n+1}$ and pushdown strings $\gamma_1, \gamma_2, \ldots, \gamma_{n+1}$ we have:

$$a_i:(q_i, \gamma_i) \,\underset{M}{\vdash}\, (q_{i+1}, \gamma_{i+1})$$

for all i between 1 and n, then we write

$$a_1 a_2 \ldots a_n:(q_1, \gamma_1) \,\underset{M}{\overset{*}{\vdash}}\, (q_{n+1}, \gamma_{n+1}).\ddagger$$

Recall that many of the a_i's may be ϵ. The subscript M will be dropped from $\underset{M}{\overset{*}{\vdash}}$ whenever the meaning remains clear.

For a pda M we define $T(M)$, the language *accepted by final state*, to be

$$\{w | w:(q_0, Z_0) \,\underset{M}{\overset{*}{\vdash}}\, (q, \gamma) \text{ for any } \gamma \text{ in } \Gamma^* \text{ and } q \text{ in } F\}.$$

Also, we define $N(M)$, the language *accepted by empty store*, to be

$$\{w | w:(q_0, Z_0) \,\underset{M}{\overset{*}{\vdash}}\, (q, \epsilon) \text{ for any } q \text{ in } K\}.$$

$\dagger$ φ denotes the empty set.
$\ddagger$ By convention, we always have $\epsilon:(q, \gamma) \,\underset{M}{\overset{*}{\vdash}}\, (q, \gamma)$.

When accepting by empty store, the set of final states is irrelevant. Thus when accepting by empty store we usually let the set of final states be the empty set.

The pda of Example 5.1 is deterministic in the sense that at most one move is possible from any configuration. Formally, we say that a pda, $M = (K, \Sigma, \Gamma, \delta, q_0, Z_0, F)$, is *deterministic* if:

1. For each q in K and Z in Γ, whenever $\delta(q, \epsilon, Z)$ is nonempty, then $\delta(q, a, Z)$ is empty for all a in Σ.
2. For no q in K, Z in Γ, and a in $\Sigma \cup \{\epsilon\}$ does $\delta(q, a, Z)$ contain more than one element.

Condition 1 prevents the possibility of a choice between a move independent of the input symbol (ϵ-move) and a move involving an input symbol. Condition 2 prevents a choice of move for any (q, a, Z) or (q, ϵ, Z).

Example 5.2. Figure 5.3 gives a nondeterministic pda that accepts $\{ww^R | w$ in $\{0, 1\}^*\}$. Rules 1 through 6 allow M to store the input on the pushdown store. In Rules 3 and 6 M has a choice of moves. If M decides that the middle of the input string has been reached, then the second choice is selected. M goes to state q_2 and tries to match the remaining input symbols with the contents of the pushdown store. If M guessed right, and if the input is of the form ww^R, then the inputs will match, M will empty its pushdown store, and thus accept the input string.

$$M = (\{q_1, q_2\}, \{0, 1\}, \{R, B, G\}, \delta, q_1, R, \varphi)$$

1. $\delta(q_1, 0, R) = \{(q_1, BR)\}$ 6. $\delta(q_1, 1, G) = \{(q_1, GG), (q_2, \epsilon)\}$
2. $\delta(q_1, 1, R) = \{(q_1, GR)\}$ 7. $\delta(q_2, 0, B) = \{(q_2, \epsilon)\}$
3. $\delta(q_1, 0, B) = \{(q_1, BB), (q_2, \epsilon)\}$ 8. $\delta(q_2, 1, G) = \{(q_2, \epsilon)\}$
4. $\delta(q_1, 0, G) = \{(q_1, BG)\}$ 9. $\delta(q_1, \epsilon, R) = \{(q_2, \epsilon)\}$
5. $\delta(q_1, 1, B) = \{(q_1, GB)\}$ 10. $\delta(q_2, \epsilon, R) = \{(q_2, \epsilon)\}$

Fig. 5.3. A nondeterministic pda that accepts $\{ww^R | w$ in $\{0, 1\}^*\}$ by empty store.

We cannot emphasize too strongly that M accepts an input if any sequence of choices causes M to empty its pushdown store. Thus M always "guesses right," because wrong guesses, in themselves, do not cause an input to be rejected. An input is only rejected if there is no "right guess." Figure 5.4 shows the accessible configurations of M when processing the string 001100.

For finite automata, the deterministic and nondeterministic models were equivalent with respect to the languages accepted. We shall see later that the same is not true for pda. In fact ww^R is accepted by a nondeterministic pda, but not by any deterministic pda.

Input	Configurations
ϵ	$(q_1, R) \rightarrow (q_2, \epsilon)$
0	(q_1, BR)
00	$(q_1, BBR)(q_2, R) \rightarrow (q_2, \epsilon)$
001	$(q_1, GBBR)$
0011	$(q_1, GGBBR)\ (q_2, BBR)$
00110	$(q_1, BGGBBR)\ (q_2, BR)$
001100	$(q_1, BBGGBBR)\ (q_2, GGBBR)\ (q_2, R) \rightarrow (q_2, \epsilon)$

Fig. 5.4. Accessible configurations for the pda of Fig. 5.3 with input 001100.

5.3 NONDETERMINISTIC PUSHDOWN AUTOMATA AND CONTEXT-FREE LANGUAGES

We shall now prove the fundamental result that the class of languages accepted by nondeterministic pda is precisely the class of context-free languages. We first show that the languages accepted by nondeterministic pushdown automata by final state are exactly the languages accepted by nondeterministic pushdown automata by empty store. We then show that the languages accepted by empty store are exactly the context-free languages.

Theorem 5.1. L is $N(M_1)$ for some pda M_1, if and only if L is $T(M_2)$ for some pda, M_2.

Proof (if). Let

$$M_2 = (K, \Sigma, \Gamma, \delta, q_0, Z_0, F)$$

be a pda such that $L = T(M_2)$. Let

$$M_1 = (K \cup \{q_e, q_0'\}, \Sigma, \Gamma \cup \{X\}, \delta', q_0', X, \varphi)$$

where δ' is defined as follows.

1. $\delta'(q_0', \epsilon, X)$ contains $(q_0, Z_0 X)$.
2. $\delta'(q, a, Z)$ includes the elements of $\delta(q, a, Z)$ for all q in K, a in Σ or $a = \epsilon$, and Z in Γ.
3. For all q in F, and Z in $\Gamma \cup \{X\}$, $\delta'(q, \epsilon, Z)$ contains (q_e, ϵ).
4. For all Z in $\Gamma \cup \{X\}$, $\delta'(q_e, \epsilon, Z)$ contains (q_e, ϵ).

Rule 1 causes M_1 to enter the initial configuration of M_2, except that M_1 will have its own bottom of the stack marker, X, which is below the symbols of M_2's pushdown store. Rule 2 allows M_1 to simulate M_2. Should M_2 ever enter a final state, Rules 3 and 4 allow M_1 the choice of entering state q_e and erasing its store, thereby accepting the input, or continuing to simulate M_2.

One should note that M_2 may possibly erase its entire store for some input x not in $T(M_2)$. This is the reason that M_1 has its own special bottom of the stack marker. Otherwise M_1, in simulating M_2, would also erase its entire store, thereby accepting x when it should not.

Now assume that x is in $T(M_2)$. Then $x:(q_0, Z_0) \left|\frac{*}{M_2}\right. (q, \gamma)$ for some q in F. Thus

$$\epsilon:(q_0', X) \left|\overline{M_1}\right. (q_0, Z_0 X) \text{ by Rule 1,}$$

$$x:(q_0, Z_0 X) \left|\frac{*}{M_1}\right. (q, \gamma X) \text{ by Rule 2,}$$

$$\epsilon:(q, \gamma X) \left|\frac{*}{M_1}\right. (q_e, \epsilon) \text{ by Rules 3 and 4,}$$

and therefore x is in $N(M_1)$. By similar reasoning, if x is in $N(M_1)$, then x is in $T(M_2)$.

Proof (only if). Let

$$M_1 = (K, \Sigma, \Gamma, \delta, q_0, Z_0, \varphi)$$

be a pda such that $L = N(M_1)$. Let

$$M_2 = (K \cup \{q_0', q_f\}, \Sigma, \Gamma \cup \{X\}, \delta', q_0', X, \{q_f\})$$

where δ' is defined as follows.

1. $\delta'(q_0', \epsilon, X)$ contains $(q_0, Z_0 X)$.
2. For all q in K, a in $\Sigma \cup \{\epsilon\}$, and Z in Γ, $\delta'(q, a, Z)$ includes the elements of $\delta(q, a, Z)$.
3. For all q in K, $\delta'(q, \epsilon, X)$ contains (q_f, ϵ).

Rule 1 causes M_2 to enter the initial configuration of M_1, except that M_2 will have its own bottom of stack marker X which is below the symbols of M_1's pushdown store. Rule 2 allows M_2 to simulate M_1. Should M_1 ever erase its entire pushdown store, then M_2, in simulating M_1, will erase its entire pushdown store except for the symbol X at the bottom. Rule 3 causes M_2, when the X appears, to enter a final state, thereby accepting the input x. The proof that $T(M_2) = N(M_1)$ is similar to the proof in the *if* part of the theorem and is left as an exercise.

Theorem 5.2. If L is a context-free language, then there exists a pda M, such that $L = N(M)$.

Proof. Let $G = (V_N, V_T, P, S)$ be a context-free grammar in Greibach normal form generating L. (We assume that ϵ is not in $L(G)$. The reader may modify the construction for the case where ϵ is in $L(G)$.) Let

$$M = (\{q_1\}, V_T, V_N, \delta, q_1, S, \varphi),$$

where $\delta(q_1, a, A)$ contains (q_1, γ) whenever $A \to a\gamma$ is in P.

To show that $L(G) = N(M)$, note that $xA\beta \underset{G}{\Rightarrow} xa\alpha\beta$ if and only if $a:(q_1, A\beta) \underset{M}{\vdash} (q_1, \alpha\beta)$. It follows immediately by induction on the number of steps of the derivation that $xA\beta \underset{G}{\overset{*}{\Rightarrow}} xy\alpha$, for any x and y in V_T^*, A in V_N, and α and β in V_N^*, if and only if $y:(q_1, A\beta) \underset{M}{\overset{*}{\vdash}} (q_1, \alpha)$. Thus $S \underset{G}{\overset{*}{\Rightarrow}} x$ if and only if $x:(q_1, S) \underset{M}{\overset{*}{\vdash}} (q_1, \epsilon).$†

Theorem 5.3. If L is $N(M)$ for some pda M, then L is a context-free language.

Proof. Let M be the pda $(K, \Sigma, \Gamma, \delta, q_0, Z_0, \varphi)$. Let $G = (V_N, \Sigma, P, S)$ be a context-free grammar. V_N is the set of objects of the form $[q, A, p]$, where q and p are in K and A is in Γ, plus the new symbol S. P is the set of productions:

1. $S \to [q_0, Z_0, q]$ for each q in K.
2. $[q, A, p] \to a[q_1, B_1, q_2][q_2, B_2, q_3] \dots [q_m, B_m, q_{m+1}]$ for each $q, q_1, q_2,$ $\dots, q_{m+1}$ in K, where $p = q_{m+1}$, each a in $\Sigma \cup \{\epsilon\}$, and $A, B_1, B_2, \dots, B_m$ in Γ, such that $\delta(q, a, A)$ contains $(q_1, B_1 B_2 \dots B_m)$. (If $m = 0$, then $q_1 = p$, $\delta(q, a, A)$ contains (p, ϵ), and the production is $[q, A, p] \to a$.)

To understand the proof it helps to know that the variables and productions of G have been defined in such a way that a leftmost derivation in G of a sentence x is a simulation of the pda M, when fed the input x. In particular, the variables that appear in any step of a leftmost derivation in G correspond to the symbols on the pushdown store of the pda at a time when the pda has seen as much of the input as the grammar has already generated.

To show that $L(G) = N(M)$, we prove by induction on the number of steps in a derivation of G or number of moves of M, that

$$[q, A, p] \underset{G}{\overset{*}{\Rightarrow}} x \qquad \text{if and only if} \qquad x:(q, A) \underset{M}{\overset{*}{\vdash}} (p, \epsilon).$$

Now if x is in $L(G)$, then

$$S \underset{G}{\Rightarrow} [q_0, Z_0, q] \underset{G}{\overset{*}{\Rightarrow}} x,$$

for some state q. Hence, $x:(q_0, Z_0) \underset{M}{\overset{*}{\vdash}} (q, \epsilon)$, and therefore, x is in $N(M)\cdot$ Similarly x in $N(M)$ implies that $x:(q_0, Z_0) \underset{M}{\overset{*}{\vdash}} (q, \epsilon)$. Hence,

$$S \underset{G}{\Rightarrow} [q_0, Z_0, q] \underset{G}{\overset{*}{\Rightarrow}} x,$$

and therefore, x is in $L(G)$.

---

† Note that the pda M makes no ϵ-moves.

First we shall undertake the "if" part of the proof. Suppose that $x:(q, A) \mathrel{\mathop{\vdash}\limits_{M}^{*}} (p, \epsilon)$ by a process taking k steps. We wish to show that $[q, A, p] \mathrel{\mathop{\Rightarrow}\limits_{G}^{*}} x$. For $k = 1$, x is either a single symbol or ϵ. Thus $\delta(q, x, A)$ must contain (p, ϵ) and hence $[q, A, p] \rightarrow x$ is a production in P. Therefore $[q, A, p] \mathrel{\mathop{\Rightarrow}\limits_{G}^{*}} x$.

Now we assume that the hypothesis is true for any process of up to $k - 1$ steps and show that it is true for processes of k steps. The first step must be of the form

$$a:(q, A) \mathrel{\mathop{\vdash}\limits_{M}} (q_1, B_1 B_2 \ldots B_l), \qquad l \geqq 1,$$

where a is ϵ or the first symbol of x. It must be that x can be written $x = a x_1 x_2 \ldots x_l$, such that for each i between 1 and l,

$$x_i:(q_i, B_i) \mathrel{\mathop{\vdash}\limits_{M}^{*}} (q_{i+1}, \epsilon)$$

by a process of fewer than k steps, where $q_1, q_2, \ldots, q_{l+1}$ are in K, and $q_{l+1} = p$. Therefore, from the inductive hypothesis, $[q_i, B_i, q_{i+1}] \mathrel{\mathop{\Rightarrow}\limits_{G}^{*}} x_i$. But

$$[q, A, p] \rightarrow a[q_1, B_1, q_2][q_2, B_2, q_3] \ldots [q_l, B_l, q_{l+1}]$$

is a production of G, so

$$[q, A, p] \mathrel{\mathop{\Rightarrow}\limits_{G}^{*}} a x_1 x_2 \ldots x_l = x.$$

The "only if" part of the proof follows in a manner similar to the "if" part, by induction on the length of a derivation, and will not be given.

Example 5.3. Let

$$M = (\{q_0, q_1\}, \{0, 1\}, \{X, Z_0\}, \delta, q_0, Z_0, \varphi)$$

where δ is given by:

$$\delta(q_0, 0, Z_0) = \{(q_0, XZ_0)\} \qquad \delta(q_1, 1, X) = \{(q_1, \epsilon)\}$$
$$\delta(q_0, 0, X) = \{(q_0, XX)\} \qquad \delta(q_1, \epsilon, X) = \{(q_1, \epsilon)\}$$
$$\delta(q_0, 1, X) = \{(q_1, \epsilon)\} \qquad \delta(q_1, \epsilon, Z_0) = \{(q_1, \epsilon)\}$$

To construct a cfg $G = (V_N, V_T, P, S)$ generating $N(M)$ let

$$V_N = \{S, [q_0, X, q_0], [q_0, X, q_1], [q_1, X, q_0], [q_1, X, q_1],$$
$$[q_0, Z_0, q_0], [q_0, Z_0, q_1], [q_1, Z_0, q_0], [q_1, Z_0, q_1]\}$$

and $V_T = \{0, 1\}$. To construct the set of productions easily, we must realize that some variables may not appear in any derivation starting from the symbol S. Thus, we can save some effort if we start with the productions for S, then add productions only for those variables that appear on the right of some production already in the set. The productions for S are

$$S \rightarrow [q_0, Z_0, q_0] \qquad S \rightarrow [q_0, Z_0, q_1].$$

Next we add productions for the variable $[q_0, Z_0, q_0]$. These are

$$[q_0, Z_0, q_0] \rightarrow 0[q_0, X, q_0][q_0, Z_0, q_0],$$
$$[q_0, Z_0, q_0] \rightarrow 0[q_0, X, q_1][q_1, Z_0, q_0].$$

These productions are required by

$$\delta(q_0, 0, Z_0) = \{(q_0, XZ_0)\}.$$

Next, the productions for $[q_0, Z_0, q_1]$ are

$$[q_0, Z_0, q_1] \rightarrow 0[q_0, X, q_0][q_0, Z_0, q_1],$$
$$[q_0, Z_0, q_1] \rightarrow 0[q_0, X, q_1][q_1, Z_0, q_1].$$

These are also required by $\delta(q_0, 0, Z_0) = \{(q_0, XZ_0)\}$. The productions for the remaining variables and the relevant moves of the pda are:

1. $[q_0, X, q_0] \rightarrow 0[q_0, X, q_0][q_0, X, q_0]$
   $[q_0, X, q_0] \rightarrow 0[q_0, X, q_1][q_1, X, q_0]$
   $[q_0, X, q_1] \rightarrow 0[q_0, X, q_0][q_0, X, q_1]$
   $[q_0, X, q_1] \rightarrow 0[q_0, X, q_1][q_1, X, q_1]$
   since $\delta(q_0, 0, X) = \{(q_0, XX)\}$
2. $[q_0, X, q_1] \rightarrow 1$ since $\delta(q_0, 1, X) = \{(q_1, \epsilon)\}$
3. $[q_1, Z_0, q_1] \rightarrow \epsilon$ since $\delta(q_1, \epsilon, Z_0) = \{(q_1, \epsilon)\}$
4. $[q_1, X, q_1] \rightarrow \epsilon$ since $\delta(q_1, \epsilon, X) = \{(q_1, \epsilon)\}$
5. $[q_1, X, q_1] \rightarrow 1$ since $\delta(q_1, 1, X) = \{(q_1, \epsilon)\}$

It should be noted that there are no productions for the variables $[q_1, X, q_0]$ and $[q_1, Z_0, q_0]$. Thus no terminal string can be derived from either $[q_0, Z_0, q_0]$ or $[q_0, X, q_0]$. Deleting all productions involving one of these four variables on either the right or left, we end up with the following productions.

$$S \rightarrow [q_0, Z_0, q_1] \qquad\qquad [q_0, X, q_1] \rightarrow 1$$
$$[q_0, Z_0, q_1] \rightarrow 0[q_0, X, q_1][q_1, Z_0, q_1] \qquad [q_1, X, q_1] \rightarrow \epsilon$$
$$[q_0, X, q_1] \rightarrow 0[q_0, X, q_1][q_1, X, q_1] \qquad [q_1, X, q_1] \rightarrow 1$$
$$[q_1, Z_0, q_1] \rightarrow \epsilon$$

We summarize Theorems 5.1, 5.2, and 5.3 as follows. The subsequent three statements are equivalent:

1. L is a context-free language.
2. $L = N(M_1)$ for some pda M_1.
3. $L = T(M_2)$ for some pda M_2.

PROBLEMS

5.1 Find pushdown automata accepting the following sets by final state.

a) $\{w|w$ in $\{0, 1\}^*$ and w consists of an equal number of 0's and 1's$\}$.

b) $\{a^n b^m | n \leq m \leq 2n\}$.

c) The set generated by the grammar

$$G = (\{S, A\}, \{a, b\}, \{S \rightarrow aAA, A \rightarrow bS, A \rightarrow aS, A \rightarrow a\}, S).$$

d) The set of well-formed FORTRAN arithmetic expressions. Assume that variable names may be of any length greater than or equal to one.

5.2 Give a grammar for the language which is $N(M)$ where

$$M = (\{q_0, q_1\}, \{0, 1\}, \{Z_0, X\}, \delta, q_0, Z_0, \varphi)$$

and δ is given by:

$$\begin{array}{ll}
\delta(q_0, 1, Z_0) = \{(q_0, XZ_0)\} & \delta(q_0, \epsilon, Z_0) = \{(q_0, \epsilon)\} \\
\delta(q_0, 1, X) = \{(q_0, XX)\} & \delta(q_1, 1, X) = \{(q_1, \epsilon)\} \\
\delta(q_0, 0, X) = \{(q_1, X)\} & \delta(q_1, 0, Z_0) = \{(q_0, Z_0)\}
\end{array}$$

5.3 Prove the "only if" portion of Theorem 5.3.

5.4 Let $L = N(M)$ for some pda. Show that $L = N(M_1)$ for some one state pda, M_1.

5.5 Let $L = T(M)$ for some pda. Show that $L = T(M_1)$ for some two-state pda, M_1. Under what conditions is $L = T(M_1)$ for some one-state pda, M_1?

5.6 Let $L = N(M)$ for some pda. Show that $L = N(M_1)$ for some pda, $M_1 = (K, \Sigma, \Gamma, \delta, q_0, Z_0, F)$ where $\delta(q, \epsilon, Z) = \varphi$ for all q in K and Z in Γ.

5.7 Is the pda of Example 5.1 deterministic? Justify your answer.

5.8 In Example 5.3, why are there no productions for the variable $[q_1, X, q_0]$?

REFERENCES

The pushdown automaton appears as a formal construction in Oettinger [1961] and Schutzenberger [1963]. Its relation to context-free languages was shown independently in Chomsky [1962] and Evey [1963].

Various generalizations of pushdown automata have appeared in the literature. Devices with two or more pushdown tapes are equivalent to Turing machines. (See Chapter 6.) The pushdown transducer is a pushdown automaton which may output symbols at each move. It has been studied in Evey [1963], Fischer [1963], Ginsburg and Rose [1966], and Ginsburg and Greibach [1966b]. The two-way pushdown automaton is a device with a pushdown store, a finite control, and an input tape on which a head can move in either direction. These devices have been studied in Hartmanis, Lewis, and Stearns [1965], Aho, Hopcroft, and Ullman [1968], and Gray, Harrison, and Ibarra [1967].

CHAPTER 6

TURING MACHINES

6.1 INTRODUCTION

In this chapter we investigate a third type of recognizing device, the Turing machine. The Turing machine has been proposed as a mathematical model for describing procedures. Since our intuitive notion of a procedure as a finite sequence of instructions which can be mechanically carried out is not mathematically precise, we can never hope to show formally that it is equivalent to the precise notion of a Turing machine. However, from the definition of a Turing machine, it will be readily apparent that any computation that can be described by means of a Turing machine can be mechanically carried out. Thus the definition is not too broad. It can also be shown that any computation that can be performed on a modern-day digital computer can be described by means of a Turing machine. Thus if one ever found a procedure that fitted the intuitive notions, but could not be described by means of a Turing machine, it would indeed be of an unusual nature since it could not possibly be programmed for any existing computer. Many other formalizations of a procedure have been proposed, and they have been shown to be equivalent to the Turing machine formalization. This strengthens our belief that the Turing machine is general enough to encompass the intuitive notion of a procedure. It has been hypothesized by Church that any process which could naturally be called a procedure can be realized by a Turing machine. Subsequently, computability by a Turing machine has become the accepted definition of a procedure. We shall accept Church's hypothesis and simply substitute the formal definition of a Turing machine for the intuitive notion of a procedure.

6.2 DEFINITIONS AND NOTATION

Specifications for the Turing machine have been given in various ways in the literature. We begin with the discussion of a basic model, as shown in Fig. 6.1. Later we investigate other models of the Turing machine, and show that all these models are equivalent. The basic model has a *finite control*, an input tape which is divided into cells, and a *tape head* which scans one cell of the tape at a time. The tape has a leftmost cell but is infinite to the right. Each cell of the tape may hold exactly one of a finite number of *tape symbols.* Initially, the *n* leftmost cells, for some finite *n*, hold the *input*, a string of symbols chosen from a subset of the tape symbols called the *input symbols*. The remaining infinity of cells hold the *blank*, a special tape symbol which is not an input symbol.

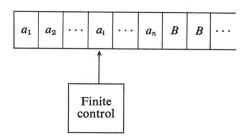

Fig. 6.1. Basic Turing machine.

In a *move* of the Turing machine, depending upon the symbol scanned by the tape head and the state of the finite control, the machine:

1. changes state.
2. prints a nonblank symbol on the tape cell scanned, replacing what was written there.
3. moves its head left or right one cell.

Note that the difference between a Turing machine and a two-way finite automaton lies in the former's ability to change symbols on its tape.

Formally, a Turing machine (Tm) is denoted $T = (K, \Sigma, \Gamma, \delta, q_0, F)$, where:

K is the finite set of *states*.

Γ is the finite set of allowable *tape symbols*. One of these, usually denoted B, is the *blank*.

Σ, a subset of Γ not including B, is the set of *input symbols*.

δ is the *next move function*, a mapping from $K \times \Gamma$ to $K \times (\Gamma - \{B\}) \times \{L, R\}$.† δ may, however, be undefined for some arguments.

q_0 in K is the *start state*.

$F \subseteq K$ is the set of *final states*.

We denote a *configuration* of the Turing machine T by (q, α, i). Here q, the current state of T, is in K. α is a string in $(\Gamma - \{B\})^*$ and is the non-blank portion of the tape. Note that if the tape head ever leaves a cell, it

---

† We have not allowed a Tm to print a blank for simplicity in defining the configurations. However, a Tm could have another symbol which is treated exactly as if it were the blank except for the fact that the Tm is allowed to print this pseudo blank symbol. Thus, no extra power results if we allow blanks to be printed. In informal discussion, we often allow the printing of a blank, knowing that one could use a different, but equivalent, symbol instead.

must print a nonblank symbol on the cell, so the tape of T will always consist of a block of nonblank symbols (here α is that block), with an infinity of blanks to the right. Finally, i is an integer, the distance of the tape head of T from the left end of α.

We define a *move* of T as follows. Let $(q, A_1A_2\ldots A_n, i)$ be a configuration of T, where $1 \leq i \leq n + 1$. If

$$1 \leq i \leq n \quad \text{and} \quad \delta(q, A_i) = (p, A, R),$$

then

$$(q, A_1A_2\ldots A_n, i) \underset{T}{\vdash} (p, A_1A_2\ldots A_{i-1}AA_{i+1}\ldots A_n, i + 1).$$

That is, T prints symbol A and moves right. If

$$\delta(q, A_i) = (p, A, L) \quad \text{and} \quad 2 \leq i \leq n,$$

then

$$(q, A_1A_2\ldots A_n, i) \underset{T}{\vdash} (p, A_1A_2\ldots A_{i-1}AA_{i+1}\ldots A_n, i - 1).$$

Here T prints A and moves left, but not off the left end of the tape. If $i = n + 1$, the tape head is scanning the blank, B. If $\delta(q, B) = (p, A, R)$, then

$$(q, A_1A_2\ldots A_n, n + 1) \underset{T}{\vdash} (p, A_1A_2\ldots A_nA, n + 2).$$

If, instead, $\delta(q, B) = (p, A, L)$, then

$$(q, A_1A_2\ldots A_n, n + 1) \underset{T}{\vdash} (p, A_1A_2\ldots A_nA, n).$$

If two configurations are related by $\underset{T}{\vdash}$, we say that the second results from the first by one move. If one configuration results from another by some finite number of moves, including zero moves, they are related by the relation $\underset{T}{\overset{*}{\vdash}}$.

The *language accepted* by T is the set of those words in Σ^* which cause T to enter a final state when placed, justified at the left, on the tape of T, with T in state q_0, and the tape head of T at the leftmost cell. Formally, the language accepted by $T = (K, \Sigma, \Gamma, \delta, q_0, F)$ is

$$\{w | w \text{ in } \Sigma^* \text{ and } (q_0, w, 1) \underset{T}{\overset{*}{\vdash}} (q, \alpha, i) \text{ for some } q \text{ in } F, \alpha \text{ in } \Gamma^* \text{ and integer } i\}.$$

Given a Tm recognizing a language L, we assume without loss of generality that the Tm *halts*, i.e., has no next move whenever the input is accepted. However, for words not accepted, it is possible that the Tm will not halt.

Example 6.1. Consider the following Tm that recognizes the context-free language $L = \{0^n1^n | n \geq 1\}$. Let $T = (K, \Sigma, \Gamma, \delta, q_0, F)$. Here,

$$K = \{q_0, q_1, \ldots, q_5\}, \quad \Sigma = \{0, 1\}, \quad \Gamma = \{0, 1, B, X, Y\}, \quad F = \{q_5\},$$

and δ is defined as follows.

1. $\delta(q_0, 0) = (q_1, X, R)$. ($T$ will alternately replace a 0 by X, then a 1 by Y. In state q_0, a 0 is replaced by an X, and T moves right in state q_1 looking for a 1.)

2. a) $\delta(q_1, 0) = (q_1, 0, R)$
   b) $\delta(q_1, Y) = (q_1, Y, R)$
   c) $\delta(q_1, 1) = (q_2, Y, L)$
   (T moves right in state q_1 (Rules 2a and 2b). When a 1 is found, it is changed to a Y, and the state becomes q_2 (Rule 2c). In q_2, we see that T moves left, looking for a 0 to convert to an X. Moving left, T will encounter a block of Y's, then, perhaps, a block of 0's, then an X.)

3. a) $\delta(q_2, Y) = (q_2, Y, L)$
   b) $\delta(q_2, X) = (q_3, X, R)$
   c) $\delta(q_2, 0) = (q_4, 0, L)$
   (T moves left, through Y's (3a). If T encounters an X while still in state q_2, there are no more 0's to convert. T goes to state q_3 to check that no

Configuration	Rule used	Configuration	Rule used
$(q_0, \dot{0}00111, 1)$	start	$(q_4, X\dot{X}0YY1, 2)$	3c
$(q_1, X\dot{0}0111, 2)$	1	$(q_0, XX\dot{0}YY1, 3)$	4b
$(q_1, X0\dot{0}111, 3)$	2a	$(q_1, XXX\dot{Y}Y1, 4)$	1
$(q_1, X00\dot{1}11, 4)$	2a	$(q_1, XXXY\dot{Y}1, 5)$	2b
$(q_2, X0\dot{0}Y11, 3)$	2c	$(q_1, XXXYY\dot{1}, 6)$	2b
$(q_4, \dot{X}00Y11, 2)$	3c	$(q_2, XXXY\dot{Y}Y, 5)$	2c
$(q_4, \dot{X}00Y11, 1)$	4a	$(q_2, XXX\dot{Y}YY, 4)$	3a
$(q_0, X\dot{0}0Y11, 2)$	4b	$(q_2, XX\dot{X}YYY, 3)$	3a
$(q_1, XX\dot{0}Y11, 3)$	1	$(q_3, XXX\dot{Y}YY, 4)$	3b
$(q_1, XX0\dot{Y}11, 4)$	2a	$(q_3, XXXY\dot{Y}Y, 5)$	5a
$(q_1, XX0Y\dot{1}1, 5)$	2b	$(q_3, XXXYY\dot{Y}, 6)$	5a
$(q_2, XX0Y\dot{Y}1, 4)$	2c	$(q_3, XXXYYY\,, 7)$	5a
$(q_2, XX\dot{0}YY1, 3)$	3a	$(q_5, XXXYYY\dot{\,}, 8)$	5b

Fig. 6.2. Computation accepting 000111.

more 1's remain (3b). If a 0 is encountered, T goes to state q_4 instead, and moves left to convert the leftmost 0 (3c).)

4. a) $\delta(q_4, 0) = (q_4, 0, L)$
   b) $\delta(q_4, X) = (q_0, X, R)$
   (T moves through the 0's (4a). If an X is encountered, T has passed the leftmost 0 and so must move right, to convert that 0 to an X. State q_0 is entered, and the process just described in Rules 1 through 4 repeats (Rule 4b).)

5. a) $\delta(q_3, Y) = (q_3, Y, R)$
   b) $\delta(q_3, B) = (q_5, Y, R)$
   (T enters state q_3 when no 0's remain (see 3b). T must move right (5a). If a blank is encountered before a 1, then no 1's remain (5b). The input is in L, and T enters state q_5, the lone accepting state.)

6. δ is undefined, except as in Rules 1 through 5.

Let us see how T acts with input 000111. The successive configurations, together with the rules used to get from one to the other are shown in Fig. 6.2. For ease of understanding, we have inserted an arrow into each configuration above the symbol scanned by the tape head.

6.3 TECHNIQUES FOR TURING MACHINE CONSTRUCTION

A Turing machine can be "programmed," in much the same manner as a computer is programmed. When one specifies the function which we usually call δ for a Tm, he is really writing a program for the Tm. In this section, we present a collection of "tricks" which, hopefully, will lead the reader to familiarity with the Turing machine.

I. STORAGE IN FINITE CONTROL. The finite control can be used to hold a finite amount of information. To do so, the state is written as a pair of elements, one exercising control and the other storing a symbol. It should be emphasized that this arrangement is for conceptual purposes only. No modification in the definition of the Turing machine has been made.

Example 6.2. Consider the Turing machine

$$T = (K, \{0, 1\}, \{0, 1, B\}, \delta, [q_0, B], F),$$

where K can be written as $\{q_0, q_1\} \times \{0, 1, B\}$. That is, K consists of the pairs $[q_0, 0]$, $[q_0, 1]$, $[q_0, B]$, $[q_1, 0]$, $[q_1, 1]$, and $[q_1, B]$. The set F is $\{[q_1, B]\}$. T looks at the first input symbol, records it in its finite control, and checks that the symbol does not appear elsewhere on its input. The second component of the state records the first input symbol. Note that T accepts a regular set, but T will serve for demonstration purposes. We define δ as follows.

1. a) $\delta([q_0, B], 0) = ([q_1, 0], 0, R)$
   b) $\delta([q_0, B], 1) = ([q_1, 1], 1, R)$
   (T stores the symbol scanned in second component of the state and moves right. The first component of T's state becomes q_1.)
2. a) $\delta([q_1, 0], 1) = ([q_1, 0], 1, R)$
   b) $\delta([q_1, 1], 0) = ([q_1, 1], 0, R)$
   (If T has a 0 stored and sees a 1, or vice versa, then T continues to move to the right.)
3. a) $\delta([q_1, 0], B) = ([q_1, B], 0, L)$
   b) $\delta([q_1, 1], B) = ([q_1, B], 0, L)$
   (T enters the final state $[q_1, B]$ if T reaches a blank symbol without having first encountered a second copy of the leftmost symbol.)

If T reaches a blank in state $[q_1, 0]$ or $[q_1, 1]$, it accepts. For state $[q_1, 0]$ and symbol 0 or for state $[q_1, 1]$ and symbol 1, δ is not defined, so if T ever sees the symbol stored, it halts without accepting.

In general, we can allow the finite control to have k components, all but one of which store information.

II. MULTIPLE TRACKS. We can imagine that the tape of the Turing machine is divided into k tracks, for any finite k. This arrangement is shown in Fig. 6.3, with $k = 3$. What is actually done is that the symbols on the tape are considered as k-tuples—one component for each track.

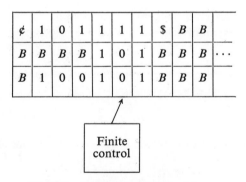

Fig. 6.3. 3-Track Turing machine.

Example 6.3. The tape in Fig. 6.3 can be imagined to be that of a Turing machine which takes a binary input greater than 2, written on the first track, and determines if it is a prime. The input is surrounded by ¢ and $ on the first track. Thus, the allowable input symbols are $[¢, B, B]$, $[0, B, B]$, $[1, B, B]$, and $[\$, B, B]$. These symbols can be identified with ¢, 0, 1, and $, respectively, when viewed as input symbols. The blank symbol can be represented by $[B, B, B]$.

To test if its input is a prime, the Tm first writes the number two in binary on the second track and copies the first track onto the third track. Then, the second track is subtracted, as many times as possible, from the third track, effectively dividing the third track by the second and leaving the remainder.

If the remainder is zero, the number on the first track is not a prime. If the remainder is nonzero, increase the number on the second track by one. If now the second track equals the first, the number on the first track is a prime, because it cannot be divided by any number between one and itself. If the second is less than the first, the whole operation is repeated for the new number on the second track.

In Fig. 6.3, the Tm is testing to determine if 47 is a prime. The Tm is dividing by 5; already 5 has been subtracted twice, so 37 appears on the third track.

III. CHECKING OFF SYMBOLS. Checking off symbols is a useful trick for visualizing how a Tm recognizes languages defined by repeated strings, such as

$$\{ww \mid w \text{ in } \Sigma^*\}, \{wcy \mid w \text{ and } y \text{ in } \Sigma^*, w \neq y\} \quad \text{or} \quad \{ww^R \mid w \text{ in } \Sigma^*\}.$$

It is also useful when lengths of substrings must be compared, such as in the languages

$$\{a^i b^i \mid i \geq 1\} \quad \text{or} \quad \{a^i b^j c^k \mid i \neq j \text{ or } j \neq k\}.$$

We introduce an extra track on the tape that holds a blank or $\sqrt{}$. The $\sqrt{}$ appears when the symbol below it has been considered by the Tm in one of its comparisons.

Example 6.4. Consider a Turing machine $T = (K, \Sigma, \Gamma, \delta, q_0, F)$, which recognizes the language $\{wcw \mid w \text{ in } \{a, b\}^*\}$. Let

$$K = \{[q, d] \mid q = q_1, q_2, \ldots, q_9 \text{ and } d = a, b, \text{ or } B\}.$$

The second component of the state is used to store an input symbol.

$$\Sigma = \{[B, d] \mid d = a, b, \text{ or } c\},$$

$$\Gamma = \{[X, d] \mid X = B \text{ or } \sqrt{} \text{ and } d = a, b, c, \text{ or } B\},$$

$$q_0 = [q_1, B], \quad \text{and} \quad F = \{[q_9, B]\}.$$

The blank symbol is identified with $[B, B]$, a is identified with $[B, a]$, b is identified with $[B, b]$, and c is identified with $[B, c]$. We define δ as follows.

1. $$\delta([q_1, B], [B, d]) = ([q_2, d], [\sqrt{}, d], R)$$

for $d = a$ or b. (T checks the symbol scanned on the tape, stores the symbol in the finite control and moves right.)

2. $$\delta([q_2, d], [B, e]) = ([q_2, d], [B, e], R)$$

for $d = a$ or b, $e = a$ or b. (T continues to move right, over unchecked symbols, looking for c.)

3. $$\delta([q_2, d], [B, c]) = ([q_3, d], [B, c], R)$$

for $d = a$ or b. (On finding c, T enters a state with first component q_3.)

4. $$\delta([q_3, d], [\sqrt{}, e]) = ([q_3, d], [\sqrt{}, e], R)$$

for $d = a$ or b, and $e = a$ or b. (T moves right over checked symbols.)

5. $$\delta([q_3, d], [B, d]) = ([q_4, B], [\sqrt{}, d], L)$$

for $d = a$ or b. (T encounters an unchecked symbol. If the unchecked symbol matches the symbol stored in the finite control, T checks it and begins moving left. If the symbols disagree, T has no next move, and so halts without accepting.)

6. $$\delta([q_4, B], [\sqrt{}, d]) = ([q_4, B], [\sqrt{}, d], L)$$

for $d = a$ or b. (T moves left over checked symbols.)

7. $$\delta([q_4, B], [B, c]) = ([q_5, B], [B, c], L)$$

(T encounters the symbol c.)

8. $$\delta([q_5, B], [B, d]) = ([q_6, B], [B, d], L)$$

for $d = a$ or b. (If the symbol immediately to the left of the c is unchecked, T proceeds left to find the leftmost unchecked symbol.)

9. $$\delta([q_6, B], [B, d]) = ([q_6, B], [B, d], L)$$

for $d = a$ or b. (T proceeds left.)

10. $$\delta([q_6, B], [\sqrt{}, d]) = ([q_1, B], [\sqrt{}, d], R)$$

for $d = a$ or b. (T encounters a checked symbol and moves right, to pick up another symbol for comparison. The first component of state becomes q_1 again.)

11. $$\delta([q_5, B], [\sqrt{}, d]) = ([q_7, B], [\sqrt{}, d], R)$$

for $d = a$ or b. (T will be in state $[q_5, B]$ immediately after crossing c moving left. (See Rule 7.) If a checked symbol appears immediately to the left of c, all symbols to the left of c have been checked. T must test if all symbols to the right have been checked. If so, they must have compared properly with the symbol to the left of c, so T will accept.)

12. $$\delta([q_7, B], [B, c]) = ([q_8, B], [B, c], R).$$

(T moves right over c.)

13. $$\delta([q_8, B], [\checkmark, d]) = ([q_8, B], [\checkmark, d], R)$$

for $d = a$ or b. (T moves to the right over checked symbols.)

14. $$\delta([q_8, B], [B, B]) = ([q_9, B], [\checkmark, B], L).$$

(If T finds $[B, B]$, the blank, it halts and accepts. If T found an unchecked symbol when its first component of state was q_8, it would have halted without accepting.)

IV. SHIFTING OVER. A Turing machine can make space on its tape by shifting all nonblank symbols a finite number of cells to the right. To do so, the tape head must make an excursion to the right, repeatedly storing the symbols read in its finite control and replacing them with symbols read from cells to the left. The Tm can then return to the vacated cells, and print symbols of its choosing. If space is available, it can push blocks of symbols left in a similar manner.

Example 6.5. We construct part of a Turing machine, $T = (K, \Sigma, \Gamma, \delta, q_0, F)$ which may occasionally have a need to shift symbols two cells to the right. Let K contain states of the form $[q, A_1, A_2]$ for $q = q_1$ or q_2, and A_1 and A_2 in Γ. Let B be the blank, and X be a special symbol not used by T except in the shifting process. We suppose that T starts the shifting process in state $[q_1, B, B]$. The relevant portions of the function δ are as follows.

1. $$\delta([q_1, B, B], A_1) = ([q_1, B, A_1], X, R)$$

for A_1 in $\Gamma - \{B, X\}$. (T stores the first symbol read in the third component of its state. X is printed on the cell scanned and T moves to the right.)

2. $$\delta([q_1, B, A_1], A_2) = ([q_1, A_1, A_2], X, R)$$

for A_1 and A_2 in $\Gamma - \{B, X\}$. (T prints an X, stores the symbol being read in the third component, shifts the symbol in the third component to the second component, and moves right.)

3. $$\delta([q_1, A_1, A_2], A_3) = ([q_1, A_2, A_3], A_1, R)$$

for A_1, A_2, and A_3 in $\Gamma - \{B, X\}$. (T now repeatedly reads a symbol A_3, stores it in the third component of state, shifts the symbol previously in third component A_2 to the second component, deposits the previous second component A_1 on the cell scanned, and moves right. It should be clear that a symbol will be deposited two cells to the right of its original position.)

4. $$\delta([q_1, A_1, A_2], B) = ([q_1, A_2, B], A_1, R)$$

for A_1 and A_2 in $\Gamma - \{B, X\}$. (When a blank is seen on the tape, the stored symbols are deposited on the tape.)

5. $\delta([q_1, A_1, B], B) = ([q_2, B, B], A_1, L)$.

(After all symbols have been deposited, T sets the first component of state to q_2, and will move left to find an X, which marks the rightmost vacated cell.)

6. $\delta([q_2, B, B], A) = ([q_2, B, B], A, L)$

for A in $\Gamma - \{B, X\}$. (T moves left until an X is found. When X is found, T will transfer to a state which we have assumed exists in K and resume its other functions.)

V. SIMULATION. Let B be an automaton which, with input w, enters in succession configurations $C_1, C_2, \ldots, C_n$. Informally, we say an automaton A *simulates* the automaton B, if A, with input w, enters in succession configurations representing $C_1, C_2, \ldots, C_n$. It is possible that A will enter other configurations between the times it enters the configurations representing those of B.

The concept of simulation is useful in showing that an automaton of one type can recognize any language recognized by an automaton of some other type. For an automaton A to simulate an automaton B, A must have two capabilities.

First, if A has in storage a configuration representing configuration C_i of B, A must be able to calculate the representation for C_{i+1}. In addition, A must be able to determine if configuration C_i of B is a configuration which implies that B accepts its input. Then A must also accept the input.

In passing, we point out that for simulation purposes it is often useful to represent a configuration of a Turing machine as $\alpha q X \beta$, where α and β are tape strings, X is a tape symbol, and q is a state. In configuration $\alpha q X \beta$, the state is q, $\alpha X \beta$ is the nonblank portion of tape, and X is the symbol scanned by the tape head. An example of the simulation of a nondeterministic Tm by a deterministic one is given in Section 6.5.

VI. DIAGONALIZATION. Another useful concept is *diagonalization*. It can be used to show that there is a language accepted by an automaton of type 2 that is accepted by no automaton of type 1. The salient features of the diagonalization are: There must be an encoding of all automata of type 1 whose input symbols are chosen from some alphabet Σ. The encoding itself uses only symbols from Σ. An example of how this encoding can be done is given in the next chapter.

Next, we construct an automaton A, of type 2, with inputs from Σ^*. The input to A is treated both as the encoding of some automaton B, of type 1, and as the input to B. A must have the ability to simulate B, that is, determine whether or not B accepts its own encoding. If B accepts, A does not accept. If B fails to accept, A accepts.

It is always true that the language accepted by A is accepted by no automaton of type 1. For suppose that B were such an automaton. B has an encoding w in Σ^*. Suppose that B accepts w. Then A simulates B with input w, and finds that B accepts w. So A does not accept w. Likewise, if B does not accept w, A does. In either case, A and B cannot accept the same language.

Incidentally, a word of explanation concerning the rationale of the term "diagonalization" is in order. One can number the words in Σ^* by the scheme—take the shortest first, and among words of equal length, use some lexicographical order (see Section 1.3). Then we can number automata of type 1 according to the numbers assigned to their encodings. The automaton A accepts the ith word if and only if the ith word is not accepted by the ith automaton. Imagine an infinite matrix for which the entry in the ith column, jth row, denoted (i, j), is 1 if the jth automaton accepts word i, and is 0 otherwise. A accepts word i if and only if the diagonal entry (i, i) is 0. Hence the word diagonalization.

VII. SUBROUTINES. It is possible for one Turing machine to be a "subroutine" of another Tm under rather general conditions. If T_1 is to be a subroutine of T_2, we require that the states of T_1 be disjoint from the states of T_2 (excluding the states of T_2's subroutine). To "call" T_1, T_2 enters the start state of T_1. The rules of T_1 are part of the rules of T_2. In addition, from a halting state of T_1, T_2 enters a state of its own and proceeds.

Example 6.6. Let us informally describe a Turing machine, T_3, which computes $n!$. That is, if we start T_3 with 01^n0 as input, T_3 will end with $0^{n+2}1^{n!}$ on the nonblank portion of its tape. T_3 will make use of a subroutine T_2, which does multiplication. Specifically, T_2, started with $01^i0^j1^k$ on its tape, with its tape head at the leftmost 0 of the block of j 0's, will halt with $01^i0^j1^{ik}$ on the tape.

From its initial configuration, T_3 moves right, past the block of 1's and the last 0, prints a 1, and moves left. T_3 now has 01^n01 on its tape. T_3 calls the subroutine T_2. When control returns to T_3, the tape of T_3 contains 01^n01^n0. From its current state, T_3 then tests to see that at least three 1's remain in the first block of 1's. If so, it changes the rightmost 1 in that block to a 0, and returns to the state from which it "calls" T_2.

After the second "call" of T_2, $01^{n-1}001^{n(n-1)}$ will appear on the tape of T_3. After the third call, $01^{n-2}0001^{n(n-1)(n-2)}$ will appear, and so on, until after the $n-1$st call, $0110^{n-1}1^{n(n-1)\cdots(2)}$ will appear. At this time, the first block of 1's has fewer than three 1's, so T_3 changes them to 0's and halts. Note that $n(n-1)\ldots(2) = n!$.

T_2 can itself be thought of as using a subroutine T_1 which, given two blocks of 1's, adds the first to the second, leaving the first intact. The technique of "checking off symbols" is useful in constructing T_1. T_2 "calls" T_1 once for each 1 in the first block, then checks it off, thus effecting a multiplication.

6.4 THE TURING MACHINE AS A PROCEDURE

So far, we have defined the Tm as a recognizing device. As mentioned earlier, we can consider the Tm as a procedure. For example, if we wish to define a procedure for determining if a number is a prime, we could construct a Tm which accepts precisely the set of all primes. Note that, in this case, whether the Tm is thought of as a recognizer or a procedure is merely a matter of preference.

In general, if one wishes to consider a procedure for manipulating strings of symbols, one can convert the procedure to a recognition problem by constructing a new Tm which accepts pairs of strings separated by a special symbol. The new Tm accepts a given pair precisely when the procedure would convert the first string in the pair to the second string and then halt. We shall leave the proof of the fact that, given a procedure, one can find a corresponding recognizer and vice-versa, as an exercise for the reader. Section 1.3 contains most of the relevant ideas.

The Tm of Example 6.1 is used as a recognizer. Note that, no matter what the input, the Tm will eventually reach a condition in which for the state of the finite control and symbol scanned by the tape head, δ is undefined. In such a condition, T is said to halt; no further moves are possible. If a language is accepted by a Tm which halts on all inputs, then the language is said to be *recursive*. It should be emphasized that there are languages which are accepted by a Tm that does not halt for some inputs not in the language, but by no Turing machine which halts on all inputs. This fact will be proved in the next chapter. A language that can be recognized by some Tm is called a *recursively enumerable* (r.e.) language. We shall see in the next chapter that the r.e. languages are exactly the languages generated by type 0 grammars.

When we consider a Tm as a procedure, if the Tm halts for all inputs, then we say that the procedure is an *algorithm*. There exist procedures for which there is no corresponding algorithm. An example is a procedure for determining if a csg generates at least one terminal string. One can construct a Tm which, given the specification of a csg, will generate all possible terminal strings in some lexicographical order. To each word, the Tm applies the algorithm given in Chapter 2, to see if the word is generated by the grammar. If the grammar generates at least one word, the Tm will find it and halt in a final state. However, if the language generated by the grammar is empty, the Tm will continue generating words and testing them forever. We show in Chapter 14 that there is no Tm that halts for every input and determines for each csg whether the language generated by the grammar is empty.

In addition to considering the Tm as a recognizing device or a procedure, we can consider the Tm as defining a function. Let $f(n)$ be a function mapping the positive integers into the positive integers. Let $T = (K, \Sigma, \Gamma, \delta, q_0, F)$ be a Tm. If, for every integer n, $(q_0, 1^n, 1) \vdash_T^* (p, 1^{f(n)}, 1)$ for some p in F, then we say that T *computes* the function $f(n)$. If some Tm T computes $f(n)$

for each n, then $f(n)$ is said to be *recursive*. If $f(n)$ is not defined for all n, then $f(n)$ is said to be a *partial* function. If some Tm T computes $f(n)$ wherever $f(n)$ is defined, but may not halt for those n for which $f(n)$ is undefined, then $f(n)$ is a *partial recursive* function.

6.5 MODIFICATIONS OF TURING MACHINES

One reason for the acceptance of the Turing machine as a general model of a computation is that the model with which we have been dealing is invariant to many modifications which would seem off-hand to increase the computing power of the device. In this section we give informal proofs of some of these equivalence theorems.

A Turing machine with a *two-way infinite tape* is denoted by $T = (K, \Sigma, \Gamma, \delta, q_0, F)$, as in the original model. As its name implies, the tape is infinite to the left as well as to the right. We denote a configuration of such a device by (q, α, i), where q is the state, α is the nonblank string of symbols on the tape, and i is the position of the tape head relative to the left end of α. That is, $i = 1$ if T is scanning the leftmost symbol of α, $i = 2$ if T is scanning the second symbol, etc. We imagine, however, that there is an infinity of blank cells both to the left and right of α. Thus, it is possible that $i = 0$, in which case T is scanning the blank immediately to the left of α.

The relation $\vdash_{T}$, which relates two configurations if the configuration on the right is obtained from the one on the left by a single move, is defined as for the original model with the following exceptions for $i \leq 1$. If

$$\delta(q, X) = (p, Y, L),$$

then

$$(q, X\alpha, 1) \vdash_{T} (p, Y\alpha, 0).$$

If

$$\delta(q, B) = (p, Y, R),$$

then

$$(q, \alpha, 0) \vdash_{T} (p, Y\alpha, 2).$$

If

$$\delta(q, B) = (p, Y, L),$$

then

$$(q, \alpha, 0) \vdash_{T} (p, Y\alpha, 0).$$

Here B is the blank. Of course, $Y \neq B$. The initial configuration is $(q_0, w, 1)$. Unlike the original model, there is no left end of the tape for the Turing machine to "fall off," so it can proceed left as far as it wishes. The relation $\vdash_{T}^{*}$, as usual, relates two configurations if the one on the right can be obtained from the one on the left by some number of moves.

Theorem 6.1. If L is recognized by a Turing machine with a two-way infinite tape, it is recognized by a Tm with a one-way infinite tape.

Proof. Let $T_2 = (K_2, \Sigma_2, \Gamma_2, \delta_2, q_2, F_2)$ be a Tm with a two-way infinite tape. We construct T_1, a Turing machine simulating T_2 and having a tape that is infinite to the right only. T_1 will have two tracks, one to represent the cells of T_2's tape to the right of, and including, the tape cell initially scanned, the other to represent, in reverse order, the cells to the left of the initial cell. If we number the initial cell of T_2 0, those cells to the right $1, 2, \ldots$, and those cells to the left $-1, -2, \ldots$, then the relationship between the tapes of T_2 and T_1 is shown in Fig. 6.4.

$\ldots$	A_{-5}	A_{-4}	A_{-3}	A_{-2}	A_{-1}	A_0	A_1	A_2	A_3	A_4	A_5	$\ldots$

(a)

	A_0	A_1	A_2	A_3	A_4	A_5	$\ldots$
	¢	A_{-1}	A_{-2}	A_{-3}	A_{-4}	A_{-5}	

Fig. 6.4. Tapes of T_1 and T_2.
(a) Tape of T_2. (b) Tape of T_1.

(b)

The first cell of the tape of T_1 will hold, in the lower track, a symbol ¢ indicating that it is the leftmost cell. The finite control of T_1 will hold information as to whether T_2 would be scanning a symbol appearing on the upper or on the lower track of T_1.

It should be fairly evident to the reader that T_1 can be constructed to simulate T_2 in the sense that while T_2 is to the right of the initial position of its input head, T_1 is working on the upper track. While T_2 is to the left of its initial tape head position, T_1 works on its lower track, moving in the direction opposite to the direction in which T_2 moves. The input symbols of T_1 are symbols with a blank on the lower track and an input symbol of T_2 on the upper track. Such a symbol can be identified with the corresponding input symbol of T_2.

We now give a formal construction of $T_1 = (K_1, \Sigma_1, \Gamma_1, \delta_1, q_1, F_1)$. The states, K_1, of T_1 are all objects of the form $[q, U]$ or $[q, L]$, where q is in K_2, plus the symbol q_1. Note that the second component will indicate whether T_1 is working on the upper or lower track.† The tape symbols in Γ_1 are all objects of the form $[X, Y]$, where X and Y are in Γ_2. In addition, Y may be

---

† Here L means "lower" and should not be confused with L in the range of δ where it means "left."

$\not c$, a symbol not in Γ_2. If B is the blank of T_2, $[B, B]$ is the blank of T_1. Σ_1 consists of all symbols $[a, B]$, where a is in Σ_2. We identify a with $[a, B]$. F_1 is $\{[q, D] | q$ in $F_2, D = U$ or $L\}$. We define δ_1 as follows.

1. $\qquad \delta_1(q_1, [a, B]) = ([q, U], [X, \not c], R), \qquad$ if $\delta_2(q_2, a) = (q, X, R)$

for each a in Σ_2. (If T_2 moves right on its first move, T_1 prints $\not c$ in the lower track to mark the end of tape, sets its second component of state to U, and moves right. The first component of T_1's state holds the state of T_2. T_1 prints the symbol X, printed by T_2, on the upper track.)

2. $\qquad \delta_1(q_1, [a, B]) = ([q, L], [X, \not c], R), \qquad$ if $\delta_2(q_2, a) = (q, X, L)$

for each a in Σ_2. (If T_2 moves left on its first move, T_1 records the next state of T_2, and the symbol printed by T_2 as in (1), but sets the second component of its state to L, and moves right. Again, $\not c$ is printed in the lower track to mark the left end of the tape.)

3. For each $[X, Y]$ in Γ_1, with $Y \neq \not c$, and $D = L$ or R,

$$\delta_1([q, U], [X, Y]) = ([p, U], [Z, Y], D), \qquad \text{if } \delta_2(q, X) = (p, Z, D).$$

(T_1 simulates T_2 on the upper track.)

4. For each $[X, Y]$ in Γ_1, with $Y \neq \not c$,

$$\delta_1([q, L], [X, Y]) = ([p, L], [X, Z], D), \qquad \text{if } \delta_2(q, Y) = (p, Z, \bar{D}).$$

If D is L, $\bar{D}$ is R. If D is R, $\bar{D}$ is L. (T_1 simulates T_2 on the lower track of T_1. The direction of head motion of T_1 is opposite to that of T_2.)

5. $\delta_1([q, U], [X, \not c]) = \delta_1([q, L], [X, \not c]) = ([p, E], [Y, \not c], R)$, if

$$\delta_2(q, X) = (p, Y, D).$$

$E = U$ if $D = R$, and $E = L$ if $D = L$. (T_1 simulates a move of T_2 on the cell initially scanned by T_2. T_1 next works on the upper or lower track, depending on the direction in which T_2 moves. T_1 will always move right in this situation.)

We leave it to the reader to show that T_1 and T_2 accept the same language.

A *multitape* Turing machine is shown in Fig. 6.5. It consists of a finite control with k tape heads and k tapes; each tape is infinite in both directions. On a single move, depending on the state of the finite control and the symbol scanned by each of the tape heads, the machine can:

1. change state.
2. print a new symbol on each of the cells scanned by its tape heads.
3. move each of its tape heads, independently, one cell to the left or right, or keep it stationary.

Initially, the input appears on the first tape and the other tapes are blank. We shall not define the device more formally. We trust that the reader can formalize the model if he desires.

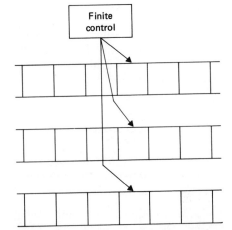

Fig. 6.5. Multitape Turing machine.

Theorem 6.2. If a language L is accepted by a multitape Turing machine, it is accepted by a single-tape Turing machine.

Proof. Let L be accepted by T_1, a Tm with k tapes. We can construct T_2, a one-tape Tm with $2k$ tracks, two tracks for each of T_1's tapes. One track records the contents of the corresponding tape of T_1 and the other is blank, except for a marker in the cell which holds the symbol scanned by the corresponding head of T_1. The arrangement is illustrated in Fig. 6.6. The finite control of T_2 stores information as to which head markers are to the left, and which are to the right of T_2's tape head. The state of T_1 is also stored in the finite control of T_2.

Head 1		X				
Tape 1	A_1	A_2	$\ldots$		$\ldots$	A_m
Head 2				X		
Tape 2	B_1	B_2	$\ldots$		$\ldots$	B_m
Head 3	X					
Tape 3	C_1	C_2	$\ldots$		$\ldots$	C_m

Fig. 6.6. Simulation of three tapes by one.

To simulate a move of T_1, T_2 must visit each of the cells with head markers, recording, in turn, the symbol scanned by each head of T_1. When

T_2 passes across a head marker, it must update the direction in which to find this marker. After gathering all the information necessary, T_2 determines the move of T_1. T_2 then visits, in turn, each of the head markers again, changing the symbols scanned and moving the markers one cell if necessary. Of course, if the new state of T_1 is accepting, T_2 accepts.

Example 6.7. Consider how much easier it is for a multitape Tm to recognize the language $L = \{ww^R | w \text{ in } \{0, 1\}^*\}$ than for a single-tape Tm.

For L to be recognized on a single-tape Tm, the tape head must go back and forth on the input, checking off symbols from both ends and comparing them. The process is similar to that of Example 6.4.

To recognize L with a two-tape Tm, the input is copied onto the second tape. The input on one tape is compared with the reversal on the other tape, and the length of the input checked to make sure it is even.

Note that the number of moves needed to recognize L by a one-tape machine is approximately the square of the input length, while with a two-tape machine, time proportional to the input length is sufficient.

A *nondeterministic* Turing machine is a device with a finite control and a single, two-way infinite tape. For a given state and tape symbol scanned by the tape head, the machine has several choices for the next move. Each choice consists of a new state, a tape symbol to print, and a direction of head motion. The nondeterministic Tm accepts its input if any sequence of choices of moves leads to an accepting state.

Theorem 6.3. If L is accepted by a nondeterministic Turing machine, T_1, then L is accepted by some deterministic Turing machine, T_2.

Proof. For any state and tape symbol of T_1, there are a finite number of choices for the next move. These can be numbered $1, 2, \ldots$. Let r be the maximum number of choices for any state–tape symbol pair. Then any finite length sequence of choices of move can be represented by a sequence of the digits 1 through r. Not all such sequences may represent choices of moves, since there may be less than r choices in some configurations.

T_2 will have three tapes. The first will hold the input. On the second, T_2 will generate sequences of digits 1 through r in a systematic manner. Specifically, the sequences will be generated with the shortest appearing first. Among sequences of equal length, they are generated in numerical order.

For each sequence generated on tape 2, T_2 copies the input onto tape 3 and then simulates T_1 on tape 3, using the sequence of tape 2 to dictate the moves of T_1. If T_1 enters an accepting state, T_2 also accepts. If there is a sequence of choices leading to acceptance, it will eventually be generated on tape 2. When simulated, T_2 will accept. But if no sequence of choices of moves of T_1 leads to acceptance, T_2 will not accept.

Note that this argument can be generalized to show how to simulate a nondeterministic multitape Tm with the usual model of a Turing machine.

Let us consider another modification of the Turing machine that adds no additional power—the *two-dimensional* Turing machine. The device consists of the usual finite control, but the tape consists of an infinity of cells in two dimensions. Depending on the state and symbol scanned, the device changes state, prints a new symbol, and moves its tape head in one of four directions. Initially, the input is on one row, and the head is at the left end of the input.

At any time, only a finite number of rows have any nonblank symbols in them, and these rows each have only a finite number of nonblank symbols. For example, consider the tape configuration shown in Fig. 6.7a. We can draw a rectangle about the nonblank symbols, as also shown in Fig. 6.7a. The rectangle can be written row by row on a single tape, as shown in Fig. 6.7b. The *'s separate the rows. One of the symbols is marked as scanned by the head.

Fig. 6.7. Two-dimensional Turing machine.

B	B	B	a_1	B	B	B
B	B	a_2	a_3	a_4	a_5	B
a_6	a_7	a_8	a_9	B	a_{10}	B
B	a_{11}	a_{12}	a_{13}	B	a_{14}	a_{15}
B	B	a_{16}	a_{17}	B	B	B

(a)

$$*BBBa_1BBB*BBa_2a_3a_4a_5B*a_6a_7a_8a_9Ba_{10}B*Ba_{11}a_{12}a_{13}Ba_{14}a_{15}*BBa_{16}a_{17}BBB*$$

(b)

If, on a given move, the head remains within the rectangle represented, it is easy to adjust the position of the head. We leave it to the reader to provide details. If the head moves vertically outside the rectangle, one adds another row of blanks to the left or right end of the linear representation. If the head leaves the rectangle to the right or left, the length of each row represented must be increased by one. Again we leave it to the reader to see how this can be done. The technique of "shifting" is useful here. The result is easily generalized to n-dimensional tapes.

We should also mention here the Turing machine with a read-only input tape and one or more read-write storage tapes. The move of the Tm is dependent on the input symbol scanned, but the Tm cannot print on the input. The input tape is usually visualized as having end markers, so the input tape head can always stay on the input, whose limits it cannot itself mark. If the input head can move in two directions, the device is called an *off-line* Turing machine. If the input head never moves left, it is an *on-line* Tm.

Clearly the off-line and on-line Tm are just varieties of multitape Tm. It should also be clear that they can simulate any multitape Tm.

6.6 RESTRICTED TURING MACHINES EQUIVALENT TO THE BASIC MODEL

So far we have considered generalizations on the basic Tm model. As we have seen, these generalizations do not increase the computational power of the model. We conclude this chapter by considering some models which at first one might think were less powerful than the Tm but indeed are just as powerful. For the most part, these models will be variations of the basic pushdown automaton defined in Chapter 5.

In passing, we note that a pushdown automaton can be thought of as a nondeterministic Tm with a read-only input on which the input head cannot move left, plus a storage tape with a rather peculiar restriction on the tape head. Whenever the storage tape head moves left, it must print a blank. Thus the storage tape to the right of the head is always completely blank. (Note that, strictly speaking, we did not allow a Tm to print a blank. We could, instead, require that a symbol with the same rules as the blank be printed.) We leave it to the reader to see that such a model is equivalent to the pushdown automaton originally introduced. The top of the pushdown store is to the right, not the left as in Chapter 5.

A *deterministic two-pushdown tape machine* is a deterministic Turing machine with a read-only input and two storage tapes. If a head moves left on either tape, a "blank" is printed on that tape.

Lemma 6.1. An arbitrary single-tape Turing machine can be simulated by a deterministic two-pushdown tape machine.

Proof. We leave it to the reader to see that the symbols to the left of the head of the Tm being simulated can be stored on one pushdown list, while the symbols on the right of the head can be placed on the other pushdown list.

We can prove a result stronger than Lemma 6.1. It concerns counter machines. A *counter machine* is a Tm whose storage tape alphabets contain only two symbols, Z and B. Furthermore, the symbol Z appears initially on the cell scanned by the tape head and may never appear on any other cell. A number i can be stored by moving the tape head i cells to the right of Z. (We again assume that this type of Tm can print a blank if it chooses.) A stored number can be incremented or decremented by moving the tape head right or left.

An example of a counter machine is shown in Fig. 6.8; ϕ and $\$$ are customarily used for end markers on the input. Here Z is the nonblank symbol on each tape.

The configuration of the counter machine can be described by the state, the position of the input head, and the distance of the storage heads from the symbol Z (shown here as d_1 and d_2). We call these distances the *counts* on the tapes. The counter machine then, can really only store a count on each tape and tell if that count is zero.

Lemma 6.2. A four-counter machine can simulate an arbitrary Turing machine.

Proof. From Lemma 6.1, it suffices to show that two counter tapes can simulate one pushdown tape. Let a pushdown tape have $k - 1$ nonblank tape symbols, $Z_1, Z_2, \ldots, Z_{k-1}$. Then we can represent the pushdown tape $Z_{i_1} Z_{i_2} \ldots Z_{i_m}$ uniquely by the "count"

$$j = i_m + k i_{m-1} + k^2 i_{m-2} + \cdots + k^{m-1} i_1.$$

Assume that j is stored on one counter. That is, the head of the tape is j cells to the right of the nonblank symbol. Assume also that the head of the second counter is at the nonblank symbol.

Fig. 6.8. Counter machine.

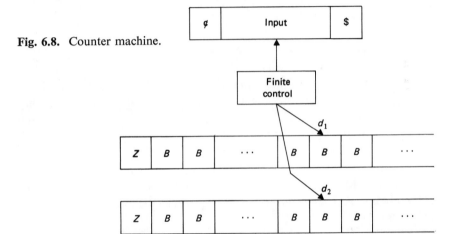

Suppose that the symbol Z_r is printed on the top (right end) of the pushdown tape $Z_{i_1} Z_{i_2} \ldots Z_{i_m}$. The count associated with $Z_{i_1} Z_{i_2} \ldots Z_{i_m} Z_r$ is $kj + r$. To get this new count, the counter machine repeatedly moves the head of the first counter one cell to the left and the head of the second, k cells to the right. When the head of the first counter reaches the nonblank symbol, the second counter will hold the count jk. It is a simple matter to add r to the count.

If, instead, the top symbol, Z_{i_m}, of the pushdown list were erased, j should be replaced by the integer part of j/k. The reader should be able to see how to do this.

To complete the description of the simulation, we must show how the four-counter machine can tell what symbol is at the top of each pushdown list. If the count j is stored on one counter, the four-counter machine can copy j to another counter, computing j modulo k in its finite control. Note that j modulo k is i_m.

Theorem 6.4. A two-counter machine can simulate an arbitrary Turing machine.

Proof. By Lemma 6.2, it is sufficient to show how to simulate four counters with two. Let four counters have counts i, j, k, and m. One counter can represent these four by the number $n = 2^i 3^j 5^k 7^m$. Since 2, 3, 5, and 7 are primes, i, j, k, and m can be uniquely recovered from n.

To increment i, j, k, or m by one, multiply n by 2, 3, 5, or 7, respectively. If we have another counter, set to zero, we can move the head of this counter 2, 3, 5, or 7 cells to the right each time we move the head of the first counter one cell to the left. When the first counter holds zero, the second will hold $2n$, $3n$, $5n$, or $7n$, respectively. To decrement i, j, k, or m by one, n is, by a similar process, divided by 2, 3, 5, or 7, respectively.

We must also show how the two-counter machine can determine the next move of the four-counter machine. The two-counter machine input head will always be at the same point on its input tape as the input head of the four-counter machine would be. The state of the four-counter machine can be stored in the finite control of the two-counter machine. Thus, to determine the move of the four-counter machine, the two-counter machine has only to determine which, if any, of i, j, k, and m are 0. By passing n from one counter to the other, the finite control of the two-counter machine can determine if n is divisible by 2, 3, 5, 7, or any product of these.

Theorem 6.5. Every Turing machine can be simulated by a Turing machine with a read-only input and a storage tape with two storage tape symbols (blank and another symbol), provided the machine can print blanks.

Proof. Most of the proof will be left to the reader. The "trick" is to encode each of the k storage symbols by r binary symbols, where $2^r \geq k$. The tape head of the Tm can visit each of the r binary symbols, representing the original symbol to determine what the original symbol was.

Remarkably, a theorem stronger than Theorem 6.5 can be proven.

Theorem 6.6. Every Turing machine can be simulated by a Turing machine with a read-only input and a storage tape with two symbols, 0 (blank) and 1. The Turing machine can print 0 or 1 where a 0 was found, but cannot print 0 where a 1 was.

Proof. We leave this to the reader. The "trick" is to create successive configurations of the original Turing machine on the tape of the new one. Tape symbols are, of course, encoded in binary. Each configuration is copied over, making the changes necessary to simulate a move of the old machine.

In addition to the binary encoding of the original symbol, the Tm doing the simulating needs cells to indicate the position of the head in the configuration being copied, and cells to indicate that the binary representation of a symbol has already been copied.

PROBLEMS

6.1 Give Turing machines of any variety accepting the following languages.

a) $\{0^n 1^n 2^n | n \geq 1\}$.

b) The set of words in $\{0, 1\}^*$ whose binary value is a perfect square.

c) $$L = \{0^i 10^j 10^k 10^m | m \geq 3 \quad \text{and} \quad i^m + j^m = k^m\}.$$

It is an unproved conjecture of number theory, known as Fermat's conjecture, that for $m \geq 3$, there are no integral solutions to the equation $i^m + j^m = k^m$. Thus L is empty if and only if Fermat's conjecture is true. Unfortunately, there is no algorithm to determine if an arbitrary Tm accepts at least one input. If there were, it could be applied to the Tm accepting L, and Fermat's conjecture could be resolved.

d) The set of FORTRAN arithmetic statements.

e) $\{a^i | i$ is a perfect number$\}$. See Section 1.2 for the definition of perfect number.

6.2 Give a complete proof of Theorem 6.6.

6.3 Show that a pushdown automaton is equivalent to a Turing machine with a read-only input on which it can move to the right only or remain stationary. The Tm is nondeterministic and has a single storage tape. Whenever the Tm moves to the left, it must print a blank.

6.4 Show that if L is accepted by a one-counter machine with a one-way input tape, L is a cfl.

6.5 Show that every Tm is equivalent to a single-tape Tm with one accepting and two nonaccepting states.

6.6 Does there exist a Tm that can diagonalize over all Turing machines? If there were an algorithm to determine if an arbitrary Tm with arbitrary input would halt, could a Tm diagonalize over all Turing machines?

REFERENCES

The basic notion of computability by Turing machine is due to A. M. Turing [1936]. Alternative formulations of the Turing machine can be found in Kleene [1936], Church [1936], and Post [1936]. For a discussion of Church's hypothesis see Kleene [1952] or Davis [1958]. The concept of Turing machines is part of the branch of mathematics called recursive function theory. See Davis [1958] and Rogers [1967].

Theorem 6.4 is found in Minsky [1961] and the proof given is taken from Fischer [1966]. A proof of Theorem 6.6 is found in Wang [1957]. An interesting theorem found in Shannon [1956] shows that every Turing machine in the formulation of this book is equivalent to one with only two nonaccepting states and one accepting state. A survey of restricted Turing machines can be found in Fischer [1965].

CHAPTER 7

TURING MACHINES:
THE HALTING PROBLEM, TYPE 0 LANGUAGES

7.1 INFORMAL DISCUSSION

In this chapter we show that there exists a Turing machine which, when presented with an encoding of an arbitrary Turing machine T and an encoding of a sentence x, will simulate the behavior of T when T is presented with x. We call such a Turing machine a *universal* Turing machine. One can think of a universal Turing machine as a general purpose computer which is powerful enough to simulate any computer, including itself.

Next we show that there is no algorithm (i.e., Turing machine that halts for all input strings) to determine, for an arbitrary Turing machine T and arbitrary input x, whether T with input x will ever halt. This result will be used extensively in Chapter 14 to show that many problems which apply to classes of languages are recursively unsolvable (i.e., no algorithm exists which will solve the problem for every member in the class).

We also show that there are recursively enumerable sets that are not recursive. In other words, there are sets that can be recognized by Turing machines, but not Turing machines that halt for all input strings.

Finally, we show the equivalence of type 0 languages and sets recognized by Turing machines.

7.2 A UNIVERSAL TURING MACHINE

We prove that a universal Turing machine exists by actual construction. First we must decide on an encoding for Turing machines and an encoding for inputs. Since a Tm T_1 may have any number of tape symbols, we assume that the tape symbols of T_1 are given some encoding using only the symbols 0 and 1. The reader should see that, for each T_1, there exists T_2 with tape symbols 0 and 1 and one additional tape symbol B (blank), which accepts exactly those strings in $\{0, 1\}^*$ that are encodings of words accepted by T_1. With this encoding of inputs in mind, it is sufficient to design a universal Turing machine for Tm's with a tape alphabet $\{0, 1, B\}$.

A Turing machine in the above class can be completely specified by a table, as shown in Fig. 7.1. Since a Turing machine may have an arbitrarily large number of states, and since we have only a fixed number of tape symbols, we encode the states 1, 11, 111, etc.

State	B	0	1
1	—	—	2, 0, R
2	3, 1, L	3, 1, L	2, 1, R
3	4, 0, R	4, 0, R	3, 1, L
4	—	—	—

Fig. 7.1. Example of a table specifying a Turing machine T with three tape symbols.

$ccc\ 0\ c\ 0\ c\ 11\ R\ 0\ cc$

$\quad 111\ L\ 1\ c\ 111\ L\ 1\ c\ 11\ R\ 1\ cc$

$\quad 1111\ R\ 0\ c\ 1111\ R\ 0\ c\ 111\ L\ 1\ cc$

$\quad 0\ c\ 0\ c\ 0\ ccc$

Fig. 7.2. Encoding of Turing machine T of Fig. 7.1.

One way to encode a state table is to mark off a number of blocks equal to the number of states, and then divide each block into three subblocks. The ith block will correspond to state i, and the three subblocks will correspond to the input symbols B, 0, and 1, respectively.

The blocks will be separated by two c's and the subblocks by a single c. Also, the beginning and end of the table will be marked by three c's. If, for the Turing machine being encoded, $\delta(i, a) = (j, b, D)$, then the subblock corresponding to state i and input symbol a will contain j 1's, followed by the symbol $D = L$ or R, followed by the symbol $b = 0$ or 1. If $\delta(i, a)$ is not defined, then the corresponding subblock will contain a single 0. Thus the encoding of the Turing machine of Fig. 7.1 would appear as shown in Fig. 7.2. The interpretation of the string $11R0$ in the subblock corresponding to state 1 and input symbol 1 is that T in state 1 scanning a 1 will change the 1 to a 0, move right, and enter state 2.

Any state with no next state for all three of the tape symbols can be interpreted as an accepting state. Such a state is 4 in Fig. 7.1. We can certainly assume (without changing the language accepted by the Tm) that a Tm, after accepting, makes no more moves. In addition, we can assume that the next state for any nonaccepting state is specified for at least one value of the tape symbol. The reader can show this. State 1 will always be taken as the start state.

Although we have used only five symbols to encode a Turing machine, our universal Turing machine will use 12 tape symbols. The additional symbols come from the fact that the universal Turing machine will have a two-track tape. The lower track will use symbols $c, 0, 1, L, R,$ and B, while the upper track will use the symbols m and B. We now informally describe the universal Turing machine.

The input to the universal Turing machine will be as follows. The lower track will contain an encoding of some Turing machine, followed by a string of 0's and 1's which will be called the *data*. The data will be separated from the encoding by three consecutive c's. Initially, the upper track will be all

B's, except for the cell containing the rightmost c at the left end of the block corresponding to state 1 and the leftmost cell containing data. These two cells will contain the symbol m. The first m is used to record the current state of the Turing machine being simulated and the second m is used to record the location of the tape head of the Turing machine being simulated. This is illustrated in Fig. 7.3.

$$m$$
$$ccc \text{ block for state 1 } cc \text{ block for state 2 } cc\ldots$$
$$m$$
$$cc \text{ block for last state } ccc \ 0110\ldots\text{(data)}$$

Fig. 7.3. Initial configuration of universal Turing machine.

Call the universal Turing machine U and the encoded Turing machine T. Now U will simulate, in the following manner, the moves that T would make, given the portion of U's input tape containing the data as input. First, U moves its input head to the right until it locates the marker in the data region over the input symbol scanned by T. This symbol, say A, is stored in U's finite control, and U moves its input head to the left until it reaches the marker recording the state of T. U erases that marker and moves its head to the right to the subblock corresponding to the symbol A and places a marker over the first symbol in that subblock, provided that it is a 1. (If the first symbol is not a 1, U halts, since there is no next move for T.) In what follows, we shall refer to this marker as m_1.

We assume that the first symbol was a 1, and see that U now moves to the left until it finds three consecutive c's. U then moves to the right, marking the rightmost of the three c's. This marker will be referred to as m_2. U continues to move its input head to the right until it finds the marker m_1. U now enters a subroutine which alternately moves m_1 one 1 to the right and m_2 one block to the right. (To distinguish the markers, both of which are m, U will record in its finite control which marker it has seen last.) When U moves m_1 to a symbol which is not 1, m_2 is located over the c just before the block corresponding to the next state of T.

At this point, U erases m_1 and records in its finite control the symbol that T will print and the direction in which T will move its input head. U then moves its head to the right, into the data region, and finds the marker which indicates the location of T's tape head. The symbol under the marker is changed appropriately and the marker is moved to the left or right one cell depending on whether T would move its head to the left or right.

U has simulated one move of T. U stores the new symbol scanned by T in its finite control, starts moving its head to the left until it reaches the marker recording the state of T, and repeats the process we have just described.

State	B						m						Notes
	0	1	c	L	R	B	0	1	c	L	R	B	
A			⟶ move right ⟶			—	—	—	B, R	—	—	—	Find marker in data region.
B			⟶ move right ⟶			—	C_0, L	C_1, L	—	—	—	C_B, L	
C_B			⟶ move left ⟶			—	—	—	$D_B, \binom{B}{c}, R$	—	—	—	Find marker in state table.
C_0			⟶ move left ⟶			—	—	—	$D_0, \binom{B}{c}, R$	—	—	—	
C_1			⟶ move left ⟶			—	—	—	$D_1, \binom{B}{c}, R$	—	—	—	
D_B	V	$E, \binom{m}{1}, L$	—	—	—	—							Find subblock corresponding to input symbol.
D_0	R	R	D_B, R	R	R	—							
D_1	R	R	D_0, R	R	R	—							
E	L	L	F, L	L	L	—							
F	E, L	E, L	G, L	E, L	E, L	—							Find state one and mark. This marker is called m_2 in text description.
G	E, L	E, L	H, R	E, L	E, L	—							
H	—	—	I, R	—	—	—							
I	—	—	$J, \binom{m}{c}, R$	—	—	—							

Fig. 7.4. State table for universal Turing machine. The entries in the table have the following meaning. A triple of state, tape symbol, and L or R indicate next state, tape symbol to be printed, and direction of motion. A pair of state and L or R indicate next state and direction of motion. The symbols L or R and the words "move left" or "move right" indicate that the Turing machine moves to the left or right without changing state or the tape symbol. The tape symbol is left unchanged. A blank indicates a situation which should never occur. State Y is the accepting state. Hence no move is possible from state Y. (The figure is continued on pages 106 and 107.)

	B						m						Remarks
	0	1	c	L	R	B	0	1	c	L	R	B	
J			←——— move right ———→			—	—	$K_L, \binom{B}{1}, R$	—	—	—	—	Begin subroutine to locate next state.
K_L	—	$M_L, \binom{m}{1}, L$	—	T_L, R	T_R, R	—	—	—	—	—	—	—	
M_L			←——— move left ———→			—	—	—	—	—	—	—	m_2 to left of m_1.
N_L	R	R	P_L, R	R	R	—	—	—	$N_L, \binom{B}{c}, R$	—	—	—	
P_L	N_L, R	N_L, R	$S_L, \binom{m}{c}, R$	N_L, R	N_L, R	—	—	N_R, R	—	—	—	—	
S_L			←——— move right ———→			—	—	$K_L, \binom{B}{1}, R$	—	—	—	—	
K_R	—	$M_R, \binom{m}{1}, R$	—	P_R, R	P_R, R	—	—	—	—	—	—	—	m_2 to right of m_1.
M_R			←——— move right ———→			—	—	—	—	—	—	—	
N_R	R	R	P_R, R	R	R	—	—	—	$N_R, \binom{B}{c}, R$	—	—	—	
P_R	N_R, R	N_R, R	$S_R, \binom{m}{c}, L$	N_R, R	N_R, R	—	—	N_R, R	—	—	—	—	
S_R			←——— move left ———→			—	—	$K_R, \binom{B}{1}, R$	—	—	—	—	Record symbol to be printed.
T_L	T_{L-0}, R	T_{L-1}, R	—	—	—	—	—	—	—	—	—	—	
T_R	T_{R-0}, R	T_{R-1}, R	—	—	—	—	—	—	—	—	—	—	

Fig. 7.4 (cont.)

	B						m						
	0	1	c	L	R	B	0	1	c	L	R	B	
T_{L-0}	——move right——			↑	↑	—	$U,(\tbinom{B}{0}),L$	$U,(\tbinom{B}{0}),L$	—	—	—	$U,(\tbinom{B}{0}),L$	⎫ Find marker in
T_{L-1}	——move right——			↑	↑	—	$U,(\tbinom{B}{1}),L$	$U,(\tbinom{B}{1}),L$	—	—	—	$U,(\tbinom{B}{1}),L$	⎬ data region.
T_{R-0}	——move right——			↑	↑	—	$U,(\tbinom{B}{0}),R$	$U,(\tbinom{B}{0}),R$	—	—	—	$U,(\tbinom{B}{0}),R$	
T_{R-1}	——move right——			↑	↑	—	$U,(\tbinom{B}{1}),R$	$U,(\tbinom{B}{1}),R$	—	—	—	$U,(\tbinom{B}{1}),R$	⎭
U	$C_0,(\tbinom{m}{0}),L$	$C_1,(\tbinom{m}{1}),L$	—	—	—	$C_B,(\tbinom{m}{B}),L$							} Adjust marker.
V	L	L	W,L	L	L	—							⎫
W	V,L	V,L	X_1,R	V,L	V,L	—							⎬ Check if
X_1	—	—	X_2,R	—	—	—							⎪ state in which
X_2	X_3,R	—	—	—	—	—							⎪ halt occurred
X_3	—	—	X_4,R	—	—	—							⎪ is accepting.
X_4	X_5,R	—	—	—	—	—							⎪
X_5	—	—	X_6,R	—	—	—							⎪
X_6	Y,R	—	—	—	—	—							⎭
Y	—	—	—	—	—	—							} Accept.

Fig. 7.4 (*concluded*)

If T halts with this particular data, U will eventually halt, and the final data portion of the tape will read exactly as T's tape. When T halts, U can tell if T is in an accepting state. If T does not halt, U will not halt or accept. Thus our universal Turing machine simulates T.

The detailed construction of the universal Turing machine which we have informally described is given in Fig. 7.4. To help understand the construction, a brief statement of the purposes of each group of states is given in the figure.

We should point out that our universal Turing machine has 12 tape symbols, but can only simulate a Turing machine with two tape symbols. However, we can find an equivalent universal Turing machine which uses only two tape symbols. To do this, we encode each tape symbol by a block of four symbols. The data portion of the initial tape will use four cells for every nonblank cell in T's original input tape.

7.3 THE UNSOLVABILITY OF THE HALTING PROBLEM

The *halting problem* for Turing machines is stated as follows: Given a Turing machine in an arbitrary configuration with a finite length string of nonblank tape symbols, will the Turing machine eventually halt? This problem is said to be *recursively unsolvable* in that there cannot exist an algorithm which, for each Tm and each configuration, will determine whether the Tm in that configuration will eventually halt. This does not mean that we cannot determine whether a specific Tm in a specific configuration will halt.

In describing the universal Turing machine, we had an encoding for each Tm with tape symbols 0, 1, and B. The encoding was a string in $\{0, 1, c, L, R\}^*$. We can number all such strings by listing them in order of length. Among strings of equal length, they are ordered according to the value of the string in base 5. (The five symbols are assumed to play the roles of integers 0, 1, 2, 3, 4 in some order.) Likewise, the strings in $\{0, 1\}^*$ can be ordered. The first few such strings are $\epsilon, 0, 1, 00, 01, 10, 11, 000, 001, \ldots$. It thus makes sense to talk about the ith string in $\{0, 1\}^*$.

If we assume that each string in $\{0, 1, c, L, R\}^*$ is a Tm (some strings will be ill formed, and are regarded as representing the Tm with no moves), then it also makes sense to talk about the jth Turing machine, i.e., the one represented by the jth string in $\{0, 1, c, L, R\}^*$.

Consider the language

$$L_1 = \{x_i | x_i \text{ is not accepted by } T_i\}.$$

Clearly, L_1 could not be accepted by a Tm. If it were, let T_j be a Tm accepting L_1. Then x_j is in L_1 if and only if x_j is not accepted by T_j. But since T_j accepts L_1, x_j is in L_1 if and only if it is accepted by T_j, a contradiction. Thus, L_1 is not an r.e. set.

Suppose that we had an algorithm (i.e., a Turing machine which always halts) for determining whether or not a Turing machine in a given configuration would ever halt. Then we could construct a Turing machine T that accepts L_1. T would operate as follows.

1. Given a sentence x, the Turing machine T would enumerate sentences, $x_1, x_2, \ldots$, until it enumerated the sentence $x_i = x$. In this way T determines that x is the ith sentence in the enumeration.
2. Next, T generates an encoding of the Turing machine T_i.
3. Control now transfers to the alleged Turing machine which can determine if T_i with input x_i halts.
4. If it is determined that T_i does not halt with input x_i, then T halts and accepts x_i. (Recall that if T_i accepts, it must halt.)
5. If it is determined that T_i eventually halts with input x_i, then control transfers to a universal Turing machine that simulates T_i with input x_i.
6. Since T_i will eventually halt, the universal Turing machine will eventually halt and determine whether or not T_i accepts x_i. In either case T halts, accepting x_i in the case that T_i rejects x_i, and rejecting x_i in the case that T_i accepts x_i.

Thus our assumption that there exists a Turing machine that can determine if an arbitrary Turing machine will halt leads us to the contradiction that L_1 is accepted by some Turing machine. This fact, in turn, leads us to the following theorem.

Theorem 7.1. There is no algorithm (Turing machine guaranteed to halt) to determine if an arbitrary Turing machine in an arbitrary configuration will eventually halt.

Proof. The theorem follows by a suitable formalization of the above discussion.

It can be shown for many other problems that no algorithm exists for their solution. We shall see some of these which involve language theory in Chapter 14.

7.4 THE CLASS OF RECURSIVE SETS

We can now show that the class of recursive sets is a proper subclass of the recursively enumerable sets. That is, there exists a set whose sentences can be recognized by a Turing machine which does not halt for some sentences not in the set, but cannot be recognized by any Tm which halts on all sentences. An example of such a set is the complement of the set L_1 used in the proof of the unsolvability of the halting problem. Before proving that L_1 is such a set we give the following two lemmas.

Lemma 7.1. If a set is recursive, its complement is recursive.

Proof. If L is a recursive set, $L \subseteq \Sigma^*$, then there is a Tm T, guaranteed to halt, accepting L. We can assume that, after accepting, T makes no more moves. Construct T_1 from T by adding a state q, which is the only accepting state of T_1. The rules of T_1 include all the rules of T, so T_1 simulates T. In addition, for each pair composed of a nonaccepting state and a tape symbol of T for which the move of T is not specified, T_1 transfers to state q and then halts.

Thus T_1 simulates T until T halts. If T halts in one of its accepting states, T_1 halts without accepting. If T halts in a nonaccepting state, it surely has not accepted its input. Thus T_1 makes one more move to state q and accepts. T_1 clearly accepts $\Sigma^* - L$.

Lemma 7.2. Let $x_1, x_2, \ldots$ be an effective enumeration of all sentences on some finite alphabet Σ with $T_1, T_2, \ldots$ representing an effective enumeration of all Turing machines with tape symbols chosen from some finite alphabet including Σ. Let L_2 be the set $\{x_i | x_i$ is accepted by $T_i\}$. L_2 is a recursively enumerable set whose complement is not recursively enumerable.

Proof. The sentences of L_2 can be accepted by the Turing machine T which operates as follows. Note that T does not necessarily halt on sentences not in L_2.

1. Given a sentence x, T enumerates sentences $x_1, x_2, \ldots$ until it finds the sentence $x_i = x$, thereby determining that x is the ith sentence in the enumeration.
2. T generates T_i and transfers control to a universal Turing machine that simulates T_i with input x_i.
3. If T_i with input x_i halts and accepts, then T halts and accepts; if T_i halts and rejects x_i, then T halts and rejects x_i. Finally, if T_i does not halt, then T does not halt.

Thus L_2 is recursively enumerable since L_2 is the set accepted by T. Now $\bar{L}_2$ cannot be recursively enumerable, since if T_j is the Turing machine accepting $\bar{L}_2$, then x_j is in $\bar{L}_2$ if and only if x_j is not accepted by T_j. This contradicts the claim that $\bar{L}_2$ is the language accepted by T_j.

Theorem 7.2. There exists a recursively enumerable set which is not recursive.

Proof. By Lemma 7.2, L_2 is a recursively enumerable set whose complement is not recursively enumerable. Now if L_2 were recursive, then by Lemma 7.1, $\bar{L}_2$ would be recursive, and hence recursively enumerable, thus contradicting the second half of Lemma 7.2.

7.5 TURING MACHINES AND TYPE 0 GRAMMARS

In this section we shall prove that a language is recognized by a Turing machine if and only if it is generated by a type 0 grammar. To prove the "if" part, we construct a nondeterministic Turing machine that will nondeterministically choose a derivation in the grammar, and see whether or not the result of that derivation is the input. If so, the Turing machine accepts.

To prove the "only if" part, we construct a grammar which will nondeterministically generate the representation of a terminal string, and then simulate the Tm on that string. If the string is accepted by the Tm, the string is converted to the terminal symbols it represents.

Theorem 7.3. If L is generated by a type 0 grammar, then L is recognized by a Turing machine.

Proof. Let $G = (V_N, V_T, P, S)$ be a type 0 grammar, with $L = L(G)$. We informally describe a Turing machine T accepting L. T will be nondeterministic. Let

$$T = (K, V_T, \Gamma, \delta, q_0, F), \qquad \text{where } \Gamma = V_N \cup V_T \cup \{B, \#, X\}.$$

The last three symbols are assumed not to be in V_N or V_T. We do not enumerate all the states in K, but designate some of them as it becomes necessary. We allow T, informally, to print the blank B, if necessary.

To begin, T has an input w in V_T^* on its tape. T inserts $\#$ before w, shifting the symbols of w to the right one cell and following it by $\#S\#$. The contents of the tape are now $\#w\#S\#$.

Now T will nondeterministically simulate a derivation in G starting with S. Each sentential form in the derivation will appear in turn between the last two $\#$'s. If some choice of moves leads to a string of terminals there, that string is compared with w. If they are the same, T accepts.

Formally, let T have $\#w\#A_1A_2\ldots A_k\#$ on its tape. T moves its head through $A_1A_2\ldots A_k$, nondeterministically choosing a position i and a constant r between 1 and the maximum length of the left side of any production in P. Then T examines the substring $A_iA_{i+1}\ldots A_{i+r-1}$. If $A_iA_{i+1}\ldots A_{i+r-1}$ is the left-hand side of some production in P, it may be replaced by the right-hand side. T may have to shift $A_{i+r}A_{i+r+1}\ldots A_k\#$ either to the left or right to make room or fill up space, should the right side of the production used have a length other than r.†

From this simple simulation of derivations in G, it should be clear that T will print on its tape a string of the form $\#w\#\alpha\#$, α in V^* exactly when $S \underset{G}{\overset{*}{\Rightarrow}} \alpha$. Also, if $\alpha = w$, T accepts.

---

† Symbol X is used in the shift right.

Theorem 7.4. If L is recognized by a Turing machine, then L is generated by a type 0 grammar.

Proof. Let L be accepted by $T = (K, \Sigma, \Gamma, \delta, q_0, F)$. We construct a grammar G, which nondeterministically generates two copies of a representation of some word in Σ^* and then simulates the action of T on one copy. If T accepts the word, then G converts the second copy to a terminal string. If T does not accept, the derivation never results in a terminal string. Again we assume without loss of generality that for each q in F and a in Σ, $\delta(q, a)$ is undefined.

Formally, let

$$G = (V_N, \Sigma, P, A_1), \qquad \text{where } V_N = ([\Sigma \cup \{\epsilon\}] \times \Gamma) \cup K \cup \{A_1, A_2, A_3\}$$

and the productions in P are:

1. $A_1 \rightarrow q_0 A_2$.
2. $A_2 \rightarrow [a, a] A_2$ for each a in Σ.
3. $A_2 \rightarrow A_3$.
4. $A_3 \rightarrow [\epsilon, B] A_3$.
5. $A_3 \rightarrow \epsilon$.
6. $q[a, C] \rightarrow [a, D]p$ for each a in $\Sigma \cup \{\epsilon\}$ and each q in K and C in Γ, such that $\delta(q, C) = (p, D, R)$.
7. $[b, E]q[a, C] \rightarrow p[b, E][a, D]$ for each C, D, and E in Γ, a and b in $\Sigma \cup \{\epsilon\}$, and q in K, such that $\delta(q, C) = (p, D, L)$.
8. $[a, C]q \rightarrow qaq$, $q[a, C] \rightarrow qaq$, and $q \rightarrow \epsilon$ for each a in $\Sigma \cup \{\epsilon\}$, C in Γ, and q in F.

Using Rules 1 and 2,

$$A_1 \xrightarrow{*} q_0[a_1, a_1][a_2, a_2] \ldots [a_n, a_n] A_2,$$

where a_i is in Σ for each i. Suppose that T accepts the string $a_1 a_2 \ldots a_n$. Then for some m, T uses no more than m cells to the right of its input. Using Rule 3, then Rule 4 m times, and finally Rule 5, we have

$$A_1 \xrightarrow{*} q_0[a_1, a_1][a_2, a_2] \ldots [a_n, a_n][\epsilon, B]^m.$$

From this point on, only Rules 6 and 7 can be used until an accepting state is generated. Note that the first components of tape symbols in $(\Sigma \cup \{\epsilon\}) \times \Gamma$ never change. We can show by induction on the number of moves made by T that if

$$(q_0, a_1 a_2 \ldots a_n, 1) \left|\frac{*}{T}\right. (q, X_1 X_2 \ldots X_s, r),$$

then

$$q_0[a_1, a_1][a_2, a_2] \ldots [a_n, a_n][\epsilon, B]^m \xrightarrow[G]{*} [a_1, X_1][a_2, X_2] \ldots$$
$$[a_{r-1}, X_{r-1}]q[a_r, X_r] \ldots [a_{n+m}, X_{n+m}],$$

where $a_1, a_2, \ldots, a_n$ are in Σ,

$$a_{n+1} = a_{n+2} = \cdots = a_{n+m} = \epsilon,$$

and $X_1, X_2, \ldots, X_{n+m}$ are in Γ with

$$X_{s+1} = X_{s+2} = \cdots = X_{n+m} = B.$$

The inductive hypothesis is trivially true for zero moves. Suppose that it is true for $k - 1$ moves. Let

$$(q_0, a_1 a_2 \ldots a_n, 1) \left|\frac{*}{T}\right. (q_1, X_1 X_2 \ldots X_r, j_1) \left|\frac{}{T}\right. (q_2, Y_1 Y_2 \ldots Y_s, j_2)$$

by a total of k moves. By the inductive hypothesis,

$$q_0[a_1, a_1] \ldots [a_n, a_n][\epsilon, B]^m \xrightarrow[G]{*} [a_1, X_1] \ldots q_1[a_{j_1}, X_{j_1}] \ldots [a_{n+m}, X_{n+m}].$$

Let $D = L$ if $j_2 = j_1 - 1$ and $D = R$ if $j_2 = j_1 + 1$. It must be the case that

$$\delta(q_1, X_{j_1}) = (q_2, Y_{j_1}, D).$$

By (6) or (7),

$$q_1[a_{j_1}, X_{j_1}] \rightarrow [a_{j_1}, Y_{j_1}]q_2$$

or

$$[a_{j_1-1}, X_{j_1-1}]q_1[a_{j_1}, X_{j_1}] \rightarrow q_2[a_{j_1-1}, X_{j_1-1}][a_{j_1}, Y_{j_1}],$$

depending on whether D is R or L. Now $X_i = Y_i$ for all $i \neq j_1$. Thus,

$$q_0[a_1, a_1] \ldots [a_n, a_n][\epsilon, B]^m \xrightarrow[G]{*} [a_1, Y_1] \ldots q_2[a_{j_2}, Y_{j_2}] \ldots [a_{n+m}, Y_{n+m}],$$

establishing the inductive hypothesis.

By (8), if q is in F, it is easy to show that

$$[a_1, X_1] \ldots q[a_j, X_j] \ldots [a_{n+m}, X_{n+m}] \xrightarrow{*} a_1 a_2 \ldots a_n.$$

Thus G can generate $a_1 a_2 \ldots a_n$, provided that $a_1 a_2 \ldots a_n$ is accepted by T. That is, $L(G)$ includes all words accepted by T.

To complete the proof of the theorem it is necessary to show that all words in $L(G)$ are accepted by T. We shall leave it to the reader to supply the induction argument that $A_1 \xrightarrow[G]{*} w$ only if w is accepted by T.

PROBLEMS

7.1 Describe the construction of a universal Turing machine U, which, when fed a binary encoding of T, an arbitrary Turing machine with input set $\{0, 1\}$, will simulate the behavior of T when T is fed an encoding of itself. What happens if U is fed an encoding of itself?

7.2 Give a formal proof of the unsolvability of the halting problem for Turing machines.

7.3 Give a set which is not recursively enumerable and whose complement is not recursively enumerable.

7.4 Construct a universal Turing machine with two nonaccepting states.

7.5 Prove that there is no algorithm to determine if an arbitrary Turing machine, starting with a blank tape, will ever halt.

7.6 Let T be the Turing machine:

$$(\{q_0, q_1, q_2, q_3\}, \{\cent, [,]\}, \{\cent, [,], X, B\}, \delta, q_0, \{q_3\}),$$

where δ is given by

$$\delta(q_0, \cent) = (q_0, \cent, R) \qquad \delta(q_1,]) = (q_2, X, L)$$
$$\delta(q_0, X) = (q_0, X, R) \qquad \delta(q_2, a) = (q_2, a, L) \text{ for all } a \neq \cent$$
$$\delta(q_0, [) = (q_1, X, R) \qquad \delta(q_2, \cent) = (q_0, \cent, R)$$
$$\delta(q_1, [) = (q_1, [, R) \qquad \delta(q_0, B) = (q_3, X, R)$$
$$\delta(q_1, X) = (q_1, X, R)$$

What words of the form $\cent w$, where w is in $\{[,]\}^*$ are accepted? Use the algorithm of Theorem 7.4 to find a grammar generating the language recognized by T. Can you find a simpler grammar for this language?

7.7 Let $G = (\{A, B\}, \{a, b\}, P, A)$, where P consists of:

$$A \rightarrow Ba \qquad B \rightarrow BB$$
$$Aa \rightarrow Bb \qquad B \rightarrow b$$
$$B \rightarrow bA \qquad A \rightarrow a$$
$$Ab \rightarrow \epsilon$$

What is $L(G)$? Find a Turing machine recognizing $L(G)$. Is $L(G)$ context free? Regular?

REFERENCES

All of the concepts of this chapter, except for the equivalence of Turing machine languages and type 0 languages, are from Turing's original paper (Turing [1936]). The latter results are from Chomsky [1959].

CHAPTER 8

LINEAR BOUNDED AUTOMATA AND CONTEXT-SENSITIVE LANGUAGES

8.1 INTRODUCTION

A *linear bounded automaton* (lba) is a nondeterministic single-tape Turing machine which never leaves those cells on which the input was placed. Formally, a linear bounded automaton is denoted by $M = (K, \Sigma, \Gamma, \delta, q_0, F)$. The symbols have essentially the same meaning as for the Turing machine of Chapter 6. The set of *states* is K. The set of *final states* is $F \subseteq K$. The set of *tape symbols* is Γ. The set of *input symbols* is $\Sigma \subseteq \Gamma$. The *start state* is q_0, in K. δ is a mapping from $K \times \Gamma$ to the subsets of $K \times \Gamma \times \{L, R\}$.

Σ contains two special symbols, usually denoted $\not\subset$ and \$, which are the *left* and *right end markers*, respectively. These symbols are initially at the ends of the input, and their function is to prevent the tape head from leaving the region of tape upon which the input appears.

A configuration of M and the relation $\vdash_{M}$, which relates two configurations if the second can be derived from the first by an application of a rule of δ, are defined essentially as they were defined for the Tm in Chapter 6. A *configuration* of M is denoted $(q, A_1 A_2 \ldots A_n, i)$, where q is in K, $A_1, A_2, \ldots, A_n$ in Γ, and i is an integer between 1 and n. Suppose that $\delta(q, A_i)$ contains (p, A, L) and $i > 1$. Then we say that

$$(q, A_1 A_2 \ldots A_n, i) \vdash_{M} (p, A_1 A_2 \ldots A_{i-1} A A_{i+1} \ldots A_n, i - 1).$$

If $\delta(q, A_i)$ contains (p, A, R) and $i < n$, we say that

$$(q, A_1 A_2 \ldots A_n, i) \vdash_{M} (p, A_1 A_2 \ldots A_{i-1} A A_{i+1} \ldots A_n, i + 1).$$

That is, M prints A over A_i, changes its state to p, and moves its head to the left or right, but not out of the region on which symbols appeared originally. As usual, we define the relation $\vdash_{M}^{*}$ by $(q, \alpha, i) \vdash_{M}^{*} (q, \alpha, i)$ and if

$$(q_1, \alpha_1, i_1) \vdash_{M}^{*} (q_2, \alpha_2, i_2) \quad \text{and} \quad (q_2, \alpha_2, i_2) \vdash_{M} (q_3, \alpha_3, i_3),$$

then

$$(q_1, \alpha_1, i_1) \vdash_{M}^{*} (q_3, \alpha_3, i_3).$$

The *language accepted by* M is

$\{w \mid w$ is in $(\Sigma - \{\cent, \$\})^*$ and $(q_0, \cent w\$, 1) \vert\frac{*}{M} (q, \alpha, i)$ for some q in F,

α in Γ^*, and integer $i\}$.

We say that M is *deterministic* if $\delta(q, A)$ contains no more than one element for any q in K, and A in Γ. It is not known whether the class of sets accepted by nondeterministic lba's properly contains the class of sets accepted by deterministic lba's. It is true, of course, that any set accepted by a nondeterministic lba is accepted by a deterministic Turing machine. However, the amount of tape required by that Tm may be an exponential function of the length of the input rather than a linear function.

8.2 RELATION OF LINEAR BOUNDED AUTOMATA TO CONTEXT-SENSITIVE LANGUAGES

Our interest in nondeterministic lba's stems from the fact that the class of sets accepted is precisely the class of context-sensitive languages. The proof is similar to the proof in Chapter 7 that a language is accepted by a Tm if and only if it is type 0.

Theorem 8.1. If L is a context-sensitive language, then L is accepted by a linear bounded automaton.

Proof. Let $G = (V_N, V_T, P, S)$ be a context-sensitive grammar. We construct an lba M such that the language accepted by M is $L(G)$. We do not go into a detailed description of M, since M is fairly complicated, but rather give a macroscopic view of how M works. The input tape will contain two tracks. Track 1 will contain the input string x with end markers. Track 2 will be used for computation. In the first step, M will place the symbol S in the leftmost cell of track 2. Next, M will enter a generation subroutine which performs the following steps.

1. The subroutine selects a consecutive substring of symbols α from track 2, such that $\alpha \rightarrow \beta$ is a production in P.
2. The substring α is replaced by β, shifting right the symbols which are to the right of α if necessary. If this operation would cause a symbol to be pushed as far as the right end marker, the lba halts.
3. The subroutine nondeterministically chooses either to go back to step 1 or to exit.

Upon M's exit from the subroutine, track 1 will still contain the string x, and track 2 will contain some string γ such that $S \xrightarrow[G]{*} \gamma$. The lba compares the symbols on track 1 with the corresponding symbols on track 2. If the comparison fails, the strings of symbols on tracks 1 and 2 are not the same, and the lba halts without accepting. If the strings are the same, the lba halts and accepts.

If x is in $L(G)$, then there exists some sequence of moves in which the lba constructs x on track 2 and accepts the input. Likewise, for the lba to accept x, there must exist a sequence of moves such that x can be constructed on track 2. Thus there must be a derivation of x from S in G.

Note the similarity of this argument to the argument used in Theorem 7.3. In the case of Theorem 7.3, we were simulating a derivation in an arbitrary grammar. In that case, intermediate sentential forms could be arbitrarily long compared with the length of the input. Hence, the full power of a Turing machine was needed. In the case of a context-sensitive grammar, intermediate sentential forms are never longer than the input.

Theorem 8.2. If L is accepted by a linear bounded automaton, then L is context-sensitive.

Proof. The construction of a csg to simulate an lba is quite similar to the construction of Theorem 7.4, in which a type 0 grammar was constructed to simulate a Turing machine. The reader can fill in the detail that is necessary because the variables of the csg must indicate not only the present and original contents of some tape cell of the lba, but also whether that cell is adjacent to an end marker on the right or left. Also, the state of the lba must be combined with the symbol scanned by the tape head. (The csg cannot have separate symbols for end markers and the state of the lba because these symbols would have to be replaced by ϵ when a string is converted to terminals.)

8.3 THE CONTEXT-SENSITIVE LANGUAGES ARE A SUBCLASS OF THE RECURSIVE SETS

In Chapter 2 we showed that every context-sensitive language is recursive. We shall now show that the converse is not true.

Theorem 8.3. There exist recursive sets that are not context sensitive.

Proof. We can number all strings in $\{0, 1\}^*$ as in Section 7.3. Let x_i be the ith word. Likewise, we can number all type 0 grammars whose terminal symbols are 0 and 1.† Since the names of variables are irrelevant, and every grammar has a finite number of them, we can assume that there is but a countable number of variables.

---

† In fact, if the set of available terminals is assumed to be countable, we can number all grammars, whatever the terminal set.

We represent the variables in a binary encoding by 01, 011, 0111, 01111, etc. We assume that 01 is always the start symbol. In addition, in this encoding, we represent the terminal 0 by 00 and the terminal 1 by 001. The symbol "→" is represented by 0011 and a "comma" by 00111. Any grammar with terminals 0 and 1 can be represented by a string of productions, using an arrow (0011) to separate left and right sides and a comma (00111) to separate productions. The strings representing symbols involved in the productions are 00, 001, and 01^i for $i = 1, 2, \ldots$. The set of variables used is defined implicitly by the productions.

Note that not all strings of 0's and 1's represent grammars, certainly not context-sensitive grammars. However, given a string, one can easily tell if it represents a csg. We can find the ith grammar by generating binary strings in the order we have described, until the ith string which is a csg is generated. Since there is an infinity of csg's, we can number the csg's $G_1, G_2, \ldots$ in a meaningful manner.

The proof of the theorem is now trivial. Define L to be $\{x_i | x_i$ is not in $L(G_i)\}$; L is recursive. Given a string x_i, one can easily determine i, and can then determine G_i. By Theorem 2.2, there is an algorithm that determines if x_i is in $L(G_i)$, since G_i is a csg. Thus, there is an algorithm to determine, for any x, whether x is in L.

Now we show that L is not generated by any csg. Suppose that L were generated by the csg G_j. First, assume that x_j is in L. Since $L(G_j) = L$, x_j is in $L(G_j)$. But then by definition of L, x_j is not in L, a contradiction. Thus, assume that x_j is not in L. Since $L(G_j) = L$, x_j is not in $L(G_j)$. But then, by definition of L, x_j is in L, again a contradiction. Thus we conclude that L is not generated by G_j. Since the above argument is valid for every csg G_j in the enumeration, and since the enumeration contains every csg, we conclude that L is not a csl. Therefore L is a recursive set that is not context sensitive.

PROBLEMS

8.1 Let M be an lba. Show that there exists an lba M_1, accepting the same language as M, which always halts, whether its input is accepted or not.

8.2 Let C be a class of devices of some sort. Suppose that:
1. there is an enumeration, $M_1, M_2, \ldots$ of all the devices in C, and
2. there is an algorithm that, given a device M in C and an input x, will determine if M accepts x.

Use the technique of Theorem 8.3 to show that not every recursive set is accepted by some device in C.

8.3 Show that every context-free language is accepted by a deterministic lba.

8.4 Specify an lba which accepts $L = \{a^i | i$ is not a prime$\}$. *Hint.* Make your lba nondeterministic. How easy is it to write down a csg generating L?

REFERENCES

Deterministic linear bounded automata were defined in Myhill [1960]. Land-weber [1963] showed that the family of context-sensitive languages includes all languages accepted by deterministic lba and that the family of csl's is closed under intersection. Kuroda [1964] generalized the lba to a nondeterministic model and showed the equivalence to context-sensitive grammars.

CHAPTER 9

OPERATIONS ON LANGUAGES

9.1 INTRODUCTION

In this chapter we apply operations such as union, concatenation, reversal, closure, etc., to languages of various types. We shall be interested in determining which operations preserve which classes of languages (i.e., map languages in a class to languages in the same class). There are a number of reasons for interest in this matter. First, knowing whether or not an operation preserves a given class of languages helps to characterize that class of languages. Second, it is often easier to determine that a complicated language is of a given class by showing that it is the result of various operations on other languages in the class, than by directly constructing a grammar for the language. Third, the knowledge obtained from a study of operations on languages can be used in proofs of theorems, as in Chapter 7, where we proved that the class of recursively enumerable sets properly contains the recursive sets by making use of the fact that the recursive sets are closed under complementation.

9.2 CLOSURE UNDER ELEMENTARY OPERATIONS

We begin by considering the operations of union, concatenation, Kleene closure, and reversal. We use the following "normal form" lemma on context-sensitive and type 0 languages.

Lemma 9.1. Every context-sensitive language is generated by a context-sensitive grammar in which all productions are either of the form $\alpha \rightarrow \beta$, where α and β are strings of variables only, or of the form $A \rightarrow b$, where A is a variable and b is a terminal. Every type 0 language is generated by a type 0 grammar whose productions are of the above form.

Proof. Let $G = (V_N, V_T, P, S)$ be a csg. For each a in V_T, let X_a be a new symbol. Consider the grammar

$$G_1 = (V_N', V_T, P_1, S),$$

where

$$V_N' = V_N \cup \{X_a | a \text{ is in } V_T\}.$$

P_1 includes all productions of the form $X_a \to a$. Also, if $\alpha \to \beta$ is in P, then $\alpha_1 \to \beta_1$ is in P_1, where α_1 and β_1 are α and β, respectively, with each a in V_T replaced by X_a. The reader can easily show that $L(G) = L(G_1)$. The proof is similar if G is a type 0 grammar.

Theorem 9.1. The classes of regular, context-free, context-sensitive, and recursively enumerable sets are closed under the operations of union, concatenation, closure, and reversal.

Proof. The proof for the class of regular sets was given in Chapter 3. Consider two grammars,

$$G_1 = (V_N^{(1)}, V_T^{(1)}, P_1, S_1) \quad \text{and} \quad G_2 = (V_N^{(2)}, V_T^{(2)}, P_2, S_2),$$

of the same type, either context free, context sensitive, or type 0. Without loss of generality we can assume that $V_N^{(1)} \cap V_N^{(2)} = \varphi$. Furthermore, by Lemma 9.1 and Theorem 4.5, we can assume that the productions of G_1 and G_2 are of the form $\alpha \to \beta$ and $A \to a$ where α and β are strings of variables, A is a single variable, and a is a single terminal symbol. Furthermore, if G_1 and G_2 are context free, then $\beta = \epsilon$ implies that α is S_1 or S_2 and that α never appears on the right-hand side of any production.

Let G_3 be the grammar

$$(V_N^{(1)} \cup V_N^{(2)} \cup \{S_3\}, V_T^{(1)} \cup V_T^{(2)}, P_3, S_3),$$

where S_3 is a new symbol not in $V_N^{(1)} \cup V_N^{(2)}$, and P_3 contains $S_3 \to S_1$, $S_3 \to S_2$, and all productions in P_1 and P_2 except $S_1 \to \epsilon$ and $S_2 \to \epsilon$, if G_1 and G_2 are context sensitive. In the case where G_1 and G_2 are context sensitive, and $S_1 \to \epsilon$ or $S_2 \to \epsilon$ is in P_1 or P_2, add $S_3 \to \epsilon$ to P_3. Now G_3 is the same type of grammar as G_1 and G_2 and $L(G_3) = L(G_1) \cup L(G_2)$.

Let G_4 be the grammar

$$(V_N^{(1)} \cup V_N^{(2)} \cup \{S_4\}, V_T^{(1)} \cup V_T^{(2)}, P_4, S_4),$$

where S_4 is a new symbol not in $V_N^{(1)} \cup V_N^{(2)}$, and P_4 contains $S_4 \to S_1 S_2$ and all productions in P_1 and P_2 except $S_1 \to \epsilon$ and $S_2 \to \epsilon$ if G_1 and G_2 are context sensitive. In the case where G_1 and G_2 are context sensitive, if $S_1 \to \epsilon$ is in P_1, add $S_4 \to S_2$ to P_4. If $S_2 \to \epsilon$ is in P_2, add $S_4 \to S_1$ to P_4. If $S_1 \to \epsilon$ and $S_2 \to \epsilon$ are in P_1 and P_2, respectively, add $S_4 \to \epsilon$ to P_4. Now G_4 is the same type of grammar as G_1 and G_2 and $L(G_4) = L(G_1)L(G_2)$. Note that since $V_N^{(1)} \cap V_N^{(2)} = \varphi$ and all productions of P_1 and P_2 have nonterminals, exclusively, on the left, it isn't possible that a string formed by the right end of a sentential form of G_1 followed by the left end of a sentential form of G_2 can be the left side of any production in P_4. The proof that $L(G_4) = L(G_1)L(G_2)$ is thus straightforward.

Let G_5 be the grammar

$$(V_N, V_T^{(1)}, P_5, S_5), \qquad \text{where} \qquad V_N = V_N^{(1)} \cup \{S_5, S_5'\}$$

and $P_5 = P_1 \cup \{S_5 \to S_1 S_5, S_5 \to \epsilon\}$ if G_5 is context free, otherwise

$$P_5 = P_1 \cup \{S_5 \to \epsilon, S_5 \to S_1, S_5 \to S_1 S_5'\} \cup$$
$$\{a S_5' \to a S_1, a S_5' \to a S_1 S_5' \text{ for each } a \text{ in } V_T^{(1)}\}.$$

However, in the case that G_1 is context sensitive the production $S_1 \to \epsilon$, if present, is deleted. G_5 is the same type of grammar as G_1 and $L(G_5) = (L(G_1))^*$.

Let

$$G_6 = (V_N^{(1)}, V_T^{(1)}, P_6, S_1),$$

where P_6 contains $\alpha^R \to \beta^R$ whenever P_1 contains $\alpha \to \beta$. G_6 is the same type of grammar as G_1 and $L(G_6) = (L(G_1))^R$.

We now consider the operations of intersection and complement.

Theorem 9.2. The class of context-free languages is not closed under intersection.

Proof. The languages

$$L_1 = \{a^n b^n c^i \,|\, n \geq 1 \text{ and } i \geq 0\}$$

and

$$L_2 = \{a^j b^n c^n \,|\, n \geq 1 \text{ and } j \geq 0\}$$

are context free, since they are generated by the grammars

$$G_1 = (\{S, T\}, \{a, b, c\}, \{S \to Sc, S \to T, T \to aTb, T \to ab\}, S)$$

and

$$G_2 = (\{S, T\}, \{a, b, c\}, \{S \to aS, S \to T, T \to bTc, T \to bc\}, S),$$

respectively. Now $L_1 \cap L_2 = \{a^n b^n c^n \,|\, n \geq 1\}$, which is not context free by Theorem 4.7.

Theorem 9.3. The class of context-free languages is not closed under complementation.

Proof. Since the class of context-free languages is closed under union but not under intersection, it cannot be closed under complementation since $L_1 \cap L_2 = \overline{\overline{L_1} \cup \overline{L_2}}$.

Although the class of cfl's is not closed under intersection, it is closed under intersection with a regular set.

Theorem 9.4. The class of cfl's is closed under intersection with a regular set.

Proof. Let L be a cfl and R a regular set. Let

$$P_1 = (K_P, \Sigma, \Gamma, \delta_P, p_0, Z_0, F_P)$$

be a nondeterministic pda accepting L and

$$A = (K_A, \Sigma, \delta_A, q_0, F_A)$$

a deterministic finite automaton accepting R. The nondeterministic pda

$$P_2 = (K_P \times K_A, \Sigma, \Gamma, \delta, [p_0, q_0], Z_0, F_P \times F_A),$$

where δ is defined below, accepts $L \cap R$. For all p in K_P, q in K_A, a in $\Sigma \cup \{\epsilon\}$, and Z in Γ, $\delta([p, q], a, Z)$ contains $([p', \delta_A(q, a)], \gamma)$ whenever $\delta_P(p, a, Z)$ contains (p', γ). (Recall that $\delta_A(q, \epsilon)$ is q for all q in K_A.) Informally, P_2 keeps track of the states of P_1 and A in its finite control.

Assume that x is in $L \cap R$. Then x can be written $a_1 a_2 \ldots a_n$, where a_i is in $\Sigma \cup \{\epsilon\}$, $1 \leq i \leq n$, such that there exist states $q_0, q_1, \ldots, q_n$ in K_A, states $p_0, p_1, \ldots, p_n$ in K_P, and strings $\gamma_0, \gamma_1, \ldots, \gamma_n$ in Γ^* for which

$$\delta_A(q_i, a_{i+1}) = q_{i+1}$$

and

$$a_{i+1} : (p_i, \gamma_i) \underset{P_1}{\overset{*}{\mid}} (p_{i+1}, \gamma_{i+1}), \qquad \text{for } 0 \leq i < n,$$

$\gamma_0 = Z_0$, q_n is in F_A, and p_n is in F_P. Thus

$$a_{i+1} : ([p_i, q_i], \gamma_i) \underset{P_2}{\mid} ([p_{i+1}, q_{i+1}], \gamma_{i+1})$$

and

$$x : ([p_0, q_0], Z_0) \underset{P_2}{\overset{*}{\mid}} ([p_n, q_n], \gamma_n).$$

Now, $[p_n, q_n]$ is in $F_P \times F_A$, so x is in $T(P_2)$.

Now assume that x is in $T(P_2)$. Then there exist configurations $([p_i, q_i], \gamma_i)$, such that

$$a_{i+1} : ([p_i, q_i], \gamma_i) \underset{P_2}{\mid} ([p_{i+1}, q_{i+1}], \gamma_{i+1}), \qquad 0 \leq i < n.$$

Also, $\gamma_0 = Z_0$ and $[p_n, q_n]$ is in $F_P \times F_A$. Thus

$$\delta_A(q_i, a_{i+1}) = q_{i+1}, \qquad 0 \leq i < n,$$

implying that $\delta_A(q_0, x) = q_n$, for some q_n in F_A. Therefore x is in R. Similarly

$$a_{i+1} : (p_i, \gamma_i) \underset{P_1}{\mid} (p_{i+1}, \gamma_{i+1}), \qquad 0 \leq i < n,$$

implying that $x : (p_0, Z_0) \underset{P_1}{\overset{*}{\mid}} (p_n, \gamma_n)$. Since p_n is in F_P, x is in L. Thus

$$T(P_2) = L \cap R_1$$

We have already seen in Chapter 3 that the class of regular sets is closed under both intersection and complement. In Chapter 7, it was shown that the class of r.e. sets is not closed under complement. Thus we have:

Theorem 9.5. The class of type 0 languages is not closed under complement.

At present it is not known whether the class of context-sensitive languages is closed under complement. However, both the class of type 0 languages and the class of context-sensitive languages are closed under intersection. The proofs for both classes are similar, and although conceptually simple, are tedious in detail. Thus only an outline of the proofs will be given.

Theorem 9.6. The class of type 0 languages and the class of context-sensitive languages are closed under intersection.

Proof. Let L_1 and L_2 be type 0 languages (context-sensitive languages). Consider two single-tape Turing machines (nondeterministic lba), M_1 and M_2, accepting L_1 and L_2, respectively. It is easy to construct a Turing machine (lba) M having one scratch tape with three tracks. The first track holds the input. M simulates M_1 using track 2. If M_1 ever reaches an accepting configuration, then M moves its tape head to the left end and simulates M_2 on track 3. If M_2 reaches an accepting configuration, then M accepts.

9.3 CLOSURE UNDER MAPPINGS

Now we consider the results of various types of mappings on languages. The first type we consider is substitution. A *substitution f* is a mapping of a finite set Σ onto subsets of Δ^* for some finite set Δ. Thus f associates some language with each symbol of Σ. The mapping f can be extended to strings in Σ^* as follows:

1. $f(\epsilon) = \epsilon$
2. $f(xa) = f(x)f(a)$.

We can further extend f to languages by defining $f(L)$ to be the set $\bigcup_{x \text{ in } L} f(x)$.

Example 9.1. $f(0) = \{a\}$, $f(1) = \{ww^R \mid w \text{ in } \{b, c\}^*\}$. The substitution f maps the set $\{0^n1^n \mid n \geq 1\}$ into the set

$$\{a^n w_1 w_1^R w_2 w_2^R \ldots w_n w_n^R \mid w_i \text{ in } \{b, c\}^* \text{ for } 1 \leq i \leq n\}.$$

A class of languages is said to be *closed under substitution* if for any language $L \subseteq \Sigma^*$ in the class and for any substitution f such that $f(a)$ is in the class for all a in Σ, the language $f(L)$ is in the class.

We shall show that the classes of regular sets, context-free languages, and type 0 languages are closed under substitution. Thus in Example 9.1, since $f(0)$ and $f(1)$ are both cfl's and since $L = \{0^n1^n \mid n \geq 1\}$ is a cfl, the set

$$f(L) = \{a^n w_1 w_1^R w_2 w_2^R \ldots w_n w_n^R \mid w_i \text{ in } \{b, c\}^*, 1 \leq i \leq n\}$$

is also a cfl.

Theorem 9.7. The classes of regular sets, context-free languages, and type 0 languages are closed under substitution.

Proof. Consider a grammar $G = (V_N, \{a_1, a_2, \ldots, a_n\}, P, S)$. Let $G_i = (V_{N_i}, V_{T_i}, P_i, S_i)$ be a grammar generating the set $f(a_i)$ for each i, $1 \leq i \leq n$. We assume without loss of generality that all nonterminal vocabularies are pairwise disjoint.

We prove the theorem for the case in which G and G_i, $1 \leq i \leq n$ are context free. The reader can prove the other cases similarly, although in each case additional details are necessary.

Construct a new grammar

$$G' = (V_N', V_T', P', S),$$

where V_N' is the union of V_{N_i}, $1 \leq i \leq n$ and V_N. V_T' is the union of V_{T_i}, $1 \leq i \leq n$. Let h be the substitution $h(a_i) = \{S_i\}$ for $1 \leq i \leq n$, and $h(A) = \{A\}$ for any A in V_N. P' contains P_i, $1 \leq i \leq n$. P' also contains $A \to h(\alpha)$ for each $A \to \alpha$ in P. Clearly, G' is context free, possibly with productions of the form $A \to \epsilon$. The reader should easily see that

$$f(L(G)) = L(G').$$

Example 9.2. Let $L = \{0^n 1^n | n \geq 1\}$. L is generated by the grammar

$$(\{S\}, \{0, 1\}, \{S \to 0S1, S \to 01\}, S).$$

As in Example 9.1, let

$$f(0) = \{a\} \qquad \text{and} \qquad f(1) = \{ww^R | w \text{ in } \{b, c\}^*\};$$

$f(0)$ is generated by

$$(\{S_1\}, \{a\}, \{S_1 \to a\}, S_1)$$

and $f(1)$ is generated by

$$(\{S_2\}, \{b, c\}, \{S_2 \to bS_2 b, S_2 \to cS_2 c, S_2 \to \epsilon\}, S_2).$$

$f(L)$ is generated by

$$(\{S, S_1, S_2\}, \{a, b, c\}, P, S),$$

where P contains $S_1 \to a$, $S_2 \to bS_2 b$, $S_2 \to cS_2 c$, $S_2 \to \epsilon$, $S \to S_1 S S_2$, and $S \to S_1 S_2$. The last two productions come from $S \to 0S1$ and $S \to 01$, with S_1 substituted for 0 and S_2 for 1.

The csl are not closed under substitution. However, we can prove a weaker result. First, a substitution f on Σ is said to be ϵ-*free* if for each a in Σ, $f(a)$ does not contain ϵ.

Theorem 9.8. The class of context-sensitive languages is closed under ϵ-free substitution.

Proof. Consider a context-sensitive grammar

$$G = (V_N, \{a_1, a_2, \ldots, a_n\}, P, S)$$

and an ϵ-free substitution f. For each i, $1 \leq i \leq n$, let

$$G_i = (V_{N_i}, V_{T_i}, P_i, S_i)$$

be a context-sensitive grammar generating the set $f(a_i)$. We assume without loss of generality that all nonterminal vocabularies are pairwise disjoint. Furthermore, we assume that all productions, with the possible exception of $S \rightarrow \epsilon$, are of the form $\alpha \rightarrow \beta$ or $A \rightarrow a$, where α, β are nonempty strings of variables, A is a single variable, and a is a single terminal symbol. We construct a grammar $G' = (V_N', V_T', P', S_L)$ where:

1. $V_N' = V_N \cup \left(\bigcup_{i=1}^n V_{N_i}\right) \cup \{A_L | A \text{ in } V_N\}$.
2. $V_T' = \bigcup_{i=1}^n V_{T_i}$.
3. P' contains
   a. $S_L \rightarrow \epsilon$ if $S \rightarrow \epsilon$ is in P.
   b. $A_L \alpha \rightarrow B_L \beta$ and $A\alpha \rightarrow B\beta$ if $A\alpha \rightarrow B\beta$ is in P. (Note that the subscript L is used to mark the leftmost symbol in a derivation of G until this symbol would be converted to a terminal symbol.)
   c. $A_L \rightarrow S_i$ if $A \rightarrow a_i$ is in P. $aA \rightarrow aS_i$ for all a in V_T' if $A \rightarrow a_i$ is in P.
   d. All productions in $P_1, P_2, \ldots, P_n$.

The grammar G' is context sensitive and $L(G') = f(L(G))$.

Theorem 9.9. The class of context-sensitive languages is not closed under substitution.

Proof. Let $G_1 = (V_N, V_T, P_1, S)$ be a type 0 grammar such that $L(G_1)$ is not a context-sensitive language. Once again, we assume without loss of generality that the productions are of the form $\alpha \rightarrow \beta$ or $A \rightarrow a$, where α is in V_N^+, β is in V_N^*, A is in V_N, and a is in V_T. Let c be a new symbol. Consider the grammar $G_2 = (V_N, V_T \cup \{c\}, P_2, S)$ where P_2 contains:

1. $\alpha \rightarrow \beta$ if $\alpha \rightarrow \beta$ is in P_1 and $|\alpha| \leq |\beta|$.
2. $\alpha \rightarrow \beta cc \ldots c$, where $|\alpha| = |\beta cc \ldots c|$ if $\alpha \rightarrow \beta$ is in P_1 and $|\alpha| > |\beta|$.
3. $cA \rightarrow Ac$ for all A in V_N.

The grammar G_2 is context sensitive, since we have forced the right-hand side of every production to be at least as long as the left-hand side. The productions $cA \rightarrow Ac$ were added to move the c's to the right end of the words so that derivations in G_2 can proceed as in G_1. Now consider the substitution

$$f(a) = \{a\} \text{ for } a \text{ in } V_T \text{ and } f(c) = \{\epsilon\}.$$

Then $f(L(G_2)) = L(G_1)$ and hence substitution does not preserve the class of csl.

Most often we are interested in special types of substitutions. A substitution f is said to be *finite* if $f(a)$ is a finite set for all a in the domain of f. If $f(a)$ is a single string for all a, then f is a *homomorphism*. Finite substitution and homomorphism are special cases of a substitution. Thus we have the following corollaries.

Corollary 9.1. The classes of regular, context-free, and type 0 languages are closed under finite substitution and homomorphism.

Proof. Obvious from Theorem 9.7.

Corollary 9.2. The class of context-sensitive languages is closed under ϵ-free finite substitution and ϵ-free homomorphism.

Proof. Obvious from Theorem 9.8.

Corollary 9.3. The class of context-sensitive languages is not closed under finite substitution or homomorphism.

Proof. The substitution used in the proof of Theorem 9.9 is a homomorphism.

We prove one more result concerning substitutions, since we need it for a later theorem. A class of languages is said to be closed under *k-limited erasing* if, for any language of the class L and any homomorphism h with the property that h never maps more than k consecutive symbols of any sentence x in L to ϵ, $h(L)$ is in the class. We show that the class of context-sensitive languages is closed under k-limited erasing. Actually a more general result is true. Let $L \subseteq \Sigma^*$ be a context-sensitive language and let $f(a)$ be context sensitive for a in Σ. $f(L)$ is context sensitive provided there exists a $k > 0$, such that for x in L and y in $f(x)$, $|y| \geqq k|x|$.

Lemma 9.2. The class of context-sensitive languages is closed under k-limited erasing.

Proof. Let $G_1 = (V_N^{(1)}, V_T^{(1)}, P_1, S_1)$ be a context-sensitive grammar. Without loss of generality, assume that the productions, with the possible exception of $S_1 \rightarrow \epsilon$, are of the form $\alpha \rightarrow \beta$ or $A \rightarrow a$, where α and β are in $V_N^{(1)+}$, A is in $V_N^{(1)}$, and a is in $V_T^{(1)}$. Let h be a homomorphism with the property that h never maps more than k consecutive symbols of any sentence x in $L(G_1)$ to ϵ. Let l be the greater of $k + 1$ and the length of the longest left-hand side of any production. Consider the grammar

$$G_2 = (V_N^{(2)}, V_T^{(2)}, P_2, S_2),$$

where

$$V_N^{(2)} = \{[\alpha] | \alpha \text{ in } (V_N^{(1)} \cup V_T^{(1)})^*, |\alpha| < 2l\},$$

$V_T^{(2)}$ contains those symbols found in strings w such that $h(a) = w$ for some a in $V_T^{(1)}$, $S_2 = [S_1]$, and P_2 contains:

1. $[S_1] \to \epsilon$ if $S_1 \to \epsilon$ is in P_1 or if there is an x in $L(G_1)$, with $h(x) = \epsilon$. (Note that $|x| \leq k$, so we can test if any such x exists.)
2. $[\alpha] \to [\beta]$ for all $[\alpha]$ and $[\beta]$ in $V_N^{(2)}$ such that $\alpha \underset{G_1}{\Longrightarrow} \beta$ and $|\beta| < 2l$.
3. $[\alpha] \to [\beta_1][\beta_2] \ldots [\beta_m]$ for all $[\alpha]$, $[\beta_1]$, $[\beta_2]$, ..., $[\beta_m]$ in $V_N^{(2)}$ such that

$$\alpha \underset{G_1}{\Longrightarrow} \beta_1 \beta_2 \ldots \beta_m,$$

$|\beta_i| = l$, $1 \leq i < m$, and $l \leq |\beta_m| < 2l$.
4. $[\alpha_1][\alpha_2] \to [\beta_1][\beta_2] \ldots [\beta_m]$ for all $[\alpha_1]$, $[\alpha_2]$, $[\beta_1]$, $[\beta_2]$, ..., $[\beta_m]$ in $V_N^{(2)}$ such that

$$\alpha_1 \alpha_2 \underset{G_1}{\Longrightarrow} \beta_1 \beta_2 \ldots \beta_m,$$

where $l \leq |\alpha_1| < 2l$, $l \leq |\alpha_2| < 2l$,

$$|\beta_i| = l, \qquad 1 \leq i < m, \qquad l \leq |\beta_m| < 2l.$$

5. $[x] \to h(x)$ for all $[x]$ in $V_N^{(2)}$, x in $V_T^{(1)*}$, $h(x) \neq \epsilon$.

The grammar G_2 is context sensitive and $L(G_2) = h(L(G_1))$. Note that G_2 is obtained by encoding blocks of at least $k + 1$ symbols of G_1 into one symbol. Since no more than k consecutive terminal symbols of G_1 are mapped to ϵ, we need never have a production in G_2 where a variable other than the sentence symbol goes to ϵ.

A *generalized sequential machine* (gsm) is a finite automaton which can output a finite number of symbols for each input symbol. Formally, a gsm is a six-tuple $S = (K, \Sigma, \Delta, \delta, q_0, F)$ where K, Σ, and Δ are the *states*, *input alphabet*, and *output alphabet*, respectively. δ is a mapping from $K \times \Sigma$ to finite subsets of $K \times \Delta^*$, q_0 is the *initial state*, and F is the set of *final states*. The interpretation of (p, w) in $\delta(q, a)$ is that S in state q with input symbol a may, as one possible choice of move, enter state p and output the string w.

We extend the domain of δ to $K \times \Sigma^*$ as follows.

1. $\delta(q, \epsilon) = \{(q, \epsilon)\}$.
2. For x in Σ^* and a in Σ,

$$\delta(q, xa) = \{(p, w) | w = w_1 w_2$$

and for some p', (p', w_1) is in $\delta(q, x)$ and (p, w_2) is in $\delta(p', a)\}$.

Let $S(x)$ denote the set

$$\{y | (p, y) \text{ is in } \delta(q_0, x) \text{ for some } p \text{ in } F\}.$$

If L is a language over Σ, let $S(L)$ denote $\{y | y \text{ is in } S(x) \text{ for some } x \text{ in } L\}$.

We say that $S(L)$ is a *gsm mapping*. Also, let

$$S^{-1}(x) = \{y \mid S(y) \text{ contains } x\}$$

and

$$S^{-1}(L) = \{y \mid x \text{ is in } S(y) \text{ for some } x \text{ in } L\}.$$

We say that $S^{-1}(L)$ is an *inverse gsm mapping*.

It is not necessarily true that $S^{-1}(S(L)) = S(S^{-1}(L)) = L$ and thus S^{-1} is not a true inverse.

Example 9.3. Let

$$S = (\{q_0, q_1\}, \{0, 1\}, \{a, b\}, \delta, q_0, \{q_1\}).$$

We define δ by

$$\delta(q_0, 0) = \{(q_0, aa), (q_1, b)\},$$
$$\delta(q_0, 1) = \{(q_0, a)\},$$
$$\delta(q_1, 0) = \varphi,$$
$$\delta(q_1, 1) = \{(q_1, \epsilon)\}.$$

Intuitively, as 0's are input to S, S has the choice of either outputting two a's or one b. If S outputs the b, it goes to state q_1. If 1 is input to S, and S is in state q_0, S can only output an a. In state q_1, S can do nothing on a 0 input, but can remain in state q_1 with no output if a 1 is input.

Let $L = \{0^n 1^n \mid n \geq 1\}$. Then

$$S(L) = \{a^{2n} b \mid n \geq 0\}.$$

If we call $S(L)$ by L_1, then

$$S^{-1}(L_1) = \{w01^i \mid i \geq 0 \text{ and } w \text{ has an even number of 1's}\}.$$

Note that $S^{-1}(S(L)) \neq L$.

A feature of gsm and inverse gsm mappings is that they preserve various classes of languages.

Lemma 9.3. Every class of languages closed under finite substitution and intersection with a regular set is closed under gsm mappings.

Proof. Let C be a class of languages closed under finite substitution (hence, homomorphism) and intersection with a regular set. Let $S = (K, \Sigma, \Delta, \delta, q_0, F)$ be a gsm. We define a finite substitution

$$f(a) = \{[q, a, x, p] \mid q \text{ and } p \text{ in } K, a \text{ in } \Sigma, x \text{ in } \Delta^*, \text{ and } (p, x) \text{ in } \delta(q, a)\}.$$

Let R be the regular set containing all strings of the form

$$[q_0, a_1, x_1, q_1][q_1, a_2, x_2, q_2] \dots [q_{n-1}, a_n, x_n, q_n]$$

such that for $1 \leq i \leq n$, a_i is in Σ, x_i is in Δ^*, q_i is in K, and (q_i, x_i) is in

$\delta(q_{i-1}, a_i)$. Also, q_0 is the start state of S and q_n is in F. Let h be the homomorphism

$$h([q, a, x, p]) = x \text{ for all } [q, a, x, p].$$

Now for L in C, $S(L) = h(f(L) \cap R)$. Since C is closed under finite substitution and intersection with a regular set, $S(L)$ is in C. Note that closure under finite substitution is required rather than ϵ-free finite substitution, since in $[q, a, x, p]$, x may be ϵ, in which case

$$h([q, a, x, p]) = \epsilon.$$

Theorem 9.10. The classes of regular, context-free, and type 0 languages are closed under gsm mappings.

Proof. The theorem is an immediate consequence of Lemma 9.3 and Theorems 9.4, 9.6, and 9.7.

Note that gsm mappings do not preserve context-sensitive languages, since every homomorphism is a gsm mapping.

A gsm mapping is said to be ϵ-*free* if (p, ϵ) is not in $\delta(q, a)$ for any q and p in K and a in Σ. Although context-sensitive languages are not closed under arbitrary gsm mappings, they are closed under ϵ-free gsm mappings.

Theorem 9.11. The class of context-sensitive languages is closed under ϵ-free gsm mappings.

Proof. In Lemma 9.3, finite substitution can be replaced by ϵ-free finite substitution provided that the gsm mapping is ϵ-free. Thus, since the class of context-sensitive languages is closed under ϵ-free finite substitution, and intersection with a regular set, the class is closed under ϵ-free gsm mappings.

We now consider inverse gsm mappings. As we shall see, regular, context-free, context-sensitive, and type 0 languages are all closed under inverse gsm mappings.

Lemma 9.4. Let C be a class of languages closed under ϵ-free substitution, k-limited erasing, and union and intersection with regular sets. Then C is closed under inverse gsm mappings.

Proof. Let $L \subseteq \Delta^*$ be a language in C and $S = (K, \Sigma, \Delta, \delta, q_0, F)$ be a gsm. We assume without loss of generality that the sets Σ and Δ are disjoint. Define a substitution f by $f(b) = \Sigma^* b$ for each b in Δ. (Note that closure under union and intersection with regular sets guarantees that all regular sets are in C and hence $\Sigma^* b$ is in C.) Let $L_1 = f(L) \cup \Sigma^*$ if ϵ is in L, and $L_1 = f(L)$ otherwise. Then L_1 is the set of all strings of the form $y_1 b_1 y_2 b_2 \ldots y_r b_r$, $r \geq 1$, where the b's are in Δ, $b_1 b_2 \ldots b_r$ is in L, and the y's are in Σ^*, plus Σ^* if ϵ is in L. We now apply Lemma 9.3 to the classes of regular, context-free, and type 0 languages.

Let R be the regular set consisting of all words of the form $a_1x_1a_2x_2\ldots$ a_mx_m, $m \geq 0$, such that

1. The a's are in Σ.
2. The x's are in Δ^*.
3. There exists states $q_0, q_1, \ldots, q_m$, such that q_m is in F and, for $1 \leq i \leq m$, $\delta(q_{i-1}, a_i)$ contains (q_i, x_i).

Note that x_i may be ϵ. The reader may easily show R to be a regular set by constructing a finite automaton accepting R.

Now $L_1 \cap R$ is the set of all words in R of the form $a_1x_1a_2x_2\ldots a_mx_m$, $m \geq 0$, where the a's are in Σ, the x's are in Δ^*, $x_1x_2\ldots x_m$ is in L, $S(a_1a_2\ldots a_m)$ contains $x_1x_2\ldots x_m$, and none of the x_i's is of length greater than k, where k is the length of the longest x such that (p, x) is in $\delta(q, a)$ for some p and q in K and a in Σ.

Finally, let h be the homomorphism which maps a to a for each a in Σ, and b to ϵ for each b in Δ. Then

$$S^{-1}(L) = h(L_1 \cap R)$$

is in C since h never causes more than k consecutive symbols to be mapped to ϵ.

Theorem 9.12. The classes of regular, context-free, context-sensitive, and type 0 languages are closed under inverse gsm mappings.

Proof. Follows immediately from Lemma 9.4 and the fact that the above classes are closed under ϵ-free substitution, k-limited erasing, and intersection and union with a regular set.

We now consider the quotient operator. Let L_1 and L_2 be any languages. We define L_1/L_2, the *quotient* of L_1 with respect to L_2, to be

$$\{x | \text{for some } y \text{ in } L_2, xy \text{ is in } L_1\}.$$

Example 9.4. Let $L_1 = \{a^nb^n | n \geq 1\}$ and $L_2 = b^*$. Then

$$L_1/L_2 = \{a^ib^j | i \geq j, i \geq 1\} \quad \text{and} \quad L_2/L_1 = \varphi.$$

Lemma 9.5. Every class of languages closed under finite substitution and intersection with a regular set is closed under quotient with a regular set.

Proof. Let C be a class of languages closed under the above operations. Let $L \subseteq \Sigma_1^*$ be a language in C and $R \subseteq \Sigma_1^*$ be a regular set. Let $\Sigma_2 = \{a' | a \text{ in } \Sigma_1\}$ and let f be the finite substitution $f(a) = \{a, a'\}$. Consider $L_2 = \Sigma_2^* R \cap f(L)$. Let h be the homomorphism defined by $h(a) = \epsilon$ and $h(a') = a$ for all a in Σ_1. Now $L/R = h(L_2)$. Since the class C is closed under finite substitution and intersection with a regular set, L/R is in C.

Closed under	Regular sets	Context-free languages	Context-sensitive languages	Type 0 languages
Union	Yes	Yes	Yes	Yes
Concatenation	Yes	Yes	Yes	Yes
Closure	Yes	Yes	Yes	Yes
Reversal	Yes	Yes	Yes	Yes
Intersection	Yes	No	Yes	Yes
Complement	Yes	No	?	No
Intersection with regular set	Yes	Yes	Yes	Yes
Substitution	Yes	Yes	No	Yes
ϵ-free substitution	Yes	Yes	Yes	Yes
gsm mappings	Yes	Yes	No	Yes
ϵ-free gsm mappings	Yes	Yes	Yes	Yes
Inverse gsm mappings	Yes	Yes	Yes	Yes
k-limited erasing	Yes	Yes	Yes	Yes
Quotient with regular set	Yes	Yes	No	Yes

Fig. 9.1. Closure properties of the classes of regular, context-free, context-sensitive, and type 0 languages.

Theorem 9.13. The classes of regular, context-free, and type 0 languages are closed under quotient with a regular set.

Proof. Follows immediately from Lemma 9.5.

Next we ask whether the class of context-sensitive languages is closed under quotient with a regular set? Once again the answer is no.

Theorem 9.14. If L_1 is any type 0 language, then there is a context-sensitive language, L_2, and a regular set R, such that $L_1 = L_2/R$.

Proof. The proof is almost identical to that of Theorem 9.9. Let

$$G_1 = (V_N, V_T, P_1, S_1)$$

be a type 0 grammar generating L_1. Let

$$G_2 = (V_N \cup \{S_2, D\}, V_T \cup \{c, d\}, P_2, S_2),$$

where P_2 is defined as follows:

1. If $\alpha \to \beta$ is in P_1 and $|\alpha| \leq |\beta|$, then $\alpha \to \beta$ is in P_2.
2. If $\alpha \to \beta$ is in P_1 and $|\alpha| - |\beta| = i, i > 0$, then $\alpha \to \beta D^i$ is in P_2.
3. For all A in V_N and a in V_T, $DA \to AD$ and $Da \to aD$ are in P_2.
4. $Dc \to cc$ and $Dc \to dc$ are in P_2.
5. $S_2 \to S_1 Dc$ is in P_2.

Note the similarity of $L(G_2)$ to the language defined in Theorem 9.9. Here, however, we can only convert all of the D's to terminal symbols if they first migrate to the right end of the sentential form. Also, once a D is converted to d, no more D's may be converted to either d or c. The theorem follows from the observation that

$$L(G_1) = L(G_2)/dc^*.$$

We summarize the closure properties for regular, context-free, context-sensitive, and type 0 languages in Fig. 9.1.

PROBLEMS

9.1 In general, the intersection of two context-free languages is not context free. However in some cases the intersection is context free. Let G be the cfg $(\{S, R, T\}, \{a, b, 0, 1\}, P, S)$ where P contains $S \to RT$, $R \to aR10$, $R \to bR0$, $R \to a10$, $R \to b0$, $T \to 0Ta$, $T \to 10Tb$, $T \to 0a$, $T \to 10b$. Is $L(G) \cap \{ww^R | w \text{ in } \{0, 1, a, b\}^*\}$ context free?

9.2 Show that the Boolean closure of the class of context-free languages is properly contained in the class of context-sensitive languages. (*Hint.* For containment consider the relation of the Boolean closure of the cfl's to the class of languages accepted by deterministic lba's. For proper containment consider the set of all cfl's over a one-symbol alphabet.)

9.3 Show that any class of languages closed under
   a) concatenation, homomorphism, inverse homomorphism, and intersection with regular set is closed under union.
   b) closure, homomorphism, inverse homomorphism, union, and intersection with regular set is closed under concatenation.
   c) homomorphism, inverse homomorphism, concatenation, and union is closed under intersection with regular set.

9.4 Let $L \subseteq \Sigma^*$ be a csl and let $f(a)$ be a csl for each a in Σ such that for some fixed $k > 0$, $|f(x)| \geq k|x|$ for all x in L. Show that $f(L)$ is context sensitive.

9.5 Let L be an arbitrary set, not necessarily recursively enumerable. Let R be regular. Show that R/L is regular. Can one always find a particular finite automaton accepting R/L?

9.6 Let L be a cfl. Show that $\{x|$ there exists some y, such that $|y| = |x|$ and xy in $L\}$ is not necessarily context free.

9.7 Show that there is no gsm which maps $\{0^i1^j|i,j \geq 0\}$ to $\{0^i1^i|i \geq 0\}$.

9.8 Let L_1 be a cfl. Show that

$$L_2 = \{a_1a_3a_5\ldots a_{2k+1}|a_1a_2a_3a_4\ldots a_{2k+1} \text{ is in } L_1\}$$

is context free.

9.9 Find a gsm that maps the word a^i to the set $\{a^jb^k|i \leq j + k < 2i\}$.

9.10 Which of the various classes of languages are closed under inverse substitution?

9.11 Let Init $(L) = \{x|$ there exists y such that xy is in $L\}$. Which classes of languages are closed under Init?

9.12 We say that y is a *proper prefix* of x if $y \neq x$ and for some $z \neq \epsilon$, $x = yz$. Let Min $(L) = \{x|x$ is in L and no proper prefix of x is in $L\}$. Which classes of languages are closed under Min?

REFERENCES

Theorems 9.2 and 9.3 are from Scheinberg [1960] and Theorem 9.4 is from Bar-Hillel, Perles, and Shamir [1961]. Theorem 9.6 for context-sensitive languages is from Landweber [1963] and Theorem 9.7 for regular and context-free languages is from Bar-Hillel, Perles, and Shamir [1961]. Theorems 9.10 and 9.12 for the latter two cases are from Ginsburg and Rose [1963b] and Theorem 9.13 for those cases is from Ginsburg and Spanier [1963]. Theorem 9.11 is from Ginsburg and Greibach [1967]. The ideas connected with Lemmas 9.3, 9.4, and 9.5 were shown in Ginsburg and Greibach [1967], but their statement in this form is from Greibach and Hopcroft [1967].

There have been several recent attempts to codify the properties of classes of languages. Ginsburg and Greibach [1967] is a study of the properties of classes of languages that are closed under union, concatenation, Kleene closure, intersection with a regular set, homomorphism, and inverse homomorphism. It is shown that each such class can be defined as the languages recognized by some class of automata with a one-way input, and that, under very broad conditions, the class of languages defined by a class of one-way automata is closed under these operations. The latter result was shown independently in Hopcroft and Ullman [1967b], and the class of languages defined by a general class of two-way automata was shown to possess certain properties such as closure under inverse gsm mappings. Extensions of these theories have appeared in Ginsburg, Greibach, and Hopcroft [1967], Ginsburg and Spanier [1967], Greibach and Hopcroft [1967], Ginsburg and Hopcroft [1968], and Hopcroft and Ullman [1968a].

CHAPTER 10

TIME- AND TAPE-BOUNDED
TURING MACHINES

10.1 INTRODUCTION

As we have seen, every recursively enumerable language is accepted by some Turing machine. However, it is reasonable to suppose that some r.e. languages can be recognized by rather "simple" Turing machines, while others cannot be recognized by any Turing machine below a certain complexity. In this section we wish to consider two formal definitions of the complexity of Turing machines. Since a Turing machine is a reasonable, although surely not perfect, model of computation, the theory of Turing machine complexity classes should shed some light on the properties of languages that are suitable as programming languages (i.e., languages that can be simply recognized).

The two measures of complexity we shall consider are bounds on the amount of tape used and bounds on the number of moves made by the Tm with a given input. Both of these bounds are functions of n, the input length.

10.2 DEFINITIONS

Consider the multitape Turing machine T of Fig. 10.1. T has a read-only input tape with end markers and k semi-infinite storage tapes. Suppose that for no input word of length n does T scan more than $L(n)$ cells on any storage tape. Then T is said to be an $L(n)$ *tape-bounded Turing machine*, or of *tape complexity* $L(n)$. The language recognized by T is likewise said to be of *tape complexity* $L(n)$.

Note that the Tm cannot rewrite on the input and that only the length of the storage tape used counts in computing the tape bound. This is done to include tape bounds of less than linear growth. If the Tm could rewrite on the input tape, then the length of the input tape would have to be included in calculating the tape bound. Thus no bound could be less than linear.

Now consider the multitape Tm T of Fig. 10.2. The Tm has k semi-infinite tapes, one of which contains the input. All tapes, including the input tape, are rewriting. Suppose that for no input word of length n does T make more than $T(n)$ moves before halting. Then T is said to be a $T(n)$ *time-bounded Turing machine*, or of *time complexity* $T(n)$. The language recognized by T is said to be of *time complexity* $T(n)$.

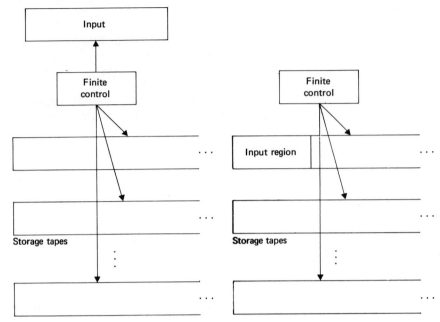

Fig. 10.1. Multitape Turing machine with read-only input.

Fig. 10.2. Multitape Turing machine.

The concepts of time- and tape-bounded Turing machines apply equally well to nondeterministic machines. A nondeterministic Tm is of time complexity $T(n)$ if no sequence of choices of moves causes the machine to make more than $T(n)$ moves. It is of tape complexity $L(n)$ if no sequence of choices enables it to scan more than $L(n)$ cells on any storage tape. Here we deal exclusively with the deterministic case. Results are analogous for the non-deterministic case. We always assume $L(n)$ and $T(n)$ to be recursive functions.

Example 10.1. Consider the language

$$L = \{wcw^R | w \text{ in } \{0, 1\}^*\}.$$

In this case L is of time complexity $n+1$, since there is a Turing machine T_1, with two tapes, which copies its input to the left of the c onto the second tape. Then, when a c is found, T_1 moves its second tape head to the left, through what it has just copied, and simultaneously continues to move its input tape head to the right. The symbols under the two heads are compared as the heads move and, if all pairs of symbols match and if, in addition, the number of symbols to the right and left of the lone c are equal, then T_1 accepts. It is easy to see that T_1 makes at most $n+1$ moves if the input is of length n.

There is another Turing machine, T_2, of tape complexity $\log_2 n$ accepting L. T_2 uses one storage tape as two binary counters. First, the input is checked to see that only one c appears. Next, the symbols on the left of the c are counted, and compared with the number on the right. If these numbers are equal, then the words on the right and the left are compared symbol by symbol.

In considering this process, we may think of the storage as having two tracks. On the upper track a binary number, i, will be written. Initially $i = 1$ and, at the last step, $i = (n - 1)/2$. For each i, the ith symbols from the right and left ends of the input are compared. These symbols can each be found by copying i from the upper track to the lower, then counting down to zero on the lower track. If all comparisons are true, the input is accepted. Since T_2 never deals with numbers greater than n, the numbers can be represented on $\log_2 n$ cells.

10.3 "SPEED UP" AND "TAPE REDUCTION" THEOREMS

In this section we show that constant factors affect nothing as far as the recognizing power of time and tape complexity classes are concerned. Thus complexity classes are defined by functional variation (logarithmic, quadratic, etc.) rather than by particular functions. We also consider the effect on time and tape bounds of reducing the number of tapes of a Tm, and see that tape bounds are independent of the number of tapes. Reducing the number of tapes of a k-tape $T(n)$ time-bounded Tm to two tapes does not increase the time to more than $T(n) \log T(n)$. Reducing the number of tapes to one does not increase the time to more than $T^2(n)$.

Theorem 10.1. If L is accepted by an $L(n)$ tape-bounded Turing machine with k storage tapes, then L is accepted by a $cL(n)$† tape-bounded Turing machine with k storage tapes, for any $c > 0$.

Proof. Let T be an $L(n)$ tape-bounded Turing machine accepting L. The proof turns on constructing a new Turing machine T_1 which simulates T, but, for some constant r, each storage tape cell of T_1 holds a symbol representing the contents of r adjacent cells of the corresponding tape of T. The finite control of T_1 can keep track of which of the cells of T, among those represented, is actually scanned by T.

Detailed construction of the rules of T_1 from the rules of T are left to the reader. Let r be such that $rc \geqq 2$. Then if $L(n) \geqq r$, T_1 can simulate T using no more than $cL(n)$ cells on any tape. T_1 can store in its finite control the contents of each tape if no more than $r - 1$ cells are used on any tape. Thus, if $L(n)$ is small enough for a particular n, so that $cL(n) < 2$, then T_1 need not use its tapes at all.

---

† We must, however, consider the tape bound to be 1 if $cL(n) < 1$. Of course, at least one cell of tape is used on each tape in any case.

Theorem 10.2. If a language L is accepted by an $L(n)$ tape-bounded Tm with k storage tapes, it is accepted by an $L(n)$ tape-bounded Tm with a single storage tape.

Proof. Let T be an $L(n)$ tape-bounded Tm with k storage tapes, accepting L. We may construct a new Tm T_1 with one storage tape which simulates the storage tapes of T on k tracks. The technique was used in Theorem 6.2. T_1 uses no more than $L(n)$ cells.

From now on we assume that any $L(n)$ tape-bounded Tm has but one storage tape. Next we turn to time bounds. First we introduce the following notation.

Let $f(n)$ be a function of n. The expression $\sup\limits_{n\to\infty} f(n)$ is taken to be the limit as $n \to \infty$ of the least upper bound of $f(n), f(n + 1), f(n + 2), \ldots$. Likewise, $\inf\limits_{n\to\infty} f(n)$ is the limit as $n \to \infty$ of the greatest lower bound of $f(n), f(n + 1), f(n + 2), \ldots$.

Example 10.2. Let $f(n) = 1/n$ for n even, and $f(n) = n$ for n odd. The least upper bound of $f(n), f(n + 1), \ldots$ is clearly ∞ for any n, because of the terms with odd arguments. Hence, $\sup\limits_{n\to\infty} f(n) = \infty$. But, because of the terms with n even, it is also true that $\inf\limits_{n\to\infty} f(n) = 0$.

Theorem 10.3. If L is accepted by a k-tape $T(n)$ time-bounded Turing machine T, then L is accepted by a k-tape $cT(n)$† time-bounded Tm T_1 for any $c > 0$, provided that $k > 1$ and $\inf\limits_{n\to\infty} T(n)/n = \infty$.

Proof. A Tm T_1 can be constructed which simulates T in the following manner. First T_1 copies the input onto a storage tape, encoding m symbols into one. (The value of m will be determined later.) From this point on, T_1 uses this storage tape as the input tape and uses the old input tape as a storage tape. T_1 will encode the contents of T's storage tapes by combining m symbols into one. The left end of each tape is marked. During the course of the simulation, T_1 will simulate a large number of moves of T in one *basic step*, which consists of eight moves of T_1. Call the cells currently scanned by each of T_1's heads the *home cells*. The finite control of T_1 records, for each tape, which of the m symbols of T, represented by each home cell, is scanned by the corresponding head of T_1.

To begin a basic step, T_1 moves each head to the left once, to the right twice, and to the left once, recording the symbols to the left and right of the home cells in its finite control. Four moves of T_1 are required.

---

† Here we must understand that $cT(n)$ is taken as $n+1$ if its actual value is less. No word can be recognized in less time than it takes to read it, except in trivial cases.

Next, T_1 determines what will be the contents of all of T's tape cells represented by the home cells and their left and right neighbors at the time when some tape head of T first leaves the region represented by the home cell and its left and right neighbors. (Note that this calculation by T_1 takes no time. It is built into the rules of T_1.) If T accepts before some tape head leaves the represented region, T_1 accepts. If T halts, T_1 halts. Otherwise T_1 then visits, on each tape, the two neighbors of the home cell, changing these symbols and that of the home cell if necessary. T_1 positions each head at the cell which represents the symbol that T's corresponding head is scanning at the end of the moves simulated. At most four moves of T_1 are needed. If T_1 was originally at the left end it only moves right then left.

It takes at least m moves for T to move a head out of the region represented by a home cell and its neighbors. Thus, in eight moves, T_1 has simulated at least m moves of T. Choose m such that $cm \geq 16$.

If T makes $T(n)$ moves, then T_1 simulates these in at most $8[T(n)/m]^+$ moves, where $[x]^+$ denotes the smallest integer greater than or equal to x. Also, T_1 must copy and encode its input (m cells to one) then return the head of the simulated input tape to the left end of the tape. This takes $n + [n/m]^+$ moves, for a total of $n + [n/m]^+ + 8[T(n)/m]^+$ moves. If $\inf_{n \to \infty} T(n)/n = \infty$, it should be clear, for some constant n_1 and all $n \geq n_1$, that

$$n + [n/m]^+ + 8[T(n)/m]^+ \leq cT(n).$$

Words of length $n < n_1$ can be accepted using only the finite control of T_1 in real time (i.e., $T(n) = n+1$).

Theorem 10.4. If a language L is accepted by a k storage tape Turing machine in time $T(n)$, and $\inf_{n \to \infty} T(n)/n = \infty$, then L is accepted by a one-tape Turing machine in time $T^2(n)$.

Proof. Let T be a k-tape $\frac{1}{2}T(n)$ time-bounded Tm accepting L. By Theorem 10.3, T exists. We can simulate T by a one-tape Tm T_1 with k tracks on its tape, one for each tape of T.

Each track will have one cell containing, in addition to the storage tape symbol of T, a marker which denotes the fact that the head of T for the corresponding tape is scanning that cell. (Head markers are shown as $\times$ in Fig. 10.3 on the next page.)

To simulate a move of T, T_1 must visit each of the cells containing a head marker to see what storage symbol is scanned. This provides T_1 with the information necessary to determine the next move of T. The head of T_1 will always be at the extreme left or extreme right head marker. T_1 crosses its tape in one direction (a *sweep*), making those changes at each head marker that have been necessitated by the previous move of T. Also, T_1 records the new symbols scanned by each of the heads of T. After completing the sweep

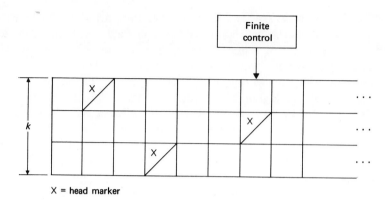

X = head marker

Fig. 10.3. Single-tape Turing machine simulating k tapes.

of its tape, T_1 can decide what move T makes next. T_1 makes these changes on its next sweep. Note that no two head markers can move apart by more than $\frac{1}{2}T(n)$ cells if T is $\frac{1}{2}T(n)$ time bounded. Thus a sweep requires no more than $\frac{1}{2}T(n)+2k$ moves. Hence, T_1 is of time complexity at most $T^2(n)$.

Theorem 10.5. If L is accepted by a k-tape $T(n)$ time-bounded Turing machine T, then L is accepted by a two storage tape Tm T_1 in time $T(n) \log T(n)$.†

Proof. The proof is complicated, and only an indication of how T_1 could simulate T in time proportional to $T(n) \log T(n)$ will be given. The Tm T_1 that we shall describe has storage tapes infinite in both directions. The construction used in Theorem 6.1 shows that T_1 could be converted to a Tm making the same number of moves as T_1, but with semi-infinite tapes. The first storage tape of T_1 will have two tracks for each storage tape of T. For convenience, we focus on two tracks corresponding to a particular tape of T. The other tapes of T are handled in exactly the same way. The second tape of T_1 is used only for scratch, to transport blocks of data on tape 1.

One particular cell of tape 1, known as B_0, will hold the storage symbols scanned by each of the heads of T. That is, rather than moving head markers, T_1 will transport data across B_0 in the direction opposite that of the motion of the head of T being simulated. To the right of cell B_0 will be blocks $B_1, B_2, \ldots$ of exponentially increasing length; that is, B_i is of length 2^{i-1}. Likewise, to the left of B_0 are blocks $B_{-1}, B_{-2}, \ldots$, with the length of B_{-i} the same as the length of B_i. The markers between blocks are assumed to exist, although they will not actually appear until the block is scanned.

---

† By Theorems 10.1 and 10.3, constant factors are irrelevant, so we do not need to specify logarithmic bases.

Let us denote the contents of the cell initially scanned by this tape head of T by a_0. The contents of the cells to the right of this cell are $a_1, a_2, \ldots$, and those to the left, $a_{-1}, a_{-2}, \ldots$. Initially these are all blank, however it is not their value, but their position on the tracks of tape 1 of T_1, that is important. Initially the upper track of T_1 for the tape of T in question is assumed to be empty, while the lower track is assumed to hold $\ldots, a_{-2}, a_{-1}, a_0, a_1, a_2, \ldots$. These are placed in blocks $\ldots, B_{-2}, B_{-1}, B_0, B_1, B_2, \ldots$ as shown in Fig. 10.4.

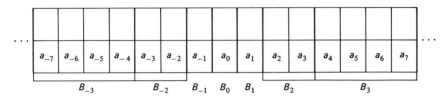

Fig. 10.4. Blocks on Tape 1.

As we mentioned previously, data will be shifted across B_0 and perhaps changed as it passes through. The method of shifting data will obey the following rules.

1. For any $i > 0$, either B_i is full (both tracks) and B_{-i} is empty, or B_i is empty and B_{-i} is full, or the bottom tracks of both B_i and B_{-i} are full, while the upper tracks are empty.
2. The contents of any B_i or B_{-i} always represents consecutive cells on the tape of T represented. For $i > 0$, the upper track represents cells to the left of those of the lower track; for $i < 0$, the upper track represents cells to the right of those of the lower track.
3. B_i represents cells to the left of those of B_j, for $-\infty < i < j < \infty$.
4. B_0 always has only its lower track filled.

To see how data is transferred, let us imagine that on successive moves the tape head of T in question moves to the left. Then T_1 must shift the corresponding data right. To do so, T_1 moves the head of tape 1 from B_0, where it rests, and goes to the right until it finds the first block, say B_i, which is not full. Then T_1 copies all the data of $B_0, B_1, \ldots, B_{i-1}$ onto tape 2 and stores it in the lower track of $B_1, B_2, \ldots, B_{i-1}$ and, if B_i is completely empty, the lower track of B_i. If the lower track of B_i is already filled, then the upper track of B_i, as well as the lower track of $B_1, B_2, \ldots, B_{i-1}$ receives all the data of $B_0, B_1, \ldots, B_{i-1}$.

Note that, in either case, there is just enough room to distribute the data. Also, the data can be picked up and stored in its new location in time proportional to the length of B_i. Finally, note that the data can be easily stored in a manner that satisfies Rules 1, 2, and 3, above.

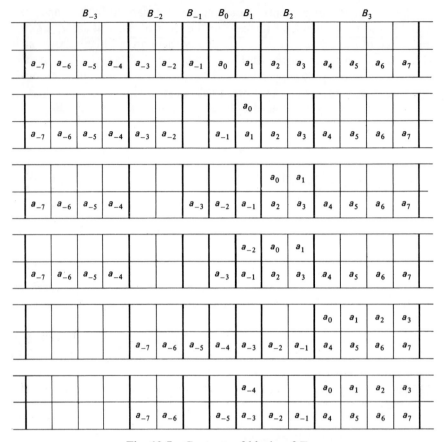

Fig. 10.5   Contents of blocks of T_1.

Next, in time proportional to the length of B_i, T_1 can find B_{-i} (using tape 2 to measure the distance from B_i to B_0 makes this easy). If B_{-i} is completely full, T_1 picks up the upper track of B_{-i} and stores it on tape 2 If B_{-i} is half full, the lower track is put on tape 2. In either case, what has been copied to tape 2 is next copied to the lower tracks of $B_{-(i-1)}$, $B_{-(i-2)}$, ..., B_0. (By Rule 1, these tracks have to be empty, since $B_1, B_2, \ldots, B_{i-1}$ were full.) Again, note that there is just enough room to store the data, and all the above operations can be carried out in time proportional to the length of B_i.

We call all that we have described above a B_i *operation*. The case in which the head of T moves to the right is analogous. The successive contents of the blocks as T moves its tape head in question five cells to the right is shown in Fig. 10.5.

We note that on any pair of tracks T_1 can perform a B_i operation at most once per 2^{i-1} moves of T, since it takes this long for $B_1, B_2, \ldots, B_{i-1}$, which are half empty after a B_i operation, to fill. Also, a B_i operation cannot be performed for the first time until the 2^{i-1}th move of T. Hence, if T operates in time $T(n)$, T_1 will perform only B_i operations, for those i such that $i \leq \log_2 T(n) + 1$.

We have seen that there is a constant m, such that T_1 uses at most $m2^i$ moves to perform a B_i operation. If T makes $T(n)$ moves, T_1 makes at most

$$T_1(n) = \sum_{i=1}^{\log_2 T(n)+1} m2^i \frac{T(n)}{2^{i-1}} \tag{10.1}$$

moves.

From (10.1), we obtain

$$T_1(n) = 2mT(n)[\log_2 T(n) + 1] \tag{10.2}$$

and from (10.2),

$$T_1(n) \leq 4mT(n) \log_2 T(n).$$

The reader should be able to see that T_1 operates in time $T_1(n)$ even when T makes moves using different storage tapes rather than only the one upon which we have concentrated.

10.4 SINGLE-TAPE TURING MACHINES AND CROSSING SEQUENCES

For single-tape Turing machines we can prove some results of the form that "such and such a language requires $T(n)$ time to be recognized by a single-tape Tm." In such a case, it is possible that the language could be recognized in less than $T(n)$ steps by a Tm with more than one tape.

First, let us give a *speed up* theorem for single-tape Tm's.

Theorem 10.6. If L is accepted by a single-tape Tm T of time complexity $T(n)$ and $\inf_{n \to \infty} T(n)/n^2 = \infty$, then, for any $c > 0$, L is accepted by a single-tape Tm of time complexity $cT(n)$.†

Proof. In n^2 steps, a single-tape Tm T_1 can condense its input by encoding m symbols into 1. The proof then proceeds as in Theorem 10.3.

For these simple machines, a useful tool has been developed known as the *crossing sequence*. We imagine that when the Tm makes its move it first overprints the symbol scanned and changes state, then moves its head. Thus, for any pair of adjacent cells on the input tape, we may list the sequence of states in which the Tm crosses from one to the other. Note that the first

---

† Again, we replace $cT(n)$ by $n+1$ if $cT(n) < n+1$.

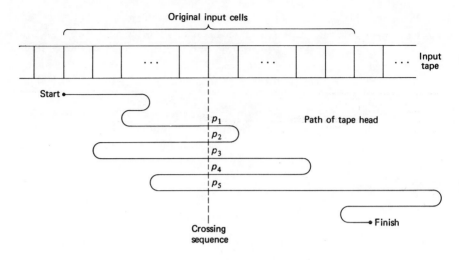

Fig. 10.6   Crossing sequence.

crossing must be left to right; subsequent crossings alternate in direction. See Fig. 10.6.

Here we assume that a word is accepted only at the right end of the cells which originally held the input. The Tm can always move to the right or left in an accepting state until that cell is reached. The number of moves necessary may almost double, but in the subsequent applications, this is of no consequence.

Lemma 10.1.   If $w = a_1a_2\ldots a_n$ is accepted by some one-tape Turing machine T, and the crossing sequence between a_i and a_{i+1} is the same as that between a_j and a_{j+1}, where $i < j$, then $a_1a_2\ldots a_ia_{j+1}a_{j+2}\ldots a_n$ is also accepted by T.

Proof.   Let the crossing sequence in question be $p_1, p_2, \ldots, p_k$. Let t_1 be the portion of the tape containing $a_1a_2\ldots a_i$, t_2 be the portion containing $a_{i+1}a_{i+2}\ldots a_j$, and t_3 be the portion containing $a_{j+1}a_{j+2}\ldots a_n$.

The computation of T on t_1t_3 is exactly the same as the computation of T on $t_1t_2t_3$ until the time that T first leaves t_1. In both cases, T leaves t_1 in state p_1. Furthermore, the contents of t_1 are the same in both cases. With input t_1t_3, T enters t_3 in state p_1 which is the same state as T with input $t_1t_2t_3$ enters t_3 for the first time. This is so since the crossing sequence between t_1 and t_2 is identical to the crossing sequence between t_2 and t_3. Thus, in both cases, T performs the same computation on t_3, leaving t_3 in the same state (namely p_2) and with the same contents. When T with input t_1t_3 reenters t_1, T will be in state p_2, which is the same state as when T with input $t_1t_2t_3$ re-enters t_1 for the first time.

By continued reasoning of this kind, eventually we see that T, with input t_1t_3, enters t_3 in state p_k, with t_3 having the same contents as when T with input $t_1t_2t_3$ enters t_3 in state p_k. But t_3 with its current content is such that T entering in state p_k will enter an accepting state.

Lemma 10.2. If $a_1a_2\ldots a_n$ and $b_1b_2\ldots b_m$ are accepted by a single-tape Tm, and the crossing sequence between a_i and a_{i+1} is the same as the crossing sequence between b_j and b_{j+1}, then $a_1a_2\ldots a_ib_{j+1}b_{j+2}\ldots b_m$ and $b_1b_2\ldots b_ja_{i+1}a_{i+2}\ldots a_n$ are also accepted.

Proof. Similar to Lemma 10.1.

Lemma 10.3. If T is $T(n)$ time bounded, then the sum of the lengths of all crossing sequences (including those outside the region of original input) is at most $T(n)$.

Proof. Each time a boundary is crossed, at least one move is made.

As an example of the use of crossing sequences, we show that the language

$$L = \{wcw^R | w \text{ in } \{0, 1\}^*\}$$

is not accepted by any single-tape Tm of time complexity $T(n)$ unless

$$\sup_{n \to \infty} \frac{T(n)}{n^2} > 0.$$

Note that we cannot prove $T(n) \geq kn^2$ since all words in L are of odd length. If a Tm first checks to see if the input is of even length, the Tm could be time bounded by a function $T_1(n)$ which is equal to n for n even and equal to n^2 for n odd.

Theorem 10.7. The language

$$L = \{wcw^R | w \text{ in } \{0, 1\}^*\}$$

is not accepted by any single-tape Turing machine of time complexity $T(n)$ unless

$$\sup_{n \to \infty} \frac{T(n)}{n^2} > 0.\dagger$$

Proof. Suppose that L is accepted by T, and T is of time complexity $T(n)$. Suppose also that there are two words $w_1w_2cw_2^Rw_1^R$ and $w_3w_4cw_4^Rw_3^R$ such that

---

† As throughout this section, we are assuming that a single-tape Tm goes to the right end of its input upon accepting. In this theorem, the assumption is without loss of generality, since the modification may only introduce a factor of two in time required for recognition, and

$$\sup_{n \to \infty} \frac{T(n)}{n^2} > 0 \quad \text{if and only if} \quad \sup_{n \to \infty} \frac{\frac{1}{2}T(n)}{n^2} > 0.$$

the crossing sequences at the boundary between w_1 and w_2 and the boundary between w_3 and w_4 are the same. Moreover,

$$|w_1| = |w_3| \qquad \text{and} \qquad w_1 \neq w_3.$$

Under these circumstances, we would have $w_1 w_4 c w_4^R w_3^R$ accepted by M, according to Lemma 10.2. Since $w_1 \neq w_3$, that situation is impossible.

Consider all words in L of length n. By the argument above, if $w_1 w_2 c w_2^R w_1^R$ and $w_3 w_4 c w_4^R w_3^R$ are two such words, with $w_1 \neq w_3$, but $|w_1| = |w_3| = i$, then the crossing sequences between w_1 and w_2 and between w_3 and w_4 must be different.

Now, let T have s states. Suppose that the average over all words in L, of the length of the crossing sequence between the ith and $i + 1$st symbols is $p(i)$. Then, for odd n, there must be $\frac{1}{2}2^{\frac{1}{2}(n-1)}$ words for which the crossing sequences between the ith and $i + 1$st symbol are of length equal to or less than $2p(i)$. (Note that there are $2^{\frac{1}{2}(n-1)}$ words of length n in L. At least one half of the words must have crossing sequences of length less than twice the average.) The number of distinct crossing sequences of length less than or equal to $2p(i)$ is less than $s^{2p(i)+1}$. Thus, there must be more than $2^{\frac{1}{2}(n-1)-1}/s^{2p(i)+1}$ words with the same crossing sequence between positions i and $i + 1$. Unless $2^{\frac{1}{2}(n-1)-1}/s^{2p(i)+1} \leq 2^{\frac{1}{2}(n-1)-i}$, there will be two words having not only the same crossing sequence between positions i and $i + 1$, but also having the same string in positions $i + 1$ through $\frac{1}{2}(n - 1)$. These words must have different strings in positions 1 through i. But we have already argued that there cannot be two words of the same length which differ in the first i positions, but have identical crossing sequences between the ith and $i + 1$st symbols.

Thus, for each i between 1 and $\frac{1}{2}(n - 1)$,

$$p(i) \geq \frac{i - 1}{3 \log_2 s}.$$

If we sum $(i - 1)/3 \log_2 s$ from $i = 1$ to $i = \frac{1}{2}(n - 1)$, we get a lower bound on the average sum of crossing sequences over all positions in the words. This sum is $(n^2 - 4n + 3)/24 \log_2 s$. There must be at least one word, the sum of the lengths of whose crossing sequences is average or more. Thus by Lemma 10.3, we have $T(n) \geq (n^2 - 4n + 3)/24 \log_2 s$ for odd n. It follows that

$$\sup_{n \to \infty} \frac{T(n)}{n^2} \geq \frac{1}{24 \log_2 s},$$

and the theorem is proven.

Note that

$$L = \{wcw^R \,|\, w \text{ in } \{0, 1\}^*\}$$

is accepted in time $T'(n) = n$ by a two-tape Tm (Example 10.1). Thus Theorem 10.4, which states that if L can be accepted by a multitape Tm in time $T(n)$, L can be accepted by a single-tape Tm in time $T^2(n)$, cannot be improved.

10.5 LOWER BOUNDS ON TAPE COMPLEXITY

It should be clear that no Tm can operate in any meaningful sense in less than $T(n) = n$, since, otherwise, the Tm could not even examine the input. However, the lower bound on $L(n)$ is certainly 1, since the regular sets can be recognized without printing on any storage tape. We might ask the question: How much tape must be used if the set accepted is not regular? The interesting fact is that a nontrivial lower bound for such sets exists and is log log n.

We define the *storage state* of a Turing machine with one semi-infinite storage tape and a read-only input to be a combination of the

1. contents of the storage tape,
2. position of storage head within the nonblank portion of storage tape, and
3. state of the finite control.

If a Tm T is $L(n)$ tape bounded, with s states and t storage tape symbols, the number of storage states possible is $sL(n)t^{L(n)}$. That is, the factor s represents the number of possible states of finite control, $L(n)$ represents the number of possible positions of the storage head, and $t^{L(n)}$ represents the number of possible contents of the nonblank portion of storage tape. (Note that the blank is counted among the t storage symbols, so this bound is valid even though not all $L(n)$ tape cells may be nonblank at a given time.)

Let r be the number of storage states for T with input of length n. Number these from 1 to r. A *transition matrix* for T (T may be nondeterministic) is an r-by-r matrix, denoted $\mathscr{T}^{(n)} = [t_{ij}]$. Each t_{ij} can take the value 00, 01, 10, or 11. The significance of the transition matrix is as follows. Let w be an input to T, where $|w| = n$, and u be a terminal suffix of w (i.e., $w = vu$ for some v). We associate a transition matrix with u as follows. If T, started in storage state i, with its input head at the leftmost symbol of u, can enter storage state j without leaving u, then the first half of t_{ij} is 1. Otherwise, the first half of t_{ij} is 0. If T, when started in storage state i at the leftmost symbol of u, can eventually move left from u, and is in storage state j the first time it reaches the rightmost symbol of v, then the second half of t_{ij} is 1. Otherwise it is 0.

Under the conditions above, we say that the matrix $\mathscr{T}^{(n)} = [t_{ij}]$ *describes* u. Note that each t_{ij} is uniquely determined, since from storage state i at the left end of u, either T can or cannot enter storage state j without leaving u, and either can or cannot enter j immediately upon leaving u. However, each u has matrices with different superscripts describing it, since the superscript determines how many storage states are considered in specifying the matrix.

Lemma 10.4. Let T be an $L(n)$ tape-bounded Tm with one storage tape and a read-only input. Suppose that w_1 and w_2 are two inputs of length n accepted by T, where $w_1 = v_1u_1$, $w_2 = v_2u_2$, and some transition matrix $\mathscr{T}^{(n)}$ describes both u_1 and u_2. Then v_1u_2 is also accepted by T.

Proof. Without loss of generality, we may assume that T makes no further moves after it accepts. Consider the sequence of configurations of T leading to acceptance of v_1u_1. If the boundary between v_1 and u_1 is never crossed, surely v_1u_2 is accepted. Suppose that, at successive times when the boundary between v_1 and u_1 is crossed, the storage states of T are $Q_1, Q_2, \ldots, Q_k$.

Now consider what happens with v_1u_2 as input to T. T will cross to u_2 in storage state Q_1. Since $\mathcal{T}^{(n)}$ describes u_1 and u_2, T must eventually move left from u_2 in storage state Q_2. Then T moves to the right to u_2 again, this time in storage state Q_3, etc.

If k is even, T will cross the boundary between v_1 and u_2 for the kth time moving left. If v_1u_1 were input, T would also cross the boundary between v_1 and u_1 for the kth and last time, then enter an accepting state while scanning v_1. With v_1u_2 as input, T will do the same, so v_1u_2 is accepted.

If k is odd, T will cross the boundary between v_1 and u_1 or u_2 for the kth and last time moving right. But T, with v_1u_1 as input, will reach u_1 in storage state Q_k and then reach an accepting state without again leaving u_1. Since $\mathcal{T}^{(n)}$ describes u_2 as well as u_1, T will reach u_2 in storage state Q_k and enter the same accepting configuration as it would if v_1u_1 were the input.

Theorem 10.8. Let T be an $L(n)$ tape-bounded Tm, possibly nondeterministic, where $L(n)$ is not bounded above by any constant. Then

$$\sup_{n \to \infty} \frac{L(n)}{\log \log n} > 0.$$

Proof. For each integer k, let n_k be the smallest n such that $L(n) \geq k$. Such an n_k must exist, since arbitrarily large values of $L(n)$ exist. Let r be the number of storage states with no more than $L(n_k)$ nonblank storage tape cells. Further, let w be an input to T, $|w| = n_k$, using at least k storage cells.

Suppose w can be written as $w = v_1v_2v_3$, with $v_2 \neq \epsilon$, and some transition matrix $\mathcal{T}^{(n_k)}$ describes both v_2v_3 and v_3. Then we claim that v_1v_3 is an input causing T to use k storage cells. For, consider the sequence of moves of T with input w causing it to enter a storage state using k storage cells. Suppose that before entering this storage state T's input head crosses the boundary between v_1 and v_2v_3 m times, $m > 0$. Since the same transition matrix describes v_3 and v_2v_3, if T is started with input v_1v_3, it can cross the boundary between v_1 and v_3 in the same sequence of storage states as it did when w was input. If m is even, T enters a storage state using k cells while scanning v_1 on its input. It can clearly do so if v_1v_3 is the input instead of w. If m is odd and v_1v_3 is input, T is moving right when it crosses the boundary between v_1 and v_3 for the mth time. Suppose T is in storage state Q at that time. $\mathcal{T}^{(n_k)}$ must indicate that if T moves its input head to v_2v_3 or any other string described by $\mathcal{T}^{(n_k)}$ when in storage state Q, T can enter a configuration using k cells. Hence T can do the same if v_3 replaces v_2v_3 on the input.

We may conclude by contradiction that w does not have two distinct proper suffixes described by the same transition matrix. Hence there must be at least $n_k - 1$ distinct r-by-r transition matrices. The number of such transition matrices is 4^{r^2}. If T has s states and t storage tape symbols, then $r \leq sL(n_k)t^{L(n_k)}$. Thus:

$$n_k - 1 \leq 4^{[sL(n_k)t^{L(n_k)}]^2}.$$

Take logarithms twice:

$$\log_2 \log_2 (n_k - 1) \leq 2[\log_2 s + \log_2 L(n_k) + L(n_k) \log_2 t] + 1.$$

For $n_k \geq 5$, the left-hand side is bounded below by $\frac{1}{2} \log_2 \log_2 n_k$. For any n_k, the right-hand side is bounded above by $3L(n_k) \log_2 2st$. Thus, for the infinity of n which are n_k for some k, we have

$$\frac{L(n)}{\log_2 \log_2 n} \geq \frac{1}{6 \log_2 2st}.$$

It is not possible that

$$\sup_{n \to \infty} \frac{L(n)}{\log \log n} = 0,$$

since the above holds for an infinity of n. Thus the theorem is proved.

Note that we have not said that $L(n)$ must be at least proportional to $\log \log n$ for all n, but just for an infinite set of n.

10.6 TAPE AND TIME HIERARCHIES

Every set accepted by a time- or tape-bounded Tm is a recursive set. Furthermore, every recursive set is accepted by some tape-bounded Tm and also by some time-bounded Tm. Since no complexity class can contain all recursive sets,† there must be an infinite hierarchy of complexity classes. In this section we show that, for small increases in the functional rate of growth of a tape or time bound, new sets can be recognized that could not be recognized before.

First we introduce the concept of constructability. A function $L(n)$ is said to be *constructable* if there is some Tm T which is $L(n)$ tape bounded, but not bounded by any smaller tape growth. The Tm T is said to *construct* $L(n)$. The set of constructable functions includes $\log n$, n^k, 2^n, $n!$, and so on. If $L_1(n)$ and $L_2(n)$ are monotonic and constructable, then so are $L_1(n) \cdot L_2(n)$, $2^{L_1(n)}$, and $(L_1(n))^{L_2(n)}$. Thus the hierarchy of constructable functions is very rich.

---

† Assume that some complexity class C contained all recursive sets. Then we could construct a Tm T which diagonalizes over the Tm's of that complexity class and which halts for all inputs. (One can tell if a Tm of given time or tape complexity class will ever halt.) This leads to a contradiction, since T accepts a recursive set which could not be in complexity class C.

Theorem 10.9. If $L_1(n)$ and $L_2(n)$ are constructable tape functions with

$$\inf_{n \to \infty} \frac{L_1(n)}{L_2(n)} = 0 \quad \text{and} \quad L_2(n) \geq \log n,$$

then there exists a set accepted by an $L_2(n)$ tape-bounded Tm, but not accepted by any $L_1(n)$ tape-bounded Tm.

Proof. We can construct an $L_2(n)$ tape-bounded Tm T which, operating as follows, accepts a set not accepted by any $L_1(n)$ tape-bounded Tm. Let T' be a Tm with input alphabet Σ' which constructs $L_2(n)$. Consider a new alphabet Σ formed from Σ' in the following manner. For each symbol a in Σ' there are two subscripted symbols a_0 and a_1 in Σ. With input x of length n, T (ignoring the subscripts) first simulates T' until T' halts. This allows T to mark off exactly $L_2(n)$ cells on its scratch tape when the proper input x is chosen. (Recall that not all inputs may cause T' to use exactly $L_2(n)$ cells.) From now on, if T ever moves to a blank cell, T halts. This ensures that T will be $L_2(n)$ tape bounded.

In what follows, T looks only at the subscripts of x. T treats x as a binary number i and generates an encoding of the ith Tm, T_i, on its scratch tape. If, in the process of generating the encoding, T attempts to use more than $L_2(n)$ cells, then T halts without accepting. We require that the method of generating the encoding of T_i be such that there always exists an input with a sufficient number of leading zeros followed by the integer i so that an encoding of T_i will be generated by T.

If T successfully generates an encoding of T_i, then T starts to simulate T_i. Since T has a fixed number of storage tape symbols and T_i may have an arbitrarily large number of storage tape symbols, T will encode T_i's symbols in binary. Thus, if T_i uses l cells, T will require $c_i l$ cells for the simulation, where c_i is a constant which depends on the number of symbols of T_i. Now T has $L_2(n)$ cells available for the simulation of T_i. If T_i happens to be $L_1(n)$ tape bounded, then the simulation requires at most $c_i L_1(n)$ cells. Since

$$\inf_{n \to \infty} \frac{L_1(n)}{L_2(n)} = 0,$$

there are an infinity of n such that $L_2(n) > c_i L_1(n)$. Thus, for any $L_1(n)$ tape-bounded Tm T_i, there is some input with a sufficient number of leading zeros followed by the integer i so that the simulation can be carried out.

An $L_1(n)$ tape-bounded Tm T_i on input x must either loop, halt in an accepting state, or halt in a nonaccepting state. If T_i has s states and t storage tape symbols and is $L_1(n)$ tape bounded, the number of possible configurations of T_i with input of length n is $snL_1(n)t^{L_1(n)}$. The factors s, n, $L_1(n)$, and $t^{L_1(n)}$ represent the state, input head position, storage head position, and storage tape contents, respectively.† Note that since

$$\inf_{n \to \infty} \frac{L_1(n)}{L_2(n)} = 0, \qquad \text{if } L_2(n) \geq \log n,$$

then there are an infinity of n such that not only is $L_2(n) > c_i L_1(n)$, but also $2^{L_2(n)} > sn L_1(n) t^{L_1(n)}$. Therefore, for the infinity of n having the above properties, T can detect the condition in which T_i loops by counting in base 2, on a separate track, the number of moves made by T_i.

Should T detect that T_i is in a loop, T halts and accepts. If T_i halts without accepting, T again halts and accepts. If T_i accepts, T halts without accepting.

The claim is made that the set accepted by T is not accepted by an $L_1(n)$ tape-bounded Tm. For assume that some $L_1(n)$ tape-bounded Tm T_i accepts the set. Then, for some n, there is an input of length n, whose subscripts (recall that input symbols of T represent two alphabets) consist of 0's followed by the binary integer i, such that:

1. T lays off $L_2(n)$ cells of tape.
2. T can construct an encoding of T_i.
3. T can simulate T_i; i.e., $L_2(n) > c_i L_1(n)$.
4. T can detect if T_i loops; i.e.,

$$2^{L_2(n)} > sn L_1(n) t^{L_1(n)}.$$

5. T accepts x if T_i does not, and T does not accept x if T_i does, thereby contradicting the claim that T_i accepts the set accepted by T.

The above proof shows that the slightest functional increase in the tape bound yields a new complexity class. However, the proof requires that $L_2(n)$ be greater than $\log n$.

It can also be shown, by another method, that between $\log \log n$ and $\log n$, a slight increase in tape yields a new complexity class.

Theorem 10.10. For each constructable function $L_2(n)$, between $\log \log n$ and $\log n$,‡ there exists a set L such that L is accepted by an $L_2(n)$ tape-bounded Tm, but not accepted by any $L_1(n)$ tape-bounded Tm, if

$$\inf_{n \to \infty} \frac{L_1(n)}{L_2(n)} = 0.$$

---

† Do not confuse configurations with storage states, as used in Section 10.5. The latter do not include input head position.
‡ By this we mean

$$\inf_{n \to \infty} \frac{\log \log n}{L_2(n)} = 0 \qquad \text{and} \qquad L_2(n) \leq \tfrac{1}{2} \log_2 n.$$

Proof. Let T be a Tm that constructs $L_2(n)$. Denote the input alphabet of T by Σ'. For each a in Σ', let a_0, a_1, and a_2 be in Σ. Let h_1 and h_2 be the homomorphisms defined by

$$h_1(a_i) = a \qquad \text{and} \qquad h_2(a_i) = i$$

for each a_i in Σ. Define L, a language over alphabet Σ, as follows. Let w be of length n and suppose that $h_1(w)$ would cause T to use k storage cells and then halt. Then w is in L if $h_2(w)$ is of the form $x2^{n-2^{k+1}}x$, where x is composed of 0's and 1's and is of length 2^k.

It is easy to see that L is accepted by an $L_2(n)$ tape-bounded Tm. The Tm first lays off k cells of memory by treating w as a word in Σ'. Next the Tm checks the format and compares the initial and terminal strings of 0's and 1's, bit by bit, using its storage tape to measure position within the initial and terminal subwords of 0's and 1's.

Suppose that L were accepted by an $L_1(n)$ tape-bounded Tm with s states and t storage tape symbols. Suppose also that

$$\inf_{n \to \infty} \frac{L_1(n)}{L_2(n)} = 0.$$

There are at most $4^{(sL_1(n)t^{L_1(n)})^2}$ transition matrices for words in Σ^* of length less than or equal to n. Let y be a word of length n over alphabet Σ' such that T' uses exactly $L_2(n)$ tape cells when processing y. Consider all w in L such that $h_1(w) = y$. There are clearly $2^{2L_2(n)}$ such w. For each of these words, the terminal string of 0's and 1's must have a unique transition matrix; otherwise, a word not in L would be accepted, by Lemma 10.4. Hence,

$$2^{2L_2(n)} \leq 4^{(sL_1(n)t^{L_1(n)})^2}.$$

Taking logarithms twice, we have

$$L_2(n) \leq 1 + 2(\log_2 s + \log_2 L_1(n) + L_1(n) \log_2 t).$$

But this contradicts the fact that

$$\inf_{n \to \infty} \frac{L_1(n)}{L_2(n)} = 0.$$

In fact, it is easy to see that

$$\inf_{n \to \infty} \frac{L_1(n)}{L_2(n)} \geq \frac{1}{\log_2 t}.$$

There is a similar hierarchy result for time complexity. However, the result is not quite as strong.

A function $T(n)$ is said to be *countable* if there is some single-tape Tm T that is $T(n)$ time bounded and marks off a block of length $\log T(n)$ on its tape. Just as for constructable functions there is a rich hierarchy of countable functions.

Theorem 10.11. For any countable function $T_2(n)$ and any k, there exists a set that can be accepted by a $T_2(n) \log (T_2(n))$ time-bounded Tm with k tapes but not by any k-tape $T_1(n)$ time-bounded Tm where

$$\inf_{n \to \infty} \frac{T_1(n)}{T_2(n)} = 0.$$

Proof. The proof is similar to that of Theorem 10.9, and only a brief sketch of the necessary construction is given. A $T_2(n) \log T_2(n)$ time-bounded Tm T is constructed to operate as follows. T treats an input x as a binary number i and generates an encoding of a Tm T_i. T simulates T_i on input x. During the simulation, T shifts a copy of the encoding of T_i along an extra track of the first storage tape in such a way that the leftmost symbol of the encoding is always immediately below the symbol scanned by T_i on that tape. Thus each time T_i moves the head on this tape to the left or right, T must move the entire encoding of T_i one space to the left or right. The reason for doing this is to keep the encoding of T_i close to a tape head of T. Otherwise, T might have to make an unbounded number of moves to access the encoding to simulate one move of T_i. The maximum number of moves T needs to simulate a move of T_i is equal to the number of moves necessary to shift the encoding plus a number of moves to access the encoding to determine the next move. Let this number be k_i.

During the simulation, T keeps a counter of length $\log T_2(n)$ on one track of the first storage tape. The leftmost symbol of this counter is always kept under the symbol scanned by the first tape head of T_i. The entire counter is shifted each time the head moves. To shift the counter and add one requires $2 \log T_2(n)$ steps. Should the contents of the counter reach $T_2(n)$, T halts. This forces the number of moves of T to be bounded by a constant times $T_2(n) \log T_2(n)$.

If, during the simulation, the Tm T_i halts without accepting, or if the counter overflows, T accepts a sentence. If, during the simulation, T_i accepts, T does not accept a sentence. Now the set accepted by T cannot be accepted by any $T_1(n)$ time-bounded Tm T_i where

$$\inf \frac{T_1(n)}{T_2(n)} = 0,$$

since there is an n and a binary string x representing the binary integer i, with $|x| = n$, such that $T_2(n) > k_i T_1(n)$. Since T simulates approximately $T_2(n)/k_i$ moves of T_i, and T_i makes at most $T_1(n)$ moves, T will complete the simulation of T_i and accept only if T_i does not accept. Thus T_i cannot accept the same set as T. '

PROBLEMS

10.1 Describe, informally, a Tm with rewriting input, but no other storage tapes, that accepts $L = \{0^m 1^m | m \geq 1\}$ with time bound $T(n) = n^2$. There is a Tm of the same type accepting L in time $T(n) = n \log n$. Can you find this machine?

10.2 Any string, w, in $\{0, 1\}^*$ beginning with 1 can be interpreted as a binary integer. Let $N(w)$ be that integer. Let $L = \{w_1 c w_2 c \ldots c w_k | N(w_i) = i\}$. (Example of a word in L: $1c10c11c100c101c110c111c1000c1001$.) Show that L belongs to tape complexity class log log n. *Hint.* It is not necessary to store all of w_i on storage tape at once to compare it with w_{i+1}.

10.3 Show that $L = \{wcw^R | w$ in $\{a, b\}^*\}$ belongs to tape complexity class log n and no smaller class, by showing that if T is a Tm with nonrewriting input and one storage tape accepting L, then no two words u_1 and u_2 in $\{a, b\}^*$ of length m can be described by the same transition matrix.

10.4 Let T be a Tm with rewriting input and no other storage tape. Suppose that for any integer $k > 0$, there is some input w to T, of length n_k, for which the crossing sequence between some two adjacent cells is at least of length k. Show that there is a constant c associated with T, such that for each k, the smallest n_k is less than c^k.

10.5 Let T be a Tm as described in Problem 10.4. Suppose that T never leaves the cells originally containing the input. Further, suppose that there is some constant k such that no matter what word is input to T, no crossing sequence ever gets longer than k. Show that T accepts a regular set.

10.6 Let T be a Tm as described in Problem 10.4. Suppose that T is of time complexity $T(n) = kn$ for some integer k. Show that T accepts a regular set. *Hint.* Use the results of Problems 10.4 and 10.5.

10.7 Let T be an $L(n)$ tape-bounded Tm with one storage tape and an input tape upon which the input head cannot move to the left (i.e., may remain stationary or move to the right). Show that if there is no constant upper bound on the amount of storage tape used by T, then

$$\inf_{n \to \infty} \frac{L(n)}{\log n} > 0.$$

10.8 Prove that the class of all languages in a given tape complexity class with a constructable tape bound is recursively enumerable (i.e., one can enumerate a class of Tm's accepting exactly these languages).

10.9 Show that for

$$\inf_{n \to \infty} \frac{T_1(n)}{T_2(n)} = 0,$$

there exists a set accepted by a $k + 1$ tape $T_2(n)$ time-bounded Tm not accepted by any k-tape $T_1(n)$ time-bounded Tm. Use this result to give an alternative proof of Theorem 10.11 for the case $k > 1$.

10.10 Show that Theorem 10.10 holds, even if the Tm's are allowed to be non-deterministic. Why does Theorem 10.9 not generalize to the nondeterministic case?

REFERENCES

Hierarchies of recursive sets have been studied by Grzegorczyk [1953], Axt [1959], and Ritchie [1963]. The classification by time-bounded Turing machines is due to Hartmanis and Stearns [1964, 1965]. Classification by tape complexity is from Hartmanis, Lewis, and Stearns [1965] and Lewis, Stearns, and Hartmanis [1965]. Theorems 10.1 and 10.9 are from Hartmanis, Lewis, and Stearns [1965]. Theorems 10.3, 10.4, and 10.11 are from Hartmanis and Stearns [1965]. Theorem 10.10 is from Hopcroft and Ullman [1968d]. The notion of crossing sequences is found in Hennie [1965] and the notion of transition matrices in Hopcroft and Ullman [1968d]. A machine-independent theory of recursive functions can be found in Blum [1964]. Interesting results on real-time computation (time complexity $T(n) = n$) can be found in Yamada [1962], Rabin [1963], and Cole [1964].

CHAPTER 11

TIME AND SPACE BOUNDS FOR
RECOGNIZING CONTEXT-FREE LANGUAGES

11.1 INTRODUCTION

Two important properties of a language are the amount of time and the amount of space necessary to recognize a sentence of the language. In this chapter we consider algorithms for recognizing sentences of a language which will be applicable to any context-free language. In particular we show that, for any cfl, we can construct a Turing machine which recognizes the sentences of the language in time n^3, and that we can construct another Turing machine which recognizes the sentences of the language using only $\log^2 n$ space. It is not known whether or not these are tight bounds, since we cannot prove that there exist cfl's requiring that much time or space.

11.2 TIME REQUIREMENTS FOR
RECOGNITION OF CONTEXT-FREE LANGUAGES

In determining the time required to recognize an arbitrary context-free language, we consider recognition by a multitape Turing machine. Our reason for doing this is that using the multitape Turing machine as a model gives answers which correspond to the number of discrete steps in the algorithm and hence, reflects the time one would need if the algorithm were run on a random access computer. Had we selected a single-tape Turing machine, we would get a different answer. With this in mind, we proceed to describe the algorithm and then its implementation on a multitape Turing machine. For simplicity, we assume that the grammar of the language to be recognized is in Chomsky normal form.

The key to the algorithm lies in an n-by-n array called the *recognition matrix*. Let $a_1 a_2 \ldots a_n$ be the sentence which we are attempting to recognize. The element in row i and column j of the recognition matrix will contain the set of all variables from which the substring $a_j a_{j+1} \ldots a_{j+i-1}$ can be derived. Note that this substring is of length i and begins at position j.

As an example, consider the grammar

$$G = (\{S, A, B, C, D, E, F\}, \{a, b\}, P, S)$$

with the following productions:

$$
\begin{array}{lll}
S \rightarrow CB & S \rightarrow FA & S \rightarrow FB \\
D \rightarrow AA & A \rightarrow CS & B \rightarrow FS \\
E \rightarrow BB & A \rightarrow FD & B \rightarrow CE \\
C \rightarrow a & A \rightarrow a & B \rightarrow b \\
F \rightarrow b. & &
\end{array}
$$

The recognition matrix for the sentence *aababb* is shown below in Fig. 11.1. The jth entry in row 1 contains some symbol H (possibly along with other symbols) if the terminal substring of length 1 starting with the jth input symbol can be derived from H. Since the grammar is in Chomsky normal form, we need only check to see if there is a rule $H \rightarrow a_j$, where a_j is the jth input symbol. The first input symbol is a, and there are productions $A \rightarrow a$ and $C \rightarrow a$ in the grammar. Thus A and C are entered in the cell $(1, 1)$. Likewise A and C are entered in the cell $(1, 2)$. The third input symbol is a b, and the grammar contains productions $B \rightarrow b$ and $F \rightarrow b$. Thus B and F are entered into the cell $(1, 3)$. The remainder of the first row is filled in similarly.

The jth entry in row 2 will contain symbol H (possibly along with some other symbols) if the substring of length 2 starting with the jth input symbol can be derived from H. The only way in which this can happen is if: $H \rightarrow IJ$ is a production of the grammar, the terminal string of length one starting in position j can be derived from I, and the terminal string of length one starting in position $j + 1$ can be derived from J. If the above conditions are fulfilled, then I will be in cell $(1, j)$ and J will be in cell $(1, j + 1)$. It is for this reason that D is entered in cell $(2, 1)$ since $D \rightarrow AA$ is a production of the grammar and A is in cell $(1, 1)$ and cell $(1, 2)$. Similarly, S is entered in cell $(2, 2)$, since $S \rightarrow CB$ is a production of the grammar and C is in cell $(1, 2)$ and B is in cell $(1, 3)$.

Position

	1	2	3	4	5	6
1	A, C	A, C	B, F	A, C	B, F	B, F
2	D	S	S	S	E, S	
3	A	A	B	A, B		
4	D	S	S, E			
5	A	A, B				
6	D, S					

Length

Fig. 11.1. Recognition matrix for the sentence *aababb*.

The jth cell of the third row will contain the symbol H if the substring of length three starting with the jth input symbol is derivable from H. There are two ways in which this can happen. Namely, if $H \to IJ$ is a production of the grammar, and either the substring of length one starting in position j is derivable from I and the substring of length two starting in position $j + 1$ is derivable from J, or the substring of length two starting in position j is derivable from I and the substring of length one starting in position $j + 2$ is derivable from J. Thus, to determine if H should go into cell $(3, j)$, we examine the pair of cells $(1, j)$ and $(2, j + 1)$ and also the pair of cells $(2, j)$ and $(1, j + 2)$.

In general, to determine the entry (i, j), $i > 1$, for each production $H \to IJ$, we examine the pairs of cells $(1, j)$ and $(i - 1, j + 1)$, $(2, j)$ and $(i - 2, j + 2), \ldots, (i - 1, j)$ and $(1, j + i - 1)$ to see if the first cell in the pair contains I and the second cell J.

Once the recognition matrix has been constructed, we need only look to see if cell $(n, 1)$ contains the symbol S to determine if the sentence is in the language. Thus the time necessary to determine if a sentence is in the language is equal to the time necessary to construct the recognition matrix.

There are n entries in the first row of the recognition matrix. Each entry takes one step to compute. There are $n - 1$ entries in the second row each requiring one step to compute. There are $n - 2$ entries in the third row each requiring two steps to compute. The ith row has $n - i + 1$ entries each requiring $i - 1$ steps to compute. Thus the total computation time is

$$n + \sum_{i=2}^{n} (n - i + 1)(i - 1) = \frac{n^3 + 5n}{6}, \quad \text{which grows as } n^3.$$

Having exhibited an algorithm for recognizing the sentences of a cfl, we implement the algorithm on a multitape Turing machine to show that we can indeed execute the algorithm in time n^3.

The real question is whether or not we can arrange the recognition matrix on the storage tapes in such a manner so as not to waste too much time moving the tape heads around. Our multitape Turing machine will have an input tape and two scratch tapes. The recognition matrix will be stored on both scratch tapes, but the elements of the matrix will be arranged in different orders on the two tapes. On tape 1, the elements of the recognition matrix will be arranged by columns. That is, $(1, 1), (2, 1), \ldots, (n, 1), (1, 2), (2, 2), \ldots$. On tape 2, the elements of the recognition matrix will be arranged by diagonals, i.e., $(1, 1), (2, 1), (1, 2), (3, 1), (2, 2), (1, 3), (4, 1), \ldots$. The elements of the recognition matrix will be computed by rows; that is, $(1, 1)$, $(1, 2), \ldots, (1, n), (2, 1), (2, 2), \ldots$.

The actual motion of the Turing machine is quite straightforward. First, the Tm fills in the $(1, 1), (1, 2), \ldots$, and $(1, n)$ entries on the appropriate cells of both tapes. This process requires the Tm to use the length of its input to

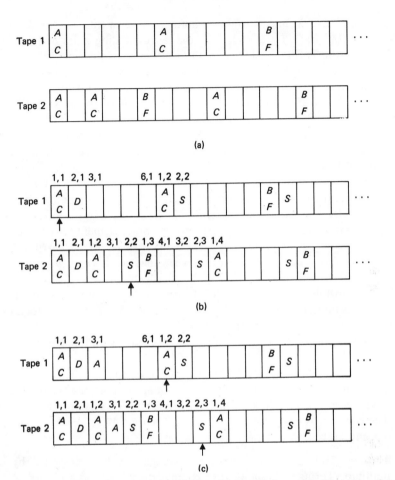

Fig. 11.2. Format of scratch tapes for n^3 recognition. (a) Contents of tapes after initialization. (b) Contents of tapes just before computation of element (3, 1). (c) Contents of tapes just after computation of element (3,1).

mark off n blocks of length n on tape 1 and blocks of lengths 1, 2, 3, ..., n on tape 2. It should be clear that this initialization phase requires a number of steps proportional to n^2. For the recognition matrix of Fig. 11.1, the initial portions of the two scratch tapes would now appear as in Fig. 11.2(a).

The Tm must now compute the remaining entries. Since there are roughly n^2 elements of the recognition matrix to be computed, we must limit ourselves to n steps per entry. Assume that we are computing element (i, j), and head 1 is at element $(1, j)$ and head 2 at element $(i - 1, j + 1)$. Head 1 moves right, scanning the elements $(1, j), (2, j), \ldots, (i - 1, j)$, until it reaches the first blank cell, which corresponds to the element (i, j) being computed.

Meanwhile, head 2 moves right scanning the elements $(i - 1, j + 1)$, $(i - 2, j + 2), \ldots, (1, j + i - 1)$. As the corresponding pairs of elements are scanned, the Turing machine computes the value of element (i, j). Since head 1 is now scanning the cell (i, j) on tape 1, this cell on tape 1 is filled in and head 1 continues to move to the right to the first nonblank cell, which will correspond to the element $(i, j + 1)$. Head 2 must move to the left to cell (i, j), which will be the first blank cell encountered, to record the answer. Head 2 then moves to the right to cell $(i - 1, j + 2)$, which is the first cell to the right of the first block of blank cells encountered. We are now ready to compute the element $(i, j + 1)$.

Figure 11.2(b) illustrates the configuration of the two scratch tapes just before the computation of the element $(3, 1)$. Head 1 is scanning element $(1, 1)$ and head 2 is scanning element $(2, 2)$. Both heads move to the right, scanning elements $(2, 1)$ and $(1, 3)$, respectively. Since element $(1, 1)$ contains C and $(2, 2)$ contains S, element $(3, 1)$ should contain A. Head 1 writes A in the cell corresponding to element $(3, 1)$ when that cell is reached, and continues to the right to the first nonblank cell which corresponds to element $(1, 2)$. Meanwhile, head 2 moves left to cell $(3, 1)$ to store the symbol A, reverses direction, and moves to the right to cell $(2, 3)$. Figure 11.2(c) illustrates the contents of the tapes at this point.

It is easily seen that at most $3n$ moves are needed to compute any element. However, when an element of the form $(i, n - i + 1)$ has been computed, both heads must be moved left approximately n^2 spaces. This will only occur n times, and thus, will only add something proportional to n^3 to the total number of steps required. Thus, the number of steps is proportional to n^3. The constant is not important since, by Theorem 10.3, we can speed up the recognition by any constant factor we desire.

Theorem 11.1. Every context-free language can be recognized by a multitape Turing machine of time complexity n^3.

Proof. The result follows from a formalization of the above discussion.

As mentioned earlier, no one has found a cfl for which there is no recognition algorithm using less than n^3 time. In fact, we do not know of any cfl that cannot be recognized in time kn (i.e., a number of steps that grows linearly with the length of the input).

11.3 SPACE REQUIREMENTS FOR RECOGNITION OF CONTEXT-FREE LANGUAGES

In this section we consider both off-line (two-way, read only input) and on-line (one-way, read only input) Turing machine models. Ideally, we would like to consider more realistic models for a computer. However, for the recognition algorithms which will be described, we see that the amount of storage required is more a function of the algorithm than of the model, except for the question of whether the model is on-line or off-line. In other words, the results are the same whether we use a single-tape Turing machine, a multitape Turing machine, or some better model of a random access computer. Specifically the results are:

1. For off-line recognition, there are context-free languages that cannot be recognized in less than log n space.
2. Log^2 n space is sufficient for off-line recognition of any context-free language.
3. For on-line recognition, there are context-free languages that cannot be recognized in less than linear space.
4. Linear space is sufficient for on-line recognition of any context-free language.

There are cfl's that cannot be recognized by an off-line Turing machine in less than log n space. See Problem 10.3. Thus we can state the following theorem.

Theorem 11.2. There are context-free languages that cannot be recognized by an off-line Turing machine in less than log n space.

Proof. The cfl $\{wcw^R | w$ is in $\{0, 1\}^*\}$ cannot be recognized in less than log n space by an off-line Turing machine (Problem 10.3).

Before showing that log^2 n space is sufficient for off-line recognition of any cfl, we prove the following lemma.

Lemma 11.1. Let α be a sentential form of length four or greater generated by a cfg in Chomsky normal form. Let $n = |\alpha|$. Then, α can be written $\alpha_1 \alpha_2 \alpha_3$, with α_1 or α_3 possibly ϵ, such that there exists a derivation of α,

$$S \xrightarrow{*} \alpha_1 A \alpha_3 \xrightarrow{*} \alpha_1 \alpha_2 \alpha_3, \qquad A \xrightarrow{*} \alpha_2 \text{ and } \tfrac{1}{3}n < |\alpha_2| \leq \tfrac{2}{3}n.$$

Proof. The first step in the derivation of α must be of the form $S \Rightarrow BC$. If either B or C generates a substring of α with length l, where $\tfrac{1}{3}n < l \leq \tfrac{2}{3}n$, then the conditions of the lemma are easily satisfied. If neither B nor C generates a substring with length l, where $\tfrac{1}{3}n < l \leq \tfrac{2}{3}n$, then either B or C must generate a string of length greater than $\tfrac{2}{3}n$. In this case, assume (without loss of generality) that B generates a string of length greater than $\tfrac{2}{3}n$. The first step in the derivation of a string from B must be of the form $B \Rightarrow DE$. Now D and E cannot both generate strings of length less than $\tfrac{1}{3}n$. Thus if neither D nor E generates a substring of α with length l, where $\tfrac{1}{3}n < l \leq \tfrac{2}{3}n$, then either D or E must generate a string of length greater than $\tfrac{2}{3}n$. By repeating the argument, we eventually must reach a variable from which an appropriate length terminal string is derived.

Theorem 11.3. Every context-free language L can be accepted by some off-line, $\log^2 n$ tape-bounded Turing machine.

Proof. The argument is quite complex, and only the essential construction will be given. We shall construct a Turing machine T that accepts L and uses at most $c \log^2 n$ cells of memory, where c is a constant to be determined by the construction. By recoding c symbols into one symbol, we can obtain a new Turing machine using only $\log^2 n$ cells. The $c \log^2 n$ cells of memory will be divided into $c \log n$ blocks. Each block will have room to contain two numbers (in binary) between 1 and n and a variable which may be either "primed" or "unprimed."

Let G be a grammar in Chomsky normal form such that $L(G) = L$. If a sentence $a_1 a_2 \ldots a_n$, $n \geq 4$, can be derived by G from S, then by Lemma 11.1 there exists a sequence of sentential forms $\delta_k, \delta_{k-1}, \ldots, \delta_1$ such that

1. $\delta_1 = a_1 a_2 \ldots a_n$.
2. $|\delta_k| \leq 3$, but $|\delta_{k-1}| \geq 4$.
3. $S \xrightarrow{*} \delta_k$.
4. For $2 \leq i \leq k$, we can write $\delta_i = \alpha_i A_i \gamma_i$ and $\delta_{i-1} = \alpha_i \beta_i \gamma_i$, where $A_i \xrightarrow{*} \beta_i$. Also, $\frac{1}{3}|\delta_{i-1}| < |\beta_i| \leq \frac{2}{3}|\delta_{i-1}|$.

Now $|\delta_i| < \frac{2}{3}|\delta_{i-1}| + 1$ for all i, with $2 \leq i \leq k$, and $|\delta_{i-1}| \geq 3$; hence, $|\delta_i| \leq \frac{4}{5}|\delta_{i-1}|$. Thus, $k \leq c \log_2 n$, where $c = 1/\log_2 \frac{5}{4}$.

The Turing machine T will determine if $S \xrightarrow[G]{*} a_1 a_2 \ldots a_n$ by locating the strings, β_i, $2 \leq i \leq k$, and replacing them by A_i. Note that β_2 is a string of terminal symbols, but that in general the strings β_i are composed of terminals and variables. When the input is reduced to a string of length 3, T's finite control can determine if S derives that string.

To determine the string β_2, T will cycle through all substrings of the input x_1 and variables of G, until a substring β_2 and variable A_2 are found, such that $A_2 \xrightarrow{*} \beta_2$ and also that $|\beta_2|$ is between $\frac{1}{3}$ and $\frac{2}{3}$ of $|x_1|$. During the cycling process, the string β_2 and variable A_2 are recorded in the first block of memory by storing the position of the first and last symbol of β_2 on the input along with the variable A_2. As soon as a suitable A_2 and β_2 are found, A_2 is primed to indicate both that $A_2 \xrightarrow{*} \beta_2$ and that the length of β_2 is satisfactory. In general, a variable is primed in any block exactly when a substring which it derives has been found. For the time being, we will postpone the explanation as to how T determines if $A_2 \xrightarrow{*} \beta_2$.

Let the string $\delta_1 = a_1 a_2 \ldots a_n$ with β_2 replaced by A_2 be δ_2. T now goes on to find a substring, β_3 of δ_2 and a variable A_3 such that $A_3 \xrightarrow{*} \beta_3$ and $|\beta_3|$ is between $\frac{1}{3}$ and $\frac{2}{3}$ the length of δ_2.

To determine the string β_3, T cycles through all substrings of δ_2 and variables of G until a substring β_3 and variable A_3 are found, such that $A_3 \overset{*}{\underset{G}{\Rightarrow}} \beta_3$ and also that $|\beta_3|$ is of suitable length. At that time, A_3 is primed. During the cycling process, the string β_3 and variable A_3 are recorded in the second block of memory. The only difference this time is that β_3 is not necessarily a string of terminal symbols since it may contain the variable A_2. Thus, to store β_3, T stores the location in the input string of the first and last symbols of the substring of the input derivable from β_3. Also, in cycling through substrings of δ_2, M must remember that δ_2 is the input with the substring β_2 replaced by A_2. Once again we postpone the explanation as to how T determines if $A_3 \overset{*}{\Rightarrow} \beta_3$.

After finding β_3, T goes on to determine β_4, β_5, etc. If, at some point, T determines that no suitable β_i exists, then T backs up to β_{i-1}, removes the prime from A_{i-1}, and starts cycling to find a different β_{i-1} or A_{i-1}. Of course, T starts the cycling from the point at which it left off. If all possible β_{i-1} and A_{i-1} are exhausted, T backs up to β_{i-2} and A_{i-2}, and so on. Should T exhaust all possible β_2 and A_2, then T concludes that the input is not derivable from S. On the other hand, if δ_1 is derivable from S, T will eventually find suitable $\beta_2, \beta_3, \ldots, \beta_k$, at which point δ_k will consist of at most three symbols. If $S \overset{*}{\Rightarrow} \delta_k$, then T accepts. Otherwise the search continues for a different β_k and A_k. Note that since $k \leq c \log n$ and since T has $c \log n$ blocks of memory, T will not run out of space to store the β_i.

It remains to explain how, at each step, T determines if $A_i \overset{*}{\Rightarrow} \beta_i$. Note that this is really the same problem as determining if $S \overset{*}{\Rightarrow} \delta_1$. If $|\beta_i| \leq 3$, the finite control can determine if $A_i \overset{*}{\Rightarrow} \beta_i$. Otherwise, by Lemma 11.1 again, there are strings $\omega_1, \omega_2, \ldots, \omega_r$, such that

1. $\omega_1 = \beta_i$.
2. $|\omega_r| \leq 3$, but $|w_{r-1}| \geq 4$.
3. $A_i \overset{*}{\Rightarrow} \omega_r$.
4. For $2 \leq j \leq r$, we can write $\omega_j = \Phi_j C_j \psi_j$ and $\omega_{j-1} = \Phi_j \theta_j \psi_j$, where $C_j \overset{*}{\Rightarrow} \theta_j$, and $\frac{1}{3}|\omega_{j-1}| < |\theta_j| \leq \frac{2}{3}|\omega_{j-1}|$.

Note that all blocks of memory to the right of block i are not in use at this time and can be used to determine if $A_i \overset{*}{\Rightarrow} \beta_i$. To determine if $A_i \overset{*}{\Rightarrow} \beta_i$, T cycles through all substrings of β_i and variables of G until it finds a substring θ_2, of suitable length, and a variable C_2 such that $C_2 \overset{*}{\Rightarrow} \theta_2$. θ_2 and C_2 are recorded in the $i + 1$st block of memory by placing the location of the first and last symbol of the substring of the input derivable from θ_2, along with the symbol C_2, into the block $i + 1$.

T determines if $C_2 \xrightarrow{*} \theta_2$ in a similar manner, by using blocks of memory from $i + 2$ on. Once $C_2 \xrightarrow{*} \theta_2$ has been determined, the blocks from $i + 2$ on are erased so that M can use these blocks for $\theta_3, \theta_4, \ldots, \theta_r$. Since $|\beta_i| \leq (4/5)^i n$, we need at most $c \log [(4/5)^i n]$ blocks which is exactly equal to the $(c \log n) - i$ blocks that are not in use. Once T has determined if $A_i \xrightarrow{*} \beta_i$, all blocks from i on are erased so that T can use these blocks for $\beta_{i+1}, \beta_{i+2}, \ldots, \beta_k$.

For on-line recognition, linear space is necessary and sufficient to recognize all cfl's.

Theorem 11.4. The context-free language,

$$L_1 = \{wcw^R | w \text{ in } \{0, 1\}^*\},$$

requires $\inf_{n \to \infty} L(n)/n > 0$ for recognition by an on-line $L(n)$ tape-bounded Turing machine.

Proof. Let M be an on-line $L(n)$ tape-bounded Turing machine that recognizes L_1. There are 2^m words w of length m, such that wcw^R is in L_1. The memory configuration of M must be different for each of these words when the input head scans the c. Thus $sL(n)t^{L(n)} \geq 2^n$, where s and t are the number of states and tape symbols of M. This implies that

$$\inf_{n \to \infty} \frac{L(n)}{n} > 0.$$

Theorem 11.5. Every context-free language can be recognized by an on-line $L(n) = n$ tape-bounded Turing machine.

Proof. First note that, for $L(n) = n$, the on-line and off-line Turing machine models are equivalent since the storage tape is long enough to store the entire input. Thus the theorem follows immediately from Theorem 11.3.

PROBLEMS

11.1 Construct the recognition matrix for the sentence *baabaabb* if the productions of the grammar are as follows.

$S \to CB$	$S \to FB$	$S \to FA$	$A \to a$
$D \to AA$	$B \to FS$	$A \to FD$	$B \to b$
$E \to BB$	$B \to CE$	$A \to CS$	$C \to a$
			$F \to b$

11.2 Prove that the language

$$L = \{w_1 c w_2 c \ldots c w_m c c w_i^R | 1 \leq i \leq m, \text{ and for } 1 \leq j \leq m, w_j \text{ is in } \{0, 1\}^*\}$$

is context free. Show that L cannot be recognized in real time† by any multitape Turing machine.

11.3 Prove that

$$L = \{xww^R | x \text{ and } w \text{ are in } \{0, 1\}^* \text{ with } w \neq \epsilon\}$$

is not accepted by a real-time multitape Tm. Is L context free?

11.4 Write an ALGOL program for the algorithm sketched in Theorem 11.3.

11.5 Consider the grammar of Problem 11.1 and the sentence *abaabbabaaababbb*. Show the contents of the memory of the Turing machine of Theorem 11.3 at the first time a variable is primed in the fourth block of memory.

REFERENCES

All the results in this chapter are from Lewis, Stearns, and Hartmanis [1965], except Theorem 11.1, which is from Younger [1967].

---

† i.e., by a Tm of time complexity n. Note that the speed-up theorem (Theorem 10.3) does not apply, so that time complexity n is different than time kn, $k > 1$.

CHAPTER 12

DETERMINISTIC PUSHDOWN AUTOMATA

12.1 INTRODUCTION

We have seen that the nondeterministic pushdown automata accept exactly the context-free languages. We might ask whether every context-free language can be accepted by a deterministic pushdown automaton. The answer is no. However, the subset of cfl's that can be accepted by deterministic pda (abbreviated dpda) is important, since these languages are very rapidly recognized in comparison with the time of n^3 given by Theorem 11.1.

Let us recall our definition of a deterministic pda. A deterministic pda is a pda for which there is only one choice of move for any triple of state, input symbol (or ϵ input), and pushdown symbol. Furthermore, there must never be a choice of using an input symbol or of using ϵ input. Formally, let

$$M = (K, \Sigma, \Gamma, \delta, q_0, Z_0, F)$$

be a pda. We say that M is *deterministic* if, for all q in K, a in Σ, and Z in Γ:

1. $\delta(q, a, Z)$ contains at most one element.
2. $\delta(q, \epsilon, Z)$ contains at most one element.
3. If $\delta(q, \epsilon, Z)$ is not empty, then $\delta(q, a, Z)$ is empty for all a in Σ.

Rules 1 and 2 prevent the existence of a choice of move for the same triple of state, input, and pushdown symbol. Rule 3 prevents a choice as to whether ϵ or a true input symbol is used.†

For the deterministic pushdown automaton, we define acceptance to be by final state. Thus

$$T(M) = \{x \mid x : (q_0, Z_0) \mathrel{\underset{M}{\overset{*}{\vdash}}} (q_f, \gamma), \text{ for some } q_f \text{ in } F \text{ and } \gamma \text{ in } \Gamma^*\}.$$

A language accepted by a dpda is called a *deterministic language*.

An example of a deterministic pda is given below.

---

† A "true" input symbol will be synonomous with a non-ϵ input symbol.

Example 12.1. Let $M = (\{q_0, q_1\}, \{a, b\}, \{Z_0, A, B\}, \delta, q_0, Z_0, \{q_0\})$. The rules of δ are:†

$$\delta(q_0, a, Z_0) = (q_1, AZ_0) \qquad \delta(q_0, b, Z_0) = (q_1, BZ_0)$$
$$\delta(q_1, a, B) = (q_1, \epsilon) \qquad \delta(q_1, b, A) = (q_1, \epsilon)$$
$$\delta(q_1, a, A) = (q_1, AA) \qquad \delta(q_1, b, B) = (q_1, BB)$$
$$\delta(q_1, \epsilon, Z_0) = (q_0, Z_0)$$

$T(M)$ is the set of strings consisting of an equal number of a's and b's. Observe that each time M uses an input symbol a, it either erases a B or prints an A on its pushdown store. Each time M uses an input symbol b, it either erases an A or prints a B. Z_0 is the top (and only) symbol on the pushdown store, if and only if P has used an equal number of a's and b's as input. In that case, M transfers to state q_0 with ϵ input.

We show several important properties of deterministic languages. First, the complement of a deterministic language is also a deterministic language. Second, the deterministic languages are preserved under the operations of intersection with a regular set, inverse deterministic gsm mapping, and quotient with a regular set. Finally, we shall define a class of unambiguous grammars, called $LR(k)$ grammars which generate exactly the deterministic languages.

12.2 COMPLEMENTS OF DETERMINISTIC LANGUAGES

To show that the complement of a deterministic language is also a deterministic language, we would like to show that interchanging the final and nonfinal states of a deterministic pda which accepts a language L results in a dpda that accepts the complement of L. There are two difficulties that complicate the above approach. The first difficulty is that the original dpda might never move beyond some point on an input string, either because it reaches a configuration in which no move is possible or it makes an infinity of moves on ϵ input and never uses another true input symbol. In either case the dpda does not accept any input with this string as a prefix and thus, a dpda accepting the complement must accept every string with this prefix.

The second difficulty is due to the fact that after seeing a sentence x, the dpda may make several moves on ϵ input. The dpda may be in final states after some of these moves and in nonfinal states after others. In this case, interchanging the final and nonfinal states results in the dpda still accepting x.

To remove the first difficulty, we prove a lemma that states that, given a dpda M, we can always find an equivalent dpda M' that will never enter a configuration from which it will not eventually use another true input symbol.

---

† Since the value of $\delta(q, a, Z)$ is either a set containing a single element or the empty set, we shall write (p, γ) for $\{(p, \gamma)\}$.

Lemma 12.1. Let M be a dpda. There exists an equivalent dpda M', such that for each input x to M' there is some configuration M' can enter, starting in its initial configuration and using the entire input x.

Proof. We can assume without loss of generality that for every configuration and input symbol, M has a next move. One can always add an end marker on the pushdown list to prevent M from erasing its pushdown store entirely and add a "dead state," q. If, for some combination of state, input symbol, and pushdown symbol, M has no next move, either using the input symbol or an ϵ input, then a transfer to state q would occur. On any true input symbol, a transfer from state q to state q is the only move possible, and no change of the pushdown store occurs. Of course, q is not an accepting state.

Now, if for every configuration and input symbol M has a next move, then the only way in which M might never reach the end of its input is if in some configuration M makes an infinity of moves on ϵ input. Two cases arise here. First, the pushdown store may grow indefinitely. Second, there may be a bound on the length of the pushdown store, but some configuration repeats.

Suppose that $M = (K, \Sigma, \Gamma, \delta, q_0, Z_0, F)$. Let r be the maximum number of pushdown symbols written in one move of M, s the number of states, and t the number of pushdown symbols of M. Now, if

$$\epsilon : (q_1, \gamma_1) \;\overset{|*}{\underset{M}{}}\; (q_2, \gamma_2), \qquad \text{where } |\gamma_2| - |\gamma_1| > rst,$$

then it should be clear that there are two intermediate configurations with the same state and the same top (leftmost) symbol on the pushdown store. Moreover, these configurations are never followed by a configuration with a shorter pushdown store. That is to say, we can find q in K and Z in Γ such that

$$\epsilon : (q_1, \gamma_1) \;\overset{|*}{\underset{M}{}}\; (q, Z\gamma_3) \qquad \text{and} \qquad \epsilon : (q, Z\gamma_3) \;\overset{|*}{\underset{M}{}}\; (q, Z\gamma_4\gamma_3)$$

by a sequence of moves in which no portion of γ_3 is erased. Finally,

$$\epsilon : (q, Z\gamma_4\gamma_3) \;\overset{|*}{\underset{M}{}}\; (q_2, \gamma_5\gamma_4\gamma_3), \qquad \text{where } \gamma_5\gamma_4\gamma_3 = \gamma_2,$$

in a manner such that no portion of γ_3 or γ_4 is ever erased.

To prove the above, it is sufficient to note that in a sequence of moves and configurations which increase the length of the pushdown store by more than rst symbols, there must be more than st configurations which have a pushdown store shorter than that of any subsequent configuration. Two of these configurations must have the same state and same top symbol on the pushdown store.

We observe that if

$$\epsilon : (q, Z\gamma_3) \;\overset{|*}{\underset{M}{}}\; (q, Z\gamma_4\gamma_3)$$

by a sequence of moves in which no portion of γ_3 is scanned, then the action of M is independent of what appears below the top symbol Z on the pushdown store. Thus we have

$$\epsilon:(q, Z\gamma_3) \;\underset{M}{\overset{*}{\vdash}}\; (q, Z\gamma_4\gamma_3)$$

$$\epsilon:(q, Z\gamma_4\gamma_3) \;\underset{M}{\overset{*}{\vdash}}\; (q, Z\gamma_4\gamma_4\gamma_3)$$

$$\vdots$$

and the pushdown store grows indefinitely. We conclude that for a fixed input word the pushdown store grows indefinitely if and only if, on ϵ input, the pushdown store grows by more than rst symbols.

Let us now consider what happens if the length of the pushdown store does not grow indefinitely. If there is a bound on the length of the pushdown store and an infinity of ϵ moves, some configuration must repeat. By the above argument, the smallest tape in the repeating loop of sequences cannot be more than rst symbols shorter than the longest tape. Hence, the loop may comprise at most $s(t + 1)^{rst}$ configurations.

We are now ready to describe a dpda M', equivalent to M, which always scans its entire input tape. Let

$$M' = (K', \Sigma, \Gamma, \delta', q'_0, Z_0, F'),$$

where $K' = \{[q, i, j] | q \text{ in } K, 0 \le i \le rst, 0 \le j \le s(t + 1)^{rst}\} \cup \{d\}, q'_0 = [q_0, 0, 0]$, $F' = \{[q, i, j] | q \text{ in } F\}$, and δ' is as defined subsequently.

The function of the i in state $[q, i, j]$ is to record the difference of the length of the current pushdown store and the length of the shortest pushdown store occurring since the last true input was used. The function of j is to count the number of moves that have been made since either a true input symbol was used or M' entered a configuration whose pushdown store was shorter than any occurring since M' last used a true input symbol. The state d is simply a dead state which will cause the input head to move to the end of the input.

For each i and j, where $0 \le i \le rst$ and $0 \le j \le s(t+1)^{rst}$, q in K, a in Σ, and Z in Γ, we define δ' as follows:

1. If $\delta(q, a, Z) = (p, \gamma)$, then $\delta'([q, i, j], a, Z) = ([p, 0, 0], \gamma)$.
2. If $\delta(q, \epsilon, Z) = (p, \gamma)$, then $\delta'([q, i, j], \epsilon, Z) = ([p, i + m - 1, j + 1], \gamma)$ where $m = |\gamma|$, unless $i + m - 1 < 0$, $i + m - 1 > rst$, or $j + 1 > s(t + 1)^{rst}$.

   Exception 1. If $i + m - 1 < 0$, then $\delta'([q, i, j], \epsilon, Z) = ([p, 0, 0], \gamma)$.

   Exception 2. If $i + m - 1 > rst$ or $j + 1 > s(t + 1)^{rst}$, then $\delta'([q, i, j], \epsilon, Z) = (d, Z)$.
3. $\delta'(d, a, Z) = (d, Z)$.

Rules 1 and 2 insure that M' will keep track of the quantities i and j properly. Exception 1 to Rule 2 causes i and j to be reset to zero each time the pushdown store becomes shorter than it has been since the last true input symbol was used. Exception 2 causes M' to detect a situation in which M will make an infinity of ϵ moves. Rule 3 causes M' to move its input head to the right end of the input whenever M reaches a point on the input from which it will never move to the right.

It is easy to check that M' is a dpda and satisfies the conditions of the lemma.

Theorem 12.1. The complement of a deterministic language is a deterministic language.

Proof. Let

$$M = (K, \Sigma, \Gamma, \delta, q_0, Z_0, F)$$

be a dpda satisfying Lemma 12.1. Let

$$M' = (K', \Sigma, \Gamma, \delta', q_0', Z_0, F')$$

be a dpda simulating M, where $K' = \{[q, k] | q \text{ in } K, k = 1, 2, \text{ or } 3\}$. Let

$$F' = \{[q, 3] | q \text{ in } K\}$$

and let

$$q_0' = \begin{cases} [q_0, 1], \text{ if } q_0 \text{ is in } F. \\ [q_0, 2], \text{ if } q_0 \text{ is not in } F. \end{cases}$$

The purpose of k in $[q, k]$ is to record, between true inputs, whether or not M has entered an accepting state. If M has entered an accepting state since the last true input, then $k = 1$. If M has not entered an accepting state since the last true input, then $k = 2$. If $k = 1$ when M reads a true input symbol, then M' uses the input symbol and changes k to 1 or 2, depending on whether the new state of M is or is not in F. If $k = 2$, M' changes k to 3 and then employs the input symbol M uses, changing k back to 1 or 2, depending on whether the new state of M is or is not in F. Thus, δ' is defined as follows, for q and p in K, and a in Σ.

1. If $\delta(q, \epsilon, Z) = (p, \gamma)$, then, for $k = 1$ or 2,

$$\delta'([q, k], \epsilon, Z) = ([p, k'], \gamma),$$

where $k' = 1$ if $k = 1$ or p is in F; otherwise $k' = 2$.

2. If $\delta(q, a, Z) = (p, \gamma)$, then

$$\delta'([q, 2], \epsilon, Z) = ([q, 3], Z)$$

and

$$\delta'([q, 1], a, Z) = \delta'([q, 3], a, Z) = ([p, k], \gamma),$$

where $k = 1$ or 2 for p in F and p not in F, respectively.

We claim that $T(M')$ is the complement of $T(M)$. Suppose that $a_1 a_2 \ldots a_n$ is in $T(M)$. Then M enters an accepting state after or upon using a_n as a true input. In that case, the second component of the state of M' will be 1 before it is possible for M' to use a true input after a_n. Therefore, M' does not accept (enter a state whose second component is 3) while a_n was the last true input used.

If $a_1 a_2 \ldots a_n$ is not in $T(M)$, by Lemma 12.1, M' will some time afterwards have no ϵ-moves to make and will have to use a true input symbol. But, at this time, the second component of M''s state is 2, since $a_1 a_2 \ldots a_n$ is not in $T(M)$. By Rule 2, M' will accept before using a true input symbol.

Before concluding this section we state the following corollary.

Corollary 12.1. Every deterministic language is accepted by some dpda which, in an accepting state, may make no move on ϵ input.

Proof. Implicit in the proof of Theorem 12.1. Note that in a final state (one in which $k = 3$) no ϵ-move is possible.

12.3 PROPERTIES OF DETERMINISTIC LANGUAGES

In addition to complement, the deterministic languages are closed under many of the operations under which cfl's are closed. One such simple operation is:

Theorem 12.2. If L is a deterministic language and R a regular set, then $L \cap R$ is a deterministic language.

Proof. From a dpda M and finite automaton A, we can create a new dpda M' whose finite control consists of the controls of M and A. M' accepts whenever both M and A accept. A schematic representation of M' is given in Fig. 12.1. The details of the proof are left to the reader.

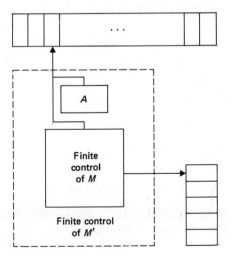

Fig. 12.1. Construction of dpda, M', from M and A.

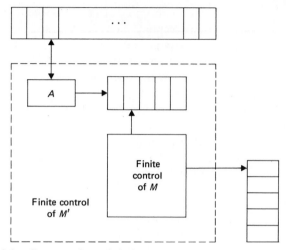

Fig. 12.2. Construction of dpda M', for the inverse gsm theorem.

We say that a gsm $A = (K_A, \Sigma, \Delta, \delta_A, q_0, F_A)$ is *deterministic* if, for each q in K_A and a in Σ, $\delta_A(q, a)$ contains at most one element. If (p, w) is in $\delta_A(q, a)$, we shall write $\delta_A(q, a) = (p, w)$, instead of $\delta_A(q, a) = \{(p, w)\}$.

Theorem 12.3. If L is a deterministic language and A a deterministic gsm mapping, then $A^{-1}(L)$ is a deterministic language.

Proof. A schematic construction of a dpda M' accepting $A^{-1}(L)$ from A, and a dpda M accepting L, is shown in Fig. 12.2. Essentially, M' passes its input through A and uses the resulting output of A as input to M. Outputs of A are stored in a buffer until they are used by M.

Formally, let

$$A = (K_A, \Sigma, \Delta, \delta_A, p_0, F_A),$$

and let

$$M = (K_M, \Delta, \Gamma, \delta_M, q_0, Z_0, F_M).$$

Assume, by Corollary 12.1, that M makes no ϵ input moves when in a final state, i.e., $\delta_M(q, \epsilon, Z) = \varphi$ for q in F_M and for Z in Γ. Let r be the maximum length of w in Δ^* such that $\delta_A(p, a) = (p_1, w)$ for some p and p_1 in K_A and a in Σ. Define

$$M' = (K, \Sigma, \Gamma, \delta, q_0', Z_0, F),$$

where K consists of all $[q, p, w]$ such that q is in K_M, p is in K_A, and w is in Δ^*, with $|w| \leq r$. Also $q_0' = [q_0, p_0, \epsilon]$, and

$$F = \{[q, p, \epsilon] | q \text{ is in } F_M \text{ and } p \text{ in } F_A\}.$$

For all q and q_1 in K_M, p and p_1 in K_A, a in Δ. w in Δ^*, b in Σ, γ in Γ^*, and Z in Γ, δ is defined by the following conditions.

1. If $\delta_M(q, \epsilon, Z) = \varphi$ and $\delta_A(p, b) = (p_1, w)$, then

$$\delta([q, p, \epsilon], b, Z) = ([q, p_1, w], Z).$$

(If M cannot move on ϵ input and the buffer is empty, M' simulates A.)

2. If $\delta_M(q, \epsilon, Z) = (q_1, \gamma)$, then

$$\delta([q, p, w], \epsilon, Z) = ([q_1, p, w], \gamma).$$

(M' simulates an ϵ-input move of M whenever possible. Note that q is not in F_M in this case.)

3. If $\delta_M(q, a, Z) = (q_1, \gamma)$, then

$$\delta([q, p, aw], \epsilon, Z) = ([q_1, p, w], \gamma).$$

(M' simulates a move of M using the leftmost buffer symbol as input. That symbol is removed from the buffer.)

It is easy to check that M' is a dpda. The reader can show by induction on the number of moves made by M or M' that x is in $T(M')$ if and only if $A(x) = y$ and y is in $T(M)$. The fact that M makes no ϵ-input moves in a final state is needed to handle the case in which some proper suffix of x, when used as input to A, yields ϵ output.

To prove that deterministic languages are closed under some other operations, we shall introduce what we call a predicting machine. If A is a finite automaton and M is a dpda, then a *predicting machine* for M and A, denoted by $\pi_A(M)$, is obtained from M by adding a second "track" to the pushdown store of M. The predicting machine $\pi_A(M)$ operates exactly as M, except whenever M writes a symbol Z on its pushdown store, $\pi_A(M)$, in addition to writing the symbol Z on its first track, writes a symbol on its second track whose use we explain below. Whenever M erases a symbol, $\pi_A(M)$ must erase the corresponding symbols on both tracks.

Let $A = (K_A, \Sigma, \delta_A, p_0, F_A)$ and $M = (K, \Sigma, \Gamma, \delta, q_0, Z_0, F)$. Define C as the set of maps from $K \times K_A$ to the set $\{0, 1\}$. The symbols that $\pi_A(M)$ writes on its second track correspond to maps in the set C.

If the pushdown store of M is $Z_i Z_{i-1} \ldots Z_1$, then the corresponding pushdown store of $\pi_A(M)$ will be $[Z_i, \alpha_i][Z_{i-1}, \alpha_{i-1}] \ldots [Z_1, \alpha_1]$. Here α_j is the map which, for q in K and p in K_A, has $\alpha_j(q, p) = 1$ if and only if there exists a w in Σ^* such that

$$w : (q, Z_{j-1} Z_{j-2} \ldots Z_1) \left|\frac{*}{M}\right. (q_f, \gamma)$$

for some q_f in F, and

$$\delta_A(p, w) = p_f$$

for some p_f in F_A. Otherwise, $\alpha_j(q, p) = 0$. In other words, $\alpha_j(q, p) = 1$ means that there exists an input sequence w, such that if M erases the jth symbol on its pushdown store and enters state q, then w will take M to an accepting configuration. Also, w takes the finite automaton from the state p to a final state.

Note that α_j depends only on the lowest $j - 1$st symbols on the pushdown store of M and not on the jth symbol. Our reason for defining α_j in this manner is to avoid having to change α_j in the case in which M changes only the top symbol on its pushdown store.

It is not obvious that $\pi_A(M)$ exists, that there is an effective procedure for constructing $\pi_A(M)$ from A and M, or that $\pi_A(M)$ is deterministic. This will be the essence of our next lemma. Since the construction of $\pi_A(M)$ is somewhat complicated, a detailed example is given in Example 12.2.

Lemma 12.2. For a finite automaton, $A = (K_A, \Sigma, \delta_A, p_0, F_A)$, and a dpda, $M = (K, \Sigma, \Gamma, \delta, q_0, Z_0, F)$, there is an effective procedure for constructing a predicting machine, $\pi_A(M)$. Furthermore, $\pi_A(M)$ is a deterministic pda.

Proof. Let $M' = (K, \Sigma, \Gamma \times C, \delta', q_0, Z'_0, F)$. C is the set of maps from $K \times K_A$ to the set $\{0, 1\}$. For q in K, a in $\Sigma \cup \{\epsilon\}$, Z in Γ, and α in C, we define δ' as follows.

1. If $\delta(q, a, Z) = (q', \epsilon)$, then $\delta'(q, a, [Z, \alpha]) = (q', \epsilon)$.
2. If $\delta(q, a, Z) = (q', Z_1 Z_2 \ldots Z_r)$, then

$$\delta'(q, a, [Z, \alpha]) = (q', [Z_1, \alpha_1][Z_2, \alpha_2] \ldots [Z_r, \alpha_r]),$$

where $\alpha_1, \alpha_2, \ldots, \alpha_r$ are appropriate tables.

The key to the proof is to show that, for $i \leq r$, α_{i-1} can be computed from Z_i and α_i. Of course, $\alpha_r = \alpha$. Suppose that we wish to compute $\alpha_{i-1}(q_1, p_1)$ for some q_1 in K and p_1 in K_A. There are two reasons why $\alpha_{i-1}(q_1, p_1)$ could be 1. Either M could reach an accepting state without ever erasing Z_i or its successors, or M will reach an accepting state after erasing Z_i or one of its successors.†

In the first case, consider

$$M_{q_1 Z_i} = (K, \Sigma, \Gamma, \delta, q_1, Z_i, F).$$

That is, M with q_1 as start state and Z_i as start symbol. Also, consider

$$A_{p_1} = (K_A, \Sigma, \delta_A, p_1, F_A).$$

There will exist w in Σ^* with $\delta_A(p_1, w)$ in F_A and $w: (q_1, Z_i) \overset{*}{\underset{M}{\vdash}} (q', \gamma)$ for some q' in F and γ in Γ^*, if and only if $T(A_{p_1}) \cap T(M_{q_1 Z_i}) \neq \varphi$. But, by

---

† By "successor," we refer to a symbol which is printed by M in the position on the pushdown store which Z_i held, without prior erasure of the symbol in that position. For example, in Rule 2 above, Z_r is the successor of Z.

Theorem 9.4, $T(A_{p_1}) \cap T(M_{q_1 Z_i})$ is certainly a cfl, and there is an algorithm to decide if a cfl is empty.

In the second case, $\alpha_{i-1}(q_1, p_1) = 1$ if there exist w_1 and w_2 in Σ^* with

1. $\delta_A(p_1, w_1) = p_2$ for some p_2 in K_A,
2. $\delta_A(p_2, w_2)$ in F_A,
3. $w_1 : (q_1, Z_i) \underset{M}{\overset{|*}{\longmapsto}} (q_2, \epsilon)$ for some q_2 in K, and
4. $w_2 : (q_2, \gamma_i) \underset{M}{\overset{|*}{\longmapsto}} (q_3, \gamma')$ for some q_3 in F and γ' in Γ^*, where γ_i is the contents of the pushdown tape after Z_i is erased.

For p_2 and q_2, α_i tells us of the existence of w_2 satisfying (2) and (4). Thus the actual value of γ_i is irrelevant, since α_i contains the necessary information about γ_i. To test for the existence of w_1 satisfying (1) and (3), it is sufficient to note that, for fixed p_2 and q_2, the set of w_1 satisfying (1) is regular, and that the set of w_1 satisfying (3) is context free, so those w_1 satisfying both (1) and (3) form a context-free language. Thus there are algorithms to determine, for any q_2 and p_2, whether w_1 and w_2 satisfying (1) through (4) exist. If any such w_1 and w_2 exist for any q_2 and p_2, then $\alpha_{i-1}(q_1, p_1) = 1$.

We must choose Z_0' properly to initialize the induction. From what has gone before, it is clear that $Z_0' = [Z_0, \alpha_0]$, where $\alpha_0(q, p) = 1$ if q is in F and p is in F_A. For all other q and p, $\alpha_0(q, p) = 0$.

Note that the addition of the mapping (element of C) on the second track does not affect the computation of M. That is, if we ignore the table, the configurations of $\pi_A(M)$ are exactly the configurations of M.

Example 12.2

$$M = (\{q_0, q_1, q_2, q_3\}, \{0, 1\}, \{X, Z_0\}, \delta, q_0, Z_0, \{q_3\}),$$

where

$$\delta(q_0, 0, Z_0) = (q_0, XZ_0) \qquad \delta(q_1, 0, X) = (q_2, \epsilon)$$
$$\delta(q_0, 0, X) = (q_0, XX) \qquad \delta(q_2, 0, X) = (q_2, \epsilon)$$
$$\delta(q_0, 1, X) = (q_1, XX) \qquad \delta(q_2, \epsilon, Z_0) = (q_3, \epsilon)$$
$$\delta(q_1, 1, X) = (q_1, XX)$$
$$T(M) = \{0^i 1^j 0^k \mid i, j > 0, i + j = k\}$$

$$A = (\{p_0, p_1\}, \{0, 1\}, \delta_A, p_0, \{p_0\})$$
$$\delta_A(p_0, 0) = p_1 \qquad \delta_A(p_0, 1) = p_0$$
$$\delta_A(p_1, 0) = p_0 \qquad \delta_A(p_1, 1) = p_1$$
$$T(A) = \{1, 01^*0\}^*$$

Figure 12.3 shows the pushdown store of $\pi_A(M)$ after the input 00011. Each pushdown symbol of $\pi_A(M)$ can be thought of as a pushdown symbol of M (the leftmost column in Fig. 12.3) plus an array of eight 0's and 1's

$$M(q, p)$$

| | q_0 | | q_1 | | q_2 | | q_3 | |
	p_0	p_1	p_0	p_1	p_0	p_1	p_0	p_1
X	1	1	1	1	1	0	1	0
X	1	1	1	1	0	1	1	0
X	1	1	1	1	1	0	1	0
X	1	1	1	1	0	1	1	0
X	1	1	0	0	1	0	1	0
Z_0	0	0	0	0	0	0	1	0

Track 1   Track 2

Fig. 12.3. Pushdown store of $\pi_A(M)$ after input 00011.

representing $\alpha(q, p)$ for the four possible values of q (q_0, q_1, q_2, or q_3) and two values of p (p_0 or p_1). The bottom symbol on the pushdown store is $[Z_0, \alpha_0]$, where $\alpha_0(q_3, p_0) = 1$, since q_3 and p_0 are accepting states of M and A, respectively, and $\alpha_0(q, p) = 0$ for all other pairs of q and p. The symbol second from the bottom is $[X, \alpha_1]$ where α_1 is computed as follows. First, if X were erased, the contents of the pushdown store would be Z_0. The first reason why $\alpha_1(q, p)$ might be 1 is if some w takes the configuration (q, Z_0) to a final configuration without erasing Z_0 and takes state p of A to the final state p_0. A careful inspection of M shows that M can enter a final configuration only by erasing Z_0. Thus, $\alpha(q, p)$ would never be 1 for this first reason, except for the degenerate case where q and p are accepting states.

The second reason why $\alpha_1(q, p)$ might be 1 is if, for some w,

$$w : (q, Z_0) \left|\frac{*}{M}\right. (q', \epsilon) \qquad \text{and} \qquad \delta_A(p, w) = p',$$

where $\alpha_0(q', p') = 1$. Thus, $\alpha_1(q_0, p_0) = 1$, since any string in $\{0^i 1^j 0^k \,|\, i, j > 0, i + j = k\}$ takes configuration (q_0, Z_0) to (q_3, ϵ) and any string in $\{1, 01*0\}*$ takes state p_0 of A to the final state p_0. The intersection of $\{0^i 1^j 0^k \,|\, i, j > 0, i + j = k\}$ and $\{1, 01*0\}*$ contains the sentence 011000. Similar reasoning implies that $\alpha_1(q_0, p_1) = 1$ and $\alpha_1(q_2, p_0) = 1$.

The maps α_2 and α_3 can be calculated in exactly the same manner using the information summarized below.

$$x : (q_0, X) \left|\frac{*}{M}\right. (q_2, \epsilon), \qquad \text{for } x \text{ in } \{0^i 1^j 0^{i+j+1} \,|\, i, j > 0\}.$$

$$x : (q_1, X) \left|\frac{*}{M}\right. (q_2, \epsilon), \qquad \text{for } x \text{ in } \{1^i 0^{i+1} \,|\, i \geq 0\}.$$

$$x : (q_2, X) \left|\frac{*}{M}\right. (q_2, \epsilon), \qquad \text{if and only if } x = 0.$$

Before proceeding, we wish to present one more lemma. The lemma asserts that we can define acceptance for a dpda by a combination of state and the top pushdown symbol; the language so defined is still a deterministic language.

Lemma 12.3. Let $M = (K, \Sigma, \Gamma, \delta, q_0, Z_0, F)$ be a dpda. Let B be any subset of $K \times \Gamma$, i.e., pairs of state and tape symbol. Define $L = \{w | w : (q_0, Z_0) \overset{|*}{\underset{|M}{}} (q, Z\gamma)$ for some (q, Z) in $B\}$. Then L is a deterministic language.

Proof. We define a dpda M', accepting L, as follows.

$$M' = (K', \Sigma, \Gamma, \delta', q_0, Z_0, F'),$$

where
$$K' = \{q, q', q'' | q \text{ in } K\} \quad \text{and} \quad F' = \{q'' | q \text{ in } K\}.$$

M' makes the same moves as M, except that M' moves from an unprimed state to a singly-primed state and then, on ϵ input, moves back to the corresponding unprimed state, either directly or through a doubly-primed version. The latter case applies only if the pair of state and top symbol of the pushdown store is in B.

Formally, if $\delta(q, a, Z) = (p, \gamma)$, then $\delta'(q, a, Z) = (p', \gamma)$.

For all q and Z such that (q, Z) is not in B, $\delta'(q', \epsilon, Z) = (q, Z)$.

For all (q, Z) in B, $\delta'(q', \epsilon, Z) = (q'', Z)$ and $\delta'(q'', \epsilon, Z) = (q, Z)$.

The reason for having three versions of each state is to ensure that M' is deterministic.

In Chapter 9 we defined the quotient of L_1 with respect to L_2, denoted L_1/L_2, as

$$\{x_1 | \text{ There exists } x_2 \text{ in } L_2 \text{ such that } x_1 x_2 \text{ is in } L_1\}.$$

In Theorem 9.13 we proved that the cfl were closed under quotient with a regular set. We shall now prove a similar result for deterministic languages.

Theorem 12.4. Let L be a deterministic language and R a regular set. The L/R is a deterministic language.

Proof. Let $M = (K, \Sigma, \Gamma, \delta, q_0, Z_0, F)$ be a dpda which never empties its pushdown store, with $T(M) = L$ and let $A = (K_A, \Sigma, \delta_A, p_0, F_A)$ be an fa with $T(A) = R$. Let $M' = \pi_A(M)$ be a predicting machine for M and A as in Lemma 12.2.

Using the same notation as in Lemma 12.2,

$$M' = (K, \Sigma, \Gamma', \delta', q_0, Z_0', F).$$

In addition, $\Gamma' = \Gamma \times C$, where C is the set of maps from $K \times K_A$ to $\{0, 1\}$. We also use the notation M_{qz} for the dpda obtained from M by using q for the initial state and Z for start symbol. That is, $M_{qz} = (K, \Sigma, \Gamma, \delta, q, Z, F)$.

Suppose that

$$w_1 : (q_0, Z'_0) \mathrel{\underset{M'}{\overset{*}{\vdash}}} (q, [Z, \alpha]\gamma).$$

Now w_1 is in L/R if and only if there is a w_2 in R such that w_2 takes M' from configuration $(q, [Z, \alpha]\gamma)$ to an accepting configuration. This can happen in one of two ways:

1. There is a w_2 in R such that $w_2 : (q, [Z, \alpha]) \mathrel{\underset{M'}{\overset{*}{\vdash}}} (q_1, \gamma_1)$ for some q_1 in F. This situation corresponds to the case where M', from configuration $(q, [Z, \alpha]\gamma)$, accepts without ever having a pushdown tape shorter than $|\gamma| + 1$, except perhaps on the last move, in which case $\gamma_1 = \epsilon$. Since M' makes exactly the moves of M, if we ignore the tables on the pushdown store, such a w_2 will exist if $R \cap T(M_{qZ}) \neq \varphi$, a condition that can be decided for any q and Z.

2. a) There is a w_2 in Σ^* such that

$$\delta_A(p_0, w_2) = p_1$$

for some p_1 in K_A and

$$w_2 : (q, [Z, \alpha]) \mathrel{\underset{M'}{\overset{*}{\vdash}}} (q_1, \epsilon)$$

for some q_1 in K. (The set of all such w_2 is a context-free language, as was mentioned in the proof of Lemma 12.2. Hence, for any p_1 and q_1, the existence of w_2 can be decided.) Also,

b) There is a w_3 in Σ^* such that $\delta_A(p_1, w_3)$ is in F_A and

$$w_3 : (q_1, \gamma) \mathrel{\underset{M'}{\overset{*}{\vdash}}} (q_2, \gamma')$$

for some q_2 in F. (The existence of such a w_3 is equivalent to $\alpha(q_1, p_1) = 1$.)

Let us, therefore, define the set $B \subseteq K \times \Gamma'$ by $(q, [Z, \alpha])$ is in B if either:

i. $R \cap T(M_{qZ}) \neq \varphi$ (Condition 1 above) or,

ii. For some p_1 in K_A and q_1 in K, $\alpha(q_1, p_1) = 1$, and there exists w_2 such that

$$\delta_A(p_0, w_2) = p_1 \qquad \text{and} \qquad w_2 : (q, [Z, \alpha]) \mathrel{\underset{M'}{\overset{*}{\vdash}}} (q_1, \epsilon).$$

(Condition 2 above.)

But we have seen that, under this definition of B, the set

$$\{w \mid w : (q_0, Z'_0) \mathrel{\underset{M'}{\overset{*}{\vdash}}} (q, [Z, \alpha]\gamma) \text{ for } (q, [Z, \alpha]) \text{ in } B\}$$

is exactly L/R. Hence, L/R is a deterministic language by Lemma 12.3.

So far we have noted that the operations of intersection with regular set, inverse deterministic gsm mapping, and quotient with a regular set preserve deterministic languages as well as context-free languages. It is trivial to show that deterministic languages are not closed under deterministic gsm mappings. The proof is left as an exercise.

We now introduce two operations which preserve deterministic languages but not arbitrary cfl's.

Let L be a language. Then

$$\text{Min} \, (L) = \{x \mid x \text{ is in } L \text{ and no } w \text{ in } L \text{ is a proper prefix of } x\}.$$

Also,

$$\text{Max} \, (L) = \{x \mid x \text{ is in } L \text{ and } x \text{ is not a proper prefix of any word in } L\}.$$

As an example, let

$$L = \{0^i 1^j 0^k \mid i, j > 0, \, i + j \geq k\}.$$

Then $\text{Min} \, (L) = 00^*1$ and $\text{Max} \, (L) = \{0^i 1^j 0^{i+j} \mid i, j > 0\}$.

Theorem 12.5. If L is a deterministic language, then $\text{Min} \, (L)$ and $\text{Max} \, (L)$ are deterministic languages.

Proof. Let $M = (K, \Sigma, \Gamma, \delta, q_0, Z_0, F)$ be a dpda with $T(M) = L$. To accept $\text{Min} \, (L)$, one simply introduces a new "dead state" p, which is non-accepting. The dpda M'', accepting $\text{Min} \, (L)$, simulates M until M enters an accepting state. Then M'' transfers to state p and can accept no subsequent input.

$\text{Max} \, (L)$ is more difficult. Let A be the finite automaton $(\{p_0\}, \Sigma, \delta_A, p_0, \{p_0\})$ accepting Σ^*. That is, $\delta_A(p_0, a) = p_0$ for all a in Σ. Let

$$M' = \pi_A(M) = (K, \Sigma, \Gamma', \delta', q_0, Z_0', F),$$

where M', Γ', Z_0', and δ' are as in Lemma 12.2.

Define the set $B \subseteq K \times \Gamma'$ as follows. $(q, [Z, \alpha])$ is in B if all three of the conditions below hold.

1. q is in F.
2. $T(M_{qZ}) = \varphi$. (M_{qZ} is as defined in Lemma 12.2.)
3. For no q_1 in K is there a w_1 in Σ^* such that

$$w_1 : (q, [Z, \alpha]) \mathrel{\vdash^*_{M'}} (q_1, \epsilon) \qquad \text{and} \qquad \alpha(q_1, p_0) = 1.$$

By Lemma 12.3, there is a dpda accepting

$$L' = \{w \mid w : (q_0, Z_0') \mathrel{\vdash^*_{M'}} (q, [Z, \alpha]\gamma) \text{ for } (q, [Z, \alpha]) \text{ in } B\}.$$

Condition 1 ensures that w is in L' only if w is in L. Conditions 2 and 3 together ensure that there is no w_2 in Σ^* such that ww_2 is in L. That is, $L' = \text{Max} \, (L)$.

12.4 CONTEXT-FREE LANGUAGES THAT ARE NOT DETERMINISTIC

It should be evident that not every cfl is a deterministic language. There are several operations which preserve deterministic languages, but which transform an arbitrary cfl into a non-context-free language. The most obvious example is complementation. If a language L has a non-context-free complement, then L cannot be a deterministic language. We know of several languages that are context free, but whose complements are not. These languages are surely not deterministic. Several examples are given in the exercises.

Also, the operations Min and Max preserve deterministic languages, but not arbitrary context-free languages. Hence, if L is context free with either Min (L) or Max (L) not context free, then L is not deterministic. An example of this situation is given in the exercises.

Certain context-free languages such as $\{a^i b^j c^k | i = j \text{ or } j = k\}$ have been shown to be inherently ambiguous. As we shall see shortly, these languages cannot be deterministic.

Finally, we might add that certain ad-hoc methods appear in the literature for showing given cfl's not to be deterministic.

12.5 *LR(k)* GRAMMARS

Often one wishes to find a parse or derivation tree for a given sentence in a given grammar. One way to do this is to start with the terminal string and replace a substring of symbols by a variable from which the substring can be derived by one application of a production of the grammar. Then, using the resulting string, one repeats the process of replacing a substring of symbols by a variable until finally the sentence symbol S is obtained. Since, at each step, there are usually many substrings that can be replaced by a variable, one must often try a large number of possible choices. For certain classes of grammars this process can be carried out in a simple, deterministic manner. One such class of grammars is called $LR(k)$, which stands for left to right parsing with k symbol look-ahead.

Intuitively, we say a cfg $G = (V_N, V_T, P, S)$ is $LR(k)$ if for any sentential form α the following holds: There is a unique way to write $\alpha = \beta\gamma\delta$ such that there is a rightmost derivation,† $S \xrightarrow{*} \beta A\delta \Rightarrow \beta\gamma\delta$, A having been replaced by γ at the last step. Moreover, A and γ can be determined uniquely by scanning α from left to right up to a point at most k symbols beyond γ. To handle the situation where the k look-ahead symbols extend beyond the end of the sentence, we look at strings derivable from the string $S\$^k$ rather than S. Here, $\$$ is a new symbol which is assumed not to be in V_N or V_T.

---

† A rightmost derivation is one in which at each step the rightmost variable is replaced.

Thus, at the right end, a string of \$'s will serve to fill out the k look-ahead symbols and will help simplify notation.

Let us give a formal definition of an $LR(k)$ grammar. (In the definition and what follows, we shall use $\overset{*}{\underset{rt}{\Rightarrow}}$ and $\underset{rt}{\Rightarrow}$ to mean "derives by a rightmost derivation.") Let $G = (V_N, V_T, P, S)$, and let \$ not be in V_N or V_T. We say that G is $LR(k)$ if the following condition holds for every string $\alpha\beta w_1 w_2$,† with $|w_1| = k$, such that $S\$^k \overset{*}{\underset{rt}{\Rightarrow}} \alpha\beta w_1 w_2$. If the next to the last step of the above derivation is $\alpha A w_1 w_2$, so that

$$S\$^k \overset{*}{\underset{rt}{\Rightarrow}} \alpha A w_1 w_2 \underset{rt}{\Rightarrow} \alpha\beta w_1 w_2,$$

and there is some other word $\alpha\beta w_1 w_3$ such that

$$S\$^k \overset{*}{\underset{rt}{\Rightarrow}} \gamma B w \underset{rt}{\Rightarrow} \alpha\beta w_1 w_3,$$

then $\gamma = \alpha$, $A = B$, and $w = w_1 w_3$.

In other words, in the rightmost derivation of two strings which agree up to k symbols beyond the point of the last replacement, the strings at the next to last step in the derivations must also agree up to k symbols beyond the point of the last replacement.

Example 12.3. Consider the language $L = \{a^i b^j | j > i\}$. L is generated by the grammar

$$G_1 = (\{S\}, \{a, b\}, P_1, S),$$

where P_1 consists of $S \rightarrow aSb$, $S \rightarrow Sb$, $S \rightarrow b$. G_1 is not $LR(1)$. (In fact, G_1 is not $LR(k)$ for any k.) For example, let $\alpha = aa$, $\gamma = aaa$, $A = B = S$, $\beta = aSb$, $w_1 = b$, $w_2 = bb\$$, $w = bbbb\$$, and $w_3 = bbb\$$.

Then

$$S\$ \overset{*}{\underset{rt}{\Rightarrow}} \alpha A w_1 w_2 \underset{rt}{\Rightarrow} \alpha\beta w_1 w_2 = aaaSbbbb\$.$$

But it is also true that

$$S\$ \overset{*}{\underset{rt}{\Rightarrow}} \gamma B w \underset{rt}{\Rightarrow} \alpha\beta w_1 w_3 = aaaSbbbbb\$.$$

Since $\gamma \neq \alpha$, G_1 is not $LR(1)$.

Now consider grammar $G_2 = (\{S, C, D\}, \{a, b\}, P_2, S)$, where P_2 consists of $S \rightarrow CD$, $C \rightarrow aCb$, $C \rightarrow \epsilon$, $D \rightarrow Db$, $D \rightarrow b$. $L(G_2) = L$, and G_2 is $LR(1)$. It is seemingly difficult to prove that G_2 is $LR(1)$. However, we shall give a method for the proof later on.

---

† Recall our convention: Greek letters are strings in V^*, lower case letters, in V_T^*, and upper case letters, in V_N.

Note that the essential difference between G_1 and G_2 is that, in G_1, productions that generate an a and a b or a b alone can be used alternately, while, in G_2, all uses of the production generating an a and a b must precede the uses of a production generating only a b. It is this "determinism," in an informal sense, that makes G_2 $LR(1)$ while G_1 is not $LR(k)$ for any k.

In the remainder of this section we show that:

1. Every $LR(k)$ grammar is unambiguous.
2. There is an algorithm to determine if a cfg is $LR(k)$ for a given k.
3. Every $LR(k)$ grammar generates a deterministic language.
4. Every deterministic language is generated by some $LR(1)$ grammar. (Thus a language is $LR(1)$ if and only if it is $LR(k)$ for some k.)

Theorem 12.6. If G is an $LR(k)$ grammar, then G is unambiguous.

Proof. The theorem follows immediately from the following two observations. First, if every sentence generated has a unique rightmost derivation, then it has a unique derivation tree; hence, a unique leftmost derivation, and so the grammar is unambiguous. Second, if in the definition of $LR(k)$ we consider the situation where $w_3 = w_2$, we see that, for a rightmost derivation of a given sentential form, the next to last line is unique. Hence, by induction on the number of steps in a derivation, the rightmost derivation is unique.

We now develop a procedure for determining if a cfg is $LR(k)$ for some fixed k. First we need the following technical result. Let $G = (V_N, V_T, P, S)$ be a cfg [not necessarily $LR(k)$] with productions in P numbered from 1 to r. Let \$ not be in V_N or V_T. For $1 \le i \le r$, w_1 in $V_T^*\$*$, and $|w_1| = k$, let the set $R_k(i, w_1)$ be defined as follows. Assume that $A \to \beta$ is the ith production in P. Then $R_k(i, w_1)$ consists of all strings γ such that γ is of the form $\alpha\beta w_1$ and there exists w_2 in $V_T^*\$*$ for which

$$S\$^k \xrightarrow[rt]{*} \alpha A w_1 w_2 \xrightarrow[rt]{} \alpha\beta w_1 w_2.$$

Lemma 12.4. The set $R_k(i, y)$ defined above is regular for any cfg G.

Proof. Surely one can assume that every variable of G derives some terminal string. Define a grammar

$$G' = (V_N', V_T', P', S'),$$

where $V_T' = V_N \cup V_T$, $S' = [S, \$^k]$, and V_N' consists of all objects of the form $[A, w]$, where A is in V_N, w is in $V_T^*\$*$, and $|w| = k$. We define P' as follows. Suppose that $A \to B_1 B_2 \dots B_m$ is in P, with each B_i, $1 \le i \le m$, in $V_N \cup V_T$. Suppose that for some particular j, $1 \le j \le m$, B_j is in V_N. Then

1. $[A, w] \to B_1 B_2 \dots B_{j-1}[B_j, w']$ is in P' for each w' of length k such that for some w'', $B_{j+1} B_{j+2} \dots B_m w \xrightarrow[G]{*} w'w''$.

2. If $C \to \delta$ is the ith production of P, then $[C, y] \to \delta y$ is in P'.

Note that every production of G' is of the form $C \to xD$ or $C \to x$, where C and D are variables and x is a terminal string (possibly ϵ). While strictly speaking, G' is not a type 3 grammar, it is easy to show, using techniques similar to Theorems 4.4 and 4.5, that $L(G')$ is a regular set. We must show that $L(G') = R_k(i, y_1)$. It suffices to show that:

$$[S, \$^k] \xrightarrow[G']{*} \alpha[A, w_1] \text{ if and only if for some } w_2, \ S\$^k \xrightarrow[rt]{*} \alpha A w_1 w_2. \qquad (*)$$

We prove (*) by induction on the number of steps in a derivation. For derivations of one step, (*) is certainly trivial in both directions.

if: Assume that (*) is true for derivations of up to r steps. Let $S\$^k \xrightarrow[rt]{*} \alpha A w_1 w_2$ by a derivation of $r + 1$ steps. Let the next to last step be $\gamma B w_3 w_4 \Rightarrow \gamma \beta w_3 w_4$ where $|w_3| = k$ and B is replaced by β. There are two cases to consider, one in which β is not V_T^*; the other in which β is in V_T^*.

In the first case, we can write β as $\beta_1 A w_5$, where $\alpha = \gamma \beta_1$ and $w_1 w_2 = w_5 w_3 w_4$. A straightforward application of the definition of P' tells us that $[B, w_3] \to \beta_1[A, w_1]$ is a production of P'. By the inductive hypothesis, $[S, \$^k] \xrightarrow[G']{*} \gamma[B, w_3]$. Thus, $[S, \$^k] \xrightarrow[G']{*} \alpha[A, w_1]$.

In the second case, let γ be of the form $\gamma_1 A y_1$. At some step in the derivation of $\alpha A w_1 w_2$, A must have been generated by some production $D \to \gamma_2 A \gamma_3$. Then, by the inductive hypothesis, $[S, \$^k] \xrightarrow[G']{*} \gamma_4[D, y_2]$, where y_2 is an appropriate string of terminals and $\gamma_1 = \gamma_4 \gamma_2$. There exists a string y_3 in V_T^* such that $\gamma_3 \xrightarrow[G]{*} y_3$ and $y_3 y_2$ is a prefix of $w_1 w_2$. But then, by the rules of construction of P', $[D, y_2] \to \gamma_2[A, w_1]$ is in P'. Note also that $\gamma_1 = \alpha$. Therefore, $[S, \$^k] \xrightarrow[G']{*} \alpha[A, w_1]$.

only if: The inductive step in this direction is straightforward, and is left to the reader.

Lemma 12.5. Let G be a context-free grammar. Then G is $LR(k)$ if and only if, for any ψ, θ, y, and z; ψ in $R_k(i, y)$ and $\psi\theta$ in $R_k(j, z)$ imply that $\theta = \epsilon$ and $i = j$.

Proof (if): Assume that ψ in $R_k(i, y)$ and $\psi\theta$ in $R_k(j, z)$ imply that $i = j$ and $\theta = \epsilon$. Let $A \to \beta$ and $B \to \delta$ be the ith and jth productions, respectively. Suppose that

$$S\$^k \xrightarrow[rt]{*} \alpha A w_1 w_2 \xrightarrow[rt]{} \alpha \beta w_1 w_2 \quad \text{and} \quad S\$^k \xrightarrow[rt]{*} \gamma B w \xrightarrow[rt]{} \gamma \delta w,$$

where $|w_1| = k$ and $\gamma \delta w$ can be written in the form $\alpha \beta w_1 w_3$. To show that G is $LR(k)$, we must show that $\gamma = \alpha$, $A = B$, and $w = w_1 w_3$.

Let w_4 be the first k symbols of w. Then $\alpha\beta w_1$ is in $R_k(i, w_1)$ and $\gamma\delta w_4$ is in $R_k(j, w_4)$. Moreover, since $\gamma\delta w = \alpha\beta w_1 w_3$, either $\gamma\delta w_4$ is a prefix of $\alpha\beta w_1$, or vice versa. In either case, we may conclude by hypothesis that $\gamma\delta w_4 = \alpha\beta w_1$ and $i = j$. Therefore, $A = B$ and $\delta = \beta$. It then follows that $\gamma = \alpha$ and $w_4 = w_1$, proving that G is $LR(k)$.

Proof (only if): Assume that G is $LR(k)$ and that, for some ψ, θ, i, and j, ψ is in $R_k(i, y)$ and $\psi\theta$ is in $R_k(j, z)$. (The case $\theta = \epsilon$ and $i = j$ is not ruled out. We show, in fact, that these relations must hold.) Let $A \to \beta$ and $B \to \delta$ be the ith and jth productions, respectively. Since ψ is in $R_k(i, y)$, we can write ψ as $\alpha\beta y$, where

$$|y| = k \quad \text{and} \quad S\$^k \xrightarrow[rt]{*} \alpha A y w_1 \underset{rt}{\Rightarrow} \alpha\beta y w_1,$$

for some w_1. Also, we can write $\psi\theta$ as $\gamma\delta z$, where

$$|z| = k \quad \text{and} \quad S\$^k \xrightarrow[rt]{*} \gamma B z w_2 \underset{rt}{\Rightarrow} \gamma\delta z w_2$$

for some w_2. But $\alpha\beta y$ is a prefix of $\gamma\delta z$, and therefore, of $\gamma\delta z w_2$. Since G is $LR(k)$, we have $\alpha = \gamma$, $A = B$, $\delta = \beta$, and $y = z$. It immediately follows that $i = j$ and $\theta = \epsilon$.

Theorem 12.7. There is an algorithm to determine whether a context-free grammar G is $LR(k)$ for a given k.

Proof. By Lemmas 12.4 and 12.5, it is sufficient to give an algorithm to test whether one of two regular sets R_1 and R_2 over the alphabet Δ contains the prefix of a string in the other. The above is true if and only if

$$R = ((R_1/\Delta\Delta^*) \cap R_2) \cup ((R_2/\Delta\Delta^*) \cap R_1)$$

is nonempty. By Theorems 3.6 and 9.13, R is regular. There is an algorithm to test if R is empty by Theorem 3.11.

Theorem 12.8. If $G = (V_N, V_T, P, S)$ is an $LR(k)$ grammar, then $L(G)$ is a deterministic language.

Proof. We construct a dpda M that accepts the language $L = \{x\$^k | x$ in $L(G)\}$, where $\$$ is a special end marker symbol not in V.† Then, by Theorem 12.4, $L(G)$ is deterministic, since $L(G) = L/\$^k$.

Let l be the length of the longest right-hand side of a production of G. We allow the pda M to look at the top $k + l$ symbols on the pushdown store. Clearly, we could accomplish this by storing the top $k + l$ symbols in the finite control. However, for the sake of exposition, it is more convenient simply to think of M as having this added capability.

---

† Recall our convention that $V = V_N \cup V_T$.

The pda M will have two tracks. On track 1, M will write symbols from V. On track 2, M will store certain mappings. Let the productions of G be numbered 1 to r. Let $A_{i,w}$ be a finite automaton accepting $R_k(i, w)$. Let N_α be the mapping from $\{1, 2, \ldots, r\} \times \{w \mid w$ in $V_T^* \$*, |w| = k\}$ to states of the $A_{i,w}$'s such that $N_\alpha(i, w)$ is the state of $A_{i,w}$ after seeing the string α.

If track 1 of the pushdown list holds string $X_1 X_2 \ldots X_n$ in V^*, then track 2 will hold $N_{X_1} N_{X_1 X_2} \ldots N_{X_1 X_2 \ldots X_n}$. If P then writes the symbol Z on track 1, it will also write the symbol $N_{\alpha Z}$ on track 2. Surely $N_{\alpha Z}$ depends only on Z and N_α. In other words, the top symbol of track 2 will always contain the states that the finite automata $A_{i,w}$, for each i and w, would be in, if given the contents of track 1 as input.

In the following discussion, we describe how M manipulates the symbols on track 1 and implicitly assume that the symbols on track 2 are appropriately manipulated. To start, M reads k input symbols and places them on the pushdown store. Next M performs the following steps.

Step 1. If the top m symbols on track 1, for some $m \leq k + l$, are $B_1 B_2 \ldots B_{m-k} a_1 a_2 \ldots a_k$, if $A \to B_1 B_2 \ldots B_{m-k}$ is the ith production in P, and if the map N on track 2 with symbol a_k is such that $N(i, a_1 a_2 \ldots a_k)$ is a final state of $A_{i, a_1 a_2 \ldots a_k}$, then the top m symbols are erased and replaced by $A a_1 a_2 \ldots a_k$. Since G is $LR(k)$, Step 1 can be done in at most one way. Step 1 is repeated until no longer applicable.

Step 2. If Step 1 is not applicable, then another input symbol is read and placed on the top of the stack. Step 1 is then repeated.

If the stack of M ever reaches the configuration $S \$^k$, then M accepts. Now M is a dpda, and is easily shown to accept $L(G)$. Thus $L(G)$ is a deterministic language.

Finally, we show that every deterministic language has an $LR(k)$ grammar. In fact, we show that every deterministic language has an $LR(1)$ grammar. Moreover, it has an $LR(0)$ grammar, provided that we adopt the convention that we can recognize the end of the sentence by noting when the look-ahead symbol is blank. To be more precise, if L is a deterministic language, we consider the language $L\$$, where $\$$ is a special end marker symbol, and show that $L\$$ has an $LR(0)$ grammar.

Theorem 12.9. If L is a deterministic language, then there exists an $LR(0)$ grammar G such that $L(G) = L\$$.

Proof. Since $L\$$ is obviously deterministic, there is a deterministic pda M that accepts $L\$$. By Corollary 12.1, we may assume that M makes no ϵ move while in a final state. Moreover, since no initial portion of a sentence of $L\$$ is in $L\$$, we can assume that M accepts with an empty stack.

Construct the grammar G from M according to the method used in the proof of Theorem 5.3, throwing away all useless nonterminals. The claim is made that G is an $LR(0)$ grammar for $L\$$.

To see this, assume that

$$S \xrightarrow[rt]{*} \alpha A w_1 \xrightarrow[rt]{} \alpha \beta w_1 \tag{12.1}$$

and

$$S \xrightarrow[rt]{*} \gamma B w_2 \xrightarrow[rt]{} \gamma \delta w_2 = \alpha \beta w_3. \tag{12.2}$$

To show that G is $LR(0)$, we must show that $\alpha = \gamma$, $w_2 = w_3$, and $A = B$. There are two cases to consider

i. $|\gamma \delta| \leq |\alpha \beta|$. Then for some t, $\gamma \delta t = \alpha \beta$ and $w_2 = t w_3$.

ii. $|\gamma \delta| \geq |\alpha \beta|$. Then for some t', $\alpha \beta t' = \gamma \delta$ and $w_3 = t' w_2$.

The cases are symmetric, and we treat only case (i). We rewrite (12.2) as

$$S \xrightarrow[rt]{*} \gamma B t w_3 \xrightarrow[rt]{} \gamma \delta t w_3. \tag{12.3}$$

Let x_α and x_β be terminal strings derivable from α and β, respectively. Then from (12.1):

$$S \xrightarrow[rt]{*} \alpha A w_1 \xrightarrow[rt]{} \alpha \beta w_1 \xrightarrow{*} x_\alpha x_\beta w_1. \tag{12.4}$$

There is a leftmost derivation whose derivation tree is the same as that of (12.4), namely:

$$S \xrightarrow{*} x_\alpha A \psi_{w_1} \xrightarrow{} x_\alpha \beta \psi_{w_1} \xrightarrow{*} x_\alpha x_\beta \psi_{w_1} \xrightarrow{*} x_\alpha x_\beta w_1. \tag{12.5}$$

Here ψ_{w_1} is a string of variables such that $\psi_{w_1} \xrightarrow{*} w_1$ by a leftmost derivation. From (12.3),

$$S \xrightarrow[rt]{*} \gamma B t w_3 \xrightarrow[rt]{} \gamma \delta t w_3 \xrightarrow{*} x_\gamma x_\delta t w_3 = x_\alpha x_\beta w_2, \tag{12.6}$$

where x_γ and x_δ are strings derivable from γ and δ such that $x_\gamma x_\delta t = x_\alpha x_\beta$. Since $\gamma \delta t = \alpha \beta$, we can surely find such strings x_γ and x_δ.

Now, consider the leftmost derivation whose derivation tree is the same as that of (12.6), namely (with some obvious stages omitted)

$$S \xrightarrow{*} x_\gamma x_\delta t \psi_{w_3} \xrightarrow{*} x_\gamma x_\delta t w_3, \tag{12.7}$$

where ψ_{w_3} is some string such that $\psi_{w_3} \xrightarrow{*} w_3$ by a leftmost derivation.

The derivations (12.5) and (12.7) are leftmost, and the grammar G was obtained from a dpda. Thus we know that $\psi_{w_1} = \psi_{w_3}$ since ψ_{w_1} and ψ_{w_3} both represent the contents of the pushdown store immediately after the dpda has seen the input $x_\alpha x_\beta$ and before the dpda has made any move on ϵ-input.

From (12.7) and the fact that $\psi_{w_1} = \psi_{w_3}$ we know that there is a leftmost derivation

$$S \xrightarrow{*} x_\gamma B \theta \xrightarrow{} x_\gamma \delta \theta \xrightarrow{*} x_\gamma x_\delta t w_1 = x_\alpha x_\beta w_1. \tag{12.8}$$

Furthermore, the derivation trees corresponding to (12.5) and (12.8) must be the same, since each step in the derivations corresponds to a move of a dpda. Thus, the rightmost derivation†

$$S \underset{rt}{\overset{*}{\Rightarrow}} \gamma Btw_1 \underset{rt}{\Rightarrow} \gamma \delta tw_1 = \alpha\beta w_2 \tag{12.9}$$

must be the same derivation as (12.1). Hence $A = B$, $\alpha = \gamma$, $\delta = \beta$, $t = \epsilon$ and $w_2 = w_3$. Therefore G is $LR(0)$.

PROBLEMS

12.1 Give an example of a deterministic language L which is not $N(M)$ for any dpda M. Under what conditions is a language $N(M)$ for some dpda M?

12.2 Can every deterministic language be accepted by some dpda which makes no moves on ϵ input? Prove your answer.

12.3 In Fig. 12.3, what would be the contents of the pushdown tape if the input sequence were 01110?

12.4 For Example 12.2, write out the complete specification of $\pi_A(M)$.

12.5 Use the concept of a predictor machine to show that every deterministic language L is accepted by a dpda M, such that if $w = a_1a_2\ldots a_n$ is in L, then upon using a_n as input after using $a_1a_2\ldots a_{n-1}$, M immediately enters an accepting state.

12.6 Show the following not to be deterministic languages.
  a) $\{a^i b^j c^k | \text{either } i \neq j \text{ or } j \neq k\}$. *Hint.* Use Theorem 12.1.
  b) $\{ww^R | w \text{ in } \Sigma^*\}$. *Hint.* Use Theorem 12.5.
  c) $\{w_1 a w_2 b w_3 | a, b \text{ in } \Sigma, a \neq b, w_1, w_2, w_3 \text{ in } \Sigma^*, |w_2| = |w_1| + |w_3|\}$. *Hint.* Use Theorem 12.1.

12.7 Show that the following languages are deterministic.
  a) $\{wcw^R | w \text{ in } \{a, b\}^*\}$
  b) $\{c0^n 1^n | n \geq 1\} \cup \{0^n 1^{2n} | n \geq 1\}$
  c) $\{w | w \text{ in } \{a, b\}^*, w \text{ consists of an equal number of } a\text{'s and } b\text{'s}\}$

12.8 Prove that deterministic languages are not closed under gsm mappings.

12.9 Give $LR(1)$ grammars for the following languages.
  a) $\{w | w \text{ consists of an equal number of } a\text{'s and } b\text{'s}\}$
  b) $\{0^i 1^j | i > j\}$
  c) $\{wcxcw^R | w \text{ and } x \text{ in } \{a, b\}^*\} \cup \{wcxdx^R | w \text{ and } x \text{ in } \{a, b\}^*\}$

---

† The existence of a rightmost derivation $S \overset{*}{\underset{rt}{\Rightarrow}} \gamma Btw_1$ follows from the fact that there is a derivation $S \overset{*}{\Rightarrow} \gamma Btw_1$. Now, if there is no rightmost derivation of γBtw_1, then there must exist γ' such that $S \overset{*}{\underset{rt}{\Rightarrow}} \gamma' Btw_1$ and $\gamma' \overset{*}{\Rightarrow} \gamma$. From this we can deduce that there is a derivation $S \overset{*}{\underset{rt}{\Rightarrow}} \gamma' Btw_3$ and thus, (12.6) is not rightmost.

12.10 Show that the grammar $G = (\{A, B\}, \{a, b, c\}, P, A)$ is not $LR(k)$ for any k, where P consists of $A \rightarrow aAb$, $A \rightarrow ab$, $A \rightarrow Bc$, $B \rightarrow aBbb$, and $B \rightarrow abb$.

12.11 Prove that the grammar G_2 of Example 12.3 is $LR(1)$.

REFERENCES

The deterministic variety of pushdown automata were first studied by Fischer [1963], Schutzenberger [1963], Haines [1965], and Ginsburg and Greibach [1966a]. Lemma 12.1 was first proven in Schutzenberger [1963]. Its consequence —that deterministic languages are closed under complement—was observed independently by various authors. The closure of deterministic languages under the various operations of Section 12.3 appears in Ginsburg and Greibach [1966a]. $LR(k)$ grammars and their equivalence to deterministic languages is from Knuth [1965]. Theorem 12.6, which concerns the unambiguity of deterministic languages, was shown independently in Haines [1965] and Ginsburg and Greibach [1966a].

An interesting theorem—that there is an algorithm to determine if the language accepted by a dpda is regular—appears in Stearns [1967]. Various subfamilies of the deterministic languages have received consideration. Among these are the precedence languages (Floyd [1963]), bounded context languages (Floyd [1964a]), and simple deterministic languages (Korenjak and Hopcroft [1966]).

STACK AUTOMATA

13.1 DEFINITIONS

The stack automaton and its various restricted forms constitute a rich class of devices. The fundamental model is shown in Fig. 13.1. It consists of:

1. A finite control.
2. An input tape with end markers and a two-way input head. The input tape is read only.
3. A storage tape, or *stack*, which can be used like a pushdown store. The storage head cannot print or erase (print a blank) unless all the cells to its right are blank. However, the storage head may move anywhere on the nonblank portion of its tape in a read-only mode.

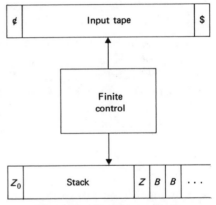

Fig. 13.1. Stack automaton.

The most general stack automation is nondeterministic, so in any situation it may have several choices of next move.

The stack automaton (referred to as an sa) can be thought of as a restricted type of nondeterministic Turing machine. One can also think of the sa as an extension of the pushdown automaton. The features which are added to the pda to get an sa are the ability of the input head to move both ways on the input and the ability to scan the pushdown list in a read-only mode. Note that while we have customarily considered the top of a pushdown list to be the left end, the top of the stack is at the right end. The formal notation for a stack automaton will resemble that for a Turing machine more than that for a pushdown automaton.

We give a formal notation for a *stack automaton* as an 8-tuple $S = (K, \Sigma, \Gamma, \delta, \delta_b, q_0, Z_0, F)$. The symbols have the following meanings.

K is the finite set of *states*.

Σ is the finite set of *input symbols*. Σ includes the *left and right end markers*, ¢ and $, respectively, which are assumed to be the first and last symbols of any input.

Γ is the finite set of nonblank *stack symbols*.

Z_0 is the *start symbol* and acts as a marker of left end of the stack.

F is the set of *final states*. $F \subseteq K$.

q_0 is the *start state*.

δ is a mapping from $K \times \Sigma \times \Gamma$ into subsets of $K \times \{L, R, S\} \times \{L, R, S\}$.

δ_b is a mapping from $K \times \Sigma \times \Gamma$ into subsets of $K \times \{L, R, S\} \times (\{L, S, E\} \cup \Gamma)$.

δ is the *next move mapping* for the condition when the storage head (which we call from now on the *stack head*) is not scanning a blank. Under this condition, the stack automaton may change state and move its two heads, so δ maps $K \times \Sigma \times \Gamma$ to the subsets of $K \times \{L, R, S\} \times \{L, R, S\}$.

The significance of (p, D_1, D_2) in $\delta(q, a, Z)$ is that, if S is in state q scanning a on its input tape and Z on its stack, it may go to state p and move its input and stack heads in directions D_1 and D_2, respectively. That is, if D_1 or D_2 has value L, R, or S, the relevant head will move to the left, to the right, or remain stationary, respectively.

δ_b is the *next move mapping* for the condition when the storage head is scanning a blank. It will always be the case that this blank is the leftmost blank on the stack. The leftmost blank will be called the *top of stack*. S has the choice of:

1. Printing a nonblank symbol and moving the stack head to the right, to the new top of stack.
2. Erasing the rightmost nonblank and moving the stack head to the left, to the new top of stack.
3. Moving its stack head to the left, into the nonblank portion of the stack.
4. Not moving the stack head.

While performing one of these four operations, S can change state and move its input head. We suppose that the next move can depend upon the rightmost nonblank symbol even though the stack head is not scanning it currently.

Thus we say that δ_b maps $K \times \Sigma \times \Gamma$ to the subsets of $K \times \{L, R, S\} \times (\{L, S, E\} \cup \Gamma)$. The significance of (p, D, X) in $\delta_b(q, a, Z)$ is that if S is in state q scanning a on its input tape and a blank on its stack, with the non-blank symbol Z immediately to the left, then S may enter state p, move its input head in direction D, and make the following motion of its stack head.

If $X = S$, no move of the stack head.

If $X = L$, the stack head moves to the left.

If $X = E$, the stack head moves to the left and prints a blank on the new cell scanned (i.e., the rightmost nonblank is erased). The cell now scanned becomes the new top of stack.

If X is a symbol of Γ, the stack head prints X over the blank and then moves to the right, to the new top of stack. We assume that X is not Z_0.

Note that the stack contents are always Z_0, followed by a nonblank string to the right and an infinite sequence of blanks to the right of that. We do not prevent S from completely erasing its tape, although it cannot make any further moves in that situation.

We define a *configuration* of a stack automaton, $S = (K, \Sigma, \Gamma, \delta, \delta_b, q_0, Z_0, F)$ with input w in $\text{¢}(\Sigma - \{\text{¢}, \$\})^*\$$, whose length is n, to be a combination of state of finite control, nonblank portion of the stack, and position of the stack and input heads. The configuration is denoted by (q, y, i, j), where q is in K, y is in Γ^*, i is an integer between 0 and $|y|$, and j is an integer between 1 and n. The position of the stack head is i cells to the left of the top of stack. That is, $i = 0$ if the head is at the top of stack, $i = 1$ if the head is at the rightmost nonblank, etc. The input head is scanning the jth symbol of w.

We say that

$$(q_1, y_1, i_1, j_1) \vert_{\overline{S,w}} (q_2, y_2, i_2, j_2)$$

if, with w as input, configuration (q_1, y_1, i_1, j_1) can become configuration (q_2, y_2, i_2, j_2) by a single move of S. Also, if (q_1, y_1, i_1, j_1) can go to (q_2, y_2, i_2, j_2) by some number of moves (including zero moves), we write

$$(q_1, y_1, i_1, j_1) \vert_{\overline{S,w}}^* (q_2, y_2, i_2, j_2).$$

S *accepts* an input w if the initial configuration, $(q_0, Z_0, 0, 1)$, is such that

$$(q_0, Z_0, 0, 1) \vert_{\overline{S,w}}^* (q, y, i, j)$$

for some q in F and any y, i, and j. We denote by $T(S)$ the set of inputs accepted by S.

Example 13.1. Let us construct a stack automaton to accept $\{\text{¢}wcw\$ \vert w$ in $\{a, b\}^*\}$. Let $S = (\{q_1, q_2, q_3\}, \{a, b, c, \text{¢}, \$\}, \{Z_0, A, B\}, \delta, \delta_b, q_1, Z_0, \{q_3\})$. Our approach will be to store on the stack everything found on the input tape to the left of c. The stack head then moves to the bottom of the stack (Z_0) and moves up the stack, comparing the subsequent input with the stack contents. If the $\$$ on the input is reached when the stack head reaches the top of stack, and all inputs have properly compared, S accepts. Formally, δ and δ_b are specified as follows:

1. $\delta_b(q_1, \text{¢}, Z_0) = \{(q_1, R, S)\}$. (Skip over ¢.)
2. $\delta_b(q_1, a, Z_0) = \delta_b(q_1, a, A) = \delta_b(q_1, a, B) = \{(q_1, R, A)\}$. (Store A on the stack if a is input.)

3. $\delta_b(q_1, b, Z_0) = \delta_b(q_1, b, A) = \delta_b(q_1, b, B) = \{(q_1, R, B)\}$. (Store B on the stack if b is input.)

4. $\delta_b(q_1, c, Z_0) = \delta_b(q_1, c, A) = \delta_b(q_1, c, B) = \{(q_1, S, L)\}$. (The stack head moves into the stack. The input head remains at c. It happens that no change of state is necessary, since only rules of δ, not δ_b, will apply while the stack head is in the stack.)

5. $\delta(q_1, c, A) = \delta(q_1, c, B) = \{(q_1, S, L)\}$. (The stack head continues to move down the stack, the input head remaining stationary.)

6. $\delta(q_1, c, Z_0) = \{(q_2, R, R)\}$. ($S$ changes to state q_2 on reaching the bottom of the stack. Also, S moves up the stack to the symbol above Z_0 and moves its input head right.)

7. $\delta(q_2, a, A) = \{(q_2, R, R)\}$. $\delta(q_2, b, B) = \{(q_2, R, R)\}$. ($S$ compares the input with the stack contents.)

8. $\delta_b(q_2, \$, Z_0) = \delta_b(q_2, \$, A) = \delta_b(q_2, \$, B) = \{(q_3, S, S)\}$. ($S$ accepts if all symbols match and the top of stack is reached.)

13.2 RESTRICTED TYPES OF STACK AUTOMATA

There are many interesting modifications which can be made upon stack automata. First, we can make the sa *deterministic*. The deterministic sa (dsa) has at most one choice of move in any situation.

If $S = (K, \Sigma, \Gamma, \delta, \delta_b, q_0, Z_0, F)$ is an sa such that, for no q, a, and Z, does $\delta_b(q, a, Z)$ contain a move of the form (p, D, E) for any D, then the sa is said to be *nonerasing*. Obviously, since no stack symbol is ever erased, a symbol once printed remains on the stack forever.

If, for no q, a, and Z, does $\delta_b(q, a, Z)$ contain a move of the form (p, L, X), nor does $\delta(q, a, Z)$ contain a move of the form (p, L, D) for any X or D, then the input head can never move to the left. We say that S is *one way*.

Note that the sa of Example 13.1 is deterministic, nonerasing, and one way. Unless otherwise stated, an sa (dsa) will be assumed to be a two-way, erasing sa (dsa).

13.3 THE POWER OF TWO-WAY STACK AUTOMATA

We would like to give informal proofs of a series of theorems to the effect that a dsa can recognize any context-sensitive language. We first show that a nonerasing dsa can simulate a deterministic lba, and, in fact, is equivalent to a Turing machine of tape complexity $n \log n$.

Next, we show that a deterministic, but erasing, sa can simulate a nondeterministic Tm of tape complexity class $n \log n$, and thus can certainly simulate any lba. Hence any context-sensitive language is accepted by a deterministic sa.

Theorem 13.1. If a language L is accepted by T, a deterministic single-tape Turing machine of tape complexity n,† then L is accepted by some nonerasing stack automaton. ‡

Proof. We can denote a configuration of T by $A_1 A_2 \ldots A_{i-1} q A_i \ldots A_n$. Here, $A_1 A_2 \ldots A_n$ is the contents of the tape cells upon which the input was originally placed, including T's end markers. The tape head is presumed to be scanning A_i, and the finite control is in state q. Suppose that such a configuration were written on the rightmost nonblank cells of the stack of S. We endeavor to show how S could construct, above this configuration of T on the stack, the configuration resulting from one move of T.

Essential to the construction of the new configuration is the ability of the stack head to find its way exactly n cells below the top of stack. Starting at the top, with the input head at the left end marker, S alternately moves its stack head one cell down the stack and its input head one cell to the right. When the right end marker of the input is reached, the stack head has reached the nth cell from the top of stack.

The new configuration is constructed by copying the old configuration symbol by symbol to the top of stack, modifying those symbols which are changed in the move of T.

Copying over tape symbols not involved in the move of T presents no problem. S moves n symbols down the stack, and one symbol more to find A_1. (Note that a configuration uses $n + 1$ cells because one is used for the state of T.) S stores A_1 in its finite control and moves to the top of stack, printing A_1. S again moves $n + 1$ cells down the stack. This time the stack head will be scanning A_2, which can be copied to the top of the stack. In succession then, by repeatedly moving $n + 1$ cells down the stack, each tape symbol of T can be copied to the top of stack.

However, we must not only copy the configuration, but also modify the configuration to simulate a move of T. After finding a tape symbol A of T, S must look at the cell to the right. If that cell holds a state of T, S must look another cell to the right to determine if T's head will move to the left. If so, the new state must be written at the top of stack before printing A. Then, above these, the symbol which T printed must be written; this makes a total of three symbols. Otherwise, the tape symbol is brought to the top of the stack in the normal way.

Also, upon moving $n + 1$ cells from the top of the stack, S may find itself scanning the state of T. S must record the state in the finite control and move one cell to the right to determine what symbol is scanned by T.

---

† For tape complexity equal to or greater than n, it should be clear that the restriction of a read-only input is unimportant. The model discussed in Chapter 10 can easily be simulated by a single tape T_m using the same number of cells.
‡ This theorem is for instruction only. We prove a more powerful result later.

It is not possible that T's head moves to the left, since, in this case, when copying the symbol to the left of the head, the new state and the symbol printed by T were also written on the top of stack.

To complete the proof, it is only necessary to state that S creates the initial configuration of T by printing the start state of T on the stack, and then copying the input onto the stack. Also, if during simulation, T enters one of its accepting states, S terminates simulation and accepts.

Before proving further results, it would be wise to develop a tool with which to describe the stack contents. We can think of the operation of the sa as a succession of moves at the top of stack (although printing and erasing may change the location of the top of stack) interspaced with sequences of moves in which the stack head remains below the top of stack. The sequence of moves whereby an sa raises its stack head from the rightmost nonblank to the top of stack will be called a "stack scan." Note that, before reaching the top of stack, the stack head may make an excursion deep into the stack.

Formally, a *stack scan* is a sequence of configurations (q_k, y_k, i_k, j_k), $0 \leq k \leq m$ such that

$$(q_k, y_k, i_k, j_k) \underset{S,w}{\big|\overline{}} (q_{k+1}, y_{k+1}, i_{k+1}, j_{k+1})$$

for each k between 0 and $m - 1$. Also, $i_0 = 1$, $i_m = 0$ and $i_k > 0$ if $0 < k < m$. We should add that S may also enter its stack and never return to the top. Perhaps S accepts within the stack, or halts without accepting, or enters an infinite loop.

For a given sa,

$$S = (K, \Sigma, \Gamma, \delta, \delta_b, q_0, Z_0, F)$$

and w in $\not\!\!c(\Sigma - \{\not\!\!c, \$\})^*\$$, with $|w| = n$, define the *transition table describing stack string* y to be a map from $K \times \{1, \ldots, n\}$ to subsets of $\{A, R\} \cup (K \times \{1, \ldots, n\})$, with the following meaning:

1. If α is the transition table, and $\alpha(q, j)$ contains A, then from configuration $(q, y, 1, j)$, S may accept without ever reaching the top of stack.
2. If $\alpha(q, j)$ contains R, then from configuration $(q, y, 1, j)$, S may enter an infinite loop or halt without reaching the top of stack.
3. If $\alpha(q, j)$ contains (p, k), then starting in configuration $(q, y, 1, j)$, S may make a stack scan, ending in configuration $(p, y, 0, k)$.

Informally, the transition table α tells us whether, given the configuration of S immediately after the stack head moves to the left from the top of stack, S will complete a stack scan, and if so, in what configurations S can be when first arriving at the top of stack. The transition table α also tells us if S can accept while below the top of stack.

In addition, if α is the transition table describing y, and yx is the stack of S, then α can be used to find what happens from the point at which S is started with its stack head at the rightmost symbol of y until the stack head reaches the leftmost symbol of x. The reason for this is that, while S's stack head is scanning the symbols of y, the operation of S does not depend on whether the top of stack or another stack symbol is to the right of y.

Suppose that, for input w, $|w| = n$, α describes stack y. Can we, for any Z in Γ, compute β, the transition table describing yZ, without knowing y, but knowing α, Z, and δ? The answer is yes, as we shall see.

Suppose that we wish to compute $\beta(q, j)$. S starts in configuration $(q, yZ, 1, j)$; that is, scanning the Z. Let S have s states. Suppose that $(q, yZ, 1, j) \left|\frac{*}{S,w}\right. (p, yZ, 0, k)$ by a sequence of moves in which the rightmost nonblank Z is scanned more than sn times before the top of stack is reached. Then there is a shorter sequence of moves making the same transition, for Z must have been twice scanned in the same state with the input head at the same position.

Therefore we compute a sequence of sets, $T_1, T_2, T_3, \ldots$, each contained in $K \times \{1, \ldots, n\}$. T_i will contain a pair (q_1, j_1) if and only if $(q, yZ, 1, j) \left|\frac{*}{S,w}\right.$ $(q_1, yZ, 1, j_1)$ by a sequence of moves for which the stack head never reaches the top of stack, and scans Z at most i times. From what has been said, a pair will not be in any T_i unless it is in T_{sn}.

Surely $T_1 = \{(q, j)\}$. We construct T_{i+1} from T_i, using α, δ, and Z to guide us. A pair (q_1, j_1) is in T_{i+1} if one of the three following conditions hold.

1. (q_1, j_1) is in T_i.
2. There is a (q_2, j_2) in T_i such that $(q_2, yZ, 1, j_2) \left|\frac{}{S,w}\right. (q_1, yZ, 1, j_1)$. ($\delta$ informs us of this condition.)
3. There is a (q_2, j_2) in T_i and some (q_3, j_3) such that $(q_2, yZ, 1, j_2) \left|\frac{}{S,w}\right.$ $(q_3, yZ, 2, j_3)$ (again, δ informs us of this possibility) and $\alpha(q_3, j_3)$ contains (q_1, j_1). (That is, the stack head will leave y, moving up the stack, in state q_1, with the input head at position j_1. Note that the fact that the top of stack is no longer immediately adjacent to y is irrelevant.)

Finally, for each (q_1, j_1) in T_{sn}, δ tells us in what pairs of state and input position S can reach the current top of stack on a single move.

In a similar manner, one can determine if A or R is in $\beta(q, j)$ for any j.

Observe that, if we know the rightmost nonblank and the transition table associated with the entire stack, we can, in a sense, simulate S, if S is non-erasing. The δ_b function tells us what moves can be made at the top of stack. If a move to the left from the top of stack is made, the transition table tells us in what combination of state and input head position S may return to the top of stack. If a new stack symbol is printed, we may construct the new transition table from δ, the symbol printed, and the old transition table. The reason we cannot so simulate an erasing sa is that when a symbol is erased, we are not necessarily able to construct the old transition table.

Suppose that we were to attempt to simulate a nonerasing stack automaton S by a Turing machine. We might ask how much space would be necessary to store the transition table associated with the stack contents. To completely specify the transition table, we must specify it for sn arguments, where s is the number of states and n the length of the input. When we specify the transition table for a given argument, we must tell whether A, R, and each of the sn pairs of state and input position are or are not in the set which is the value of the transition table for the argument in question. The information can be given by a binary array of length $2 + sn$. That is, each cell represents either A, R, or a state-position pair. It holds 1 if what it represents is in the set; 0, otherwise.

Therefore we can represent an entire transition table by sn arrays each of length $2 + sn$. The total number of cells is thus $s^2n^2 + 2sn$. This number is surely bounded above by $3s^2n^2$.

In addition, suppose that S is a deterministic nonerasing sa. Then if α is a transition table, $\alpha(q, j)$ can have only one element, either A, R, or a state-position pair. By encoding these in binary, the value of $\delta(q, j)$ can be represented in $\log_2 (2 + sn)$ cells. Since α must be specified for sn arguments, it takes a total of $sn \log_2 (2 + sn)$ cells. We can show this figure to be bounded above by $3s^2n \log_2 n$. We thus point out two simulation theorems.

Theorem 13.2. If a language L is accepted by a deterministic nonerasing stack automaton S, it is accepted by a deterministic Turing machine of tape complexity class $n \log n$.

Proof. We can specify a multitape Tm T, which keeps track of the transition table for the stack contents, beginning with the transition table for the initial stack, Z_0. As we mentioned, for a dsa, the transition table can be stored in a number of cells proportional to $n \log n$. (Recall from Theorem 10.1 that constants of proportionality are irrelevant as far as tape complexity classes are concerned.)

When S makes a stationary move at the top of stack, T simply changes state. If S moves to the left from the top of stack, T references the current transition table to see if S accepts, rejects, or completes a stack scan. If S accepts or rejects, T does likewise. If S completes a stack scan, T knows in what state-input head position pair S will be when it completes the stack scan. Lastly, if S prints a symbol at the top of stack, T must update the transition table to include the new stack symbol, using the algorithm described in this section. At all times when the stack head of S is at the top of stack, T stores the top stack symbol and state of S in T's finite control for reference. Also, the input head of T will be positioned at the cell scanned by the input head of S.

We have not yet shown that T can reference and update the transition table in the $n \log n$ storage cells allotted. However, such is the case, and a proof appears in the literature. As an exercise, the reader might choose a representation for a transition table, and then show how referencing and updating might be performed.

Theorem 13.3. If L is accepted by a nondeterministic, nonerasing sa S, then it is accepted by a nondeterministic Tm T of tape complexity class n^2.

Proof. Again we give only an indication of how the theorem is proved. T will use a length of tape proportional to n^2 to store a transition table. The state and top stack symbol of S will be stored in the finite control of T. For each configuration $(q, yZ, 0, j)$ which S can enter, T can enter a configuration with q and Z stored in its finite control, its input head at position j, and the transition table for yZ stored on one of T's storage tapes.

Suppose that the above is true for some configuration of S. S may make various moves from this configuration, nondeterministically. For each choice of S for which the stack head remains stationary, T has a choice which changes its input head position and the state of S recorded in T's finite control, in conformity with the move of S.

If S chooses to move into the stack, T has a choice of referencing the transition table and returning to the top of stack, nondeterministically, in those pairs of state of S and input position which the transition table says is possible. If, according to the transition table, S may enter the stack and accept without completing a stack scan, T accepts.

Finally, if S chooses to print another stack symbol, then T updates the transition table in accordance with the symbol S chose to print.

Initially, T is in a configuration representing the initial configuration of S. We may show by induction on the sum of the number of moves made at the top of stack plus the number of stack scans that, if S enters a configuration with the stack head at the top of stack, T will enter a configuration representing that of S. (i.e., T will have the proper state of S, top stack symbol, input position, and transition table.) If this configuration has an accepting state, T accepts. Also, if S can, from this configuration, enter an accepting state somewhere within the stack, the transition table will so indicate, and T will accept.

Again the hardest part of the proof, the updating of the transition table, has not been explained. It is also found in the literature.

We would like to show the converses of Theorems 13.2 and 13.3. The result of these two theorems and the next two theorems will be to show the equivalence of:

1. The nonerasing dsa and the Tm of tape complexity class $n \log n$.
2. The nonerasing sa and the nondeterministic Tm of tape complexity class n^2.

We prove the easier result first.

Theorem 13.4. If a language L is accepted by T, a nondeterministic Turing machine of tape complexity n^2, it is accepted by S, a nonerasing sa.

Proof. We may assume without loss of generality that T is a single-tape Tm. That is, given an off-line Tm of tape complexity n^2, one can find an equivalent single-tape Tm using no more than n^2 cells of tape when the input is of length n. We represent a configuration of T in Fig. 13.2. If T's input is of length n, the n^2 cells of tape used by T are divided into n blocks of n cells, separated by the symbol $*$. The entire configuration is surrounded by $**$. The state of T and the position of its tape head are indicated by a state symbol to the left of the symbol scanned. In Fig. 13.2, the symbol scanned is A_{ij}.

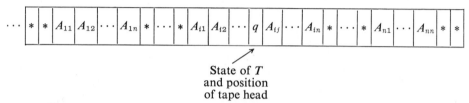

State of T
and position
of tape head

Fig. 13.2. Representation of the configuration of T on the stack of S.

The proof is similar to that of Theorem 13.1. S starts with the initial configuration of T on the stack of S. Here the initial configuration consists of the initial state of T followed by the input to T and a sufficient number of blanks to make up n blocks. The reader can verify that this configuration can be printed by S. S will copy each configuration to the top of stack, nondeterministically making those changes which could be brought about by one move of T. The procedure of alteration is the same as in Theorem 13.1, except that T may have a choice of next moves. When copying the symbols involved in the move, S will nondeterministically change them to reflect one of these moves.

The method of making changes having been previously discussed, we explain here only how to copy one entire configuration. Suppose that S has copied i entire blocks, and j tape symbols of the next block. First, S may test if $j = n$ by comparing the number of tape symbols written above the last $*$ with the length of the input. That is, starting with the input head at $\mathcal{e}$, S moves its stack head down the stack. Each time a tape symbol of T is found, S's input head moves one cell to the right. If a $*$ is found on the stack before the right end marker of the input is reached, then $j < n$. If $j = n$, S must print $*$ on the top of stack.

Similarly, S can test if $i = n$ by comparing the number of single $*$'s written on its stack above the top $**$ with the length of its input. If $i = n$, S prints $**$ and proceeds to create a new configuration.

Let us suppose that $i < n$ and $j < n$. S uses the length of the input to count blocks down the stack until the nth complete block (i.e., not counting the block being formed) from the top of stack is reached. S nondeterministically selects a tape symbol in this block in such a manner that S has the option of choosing any symbol. This symbol is stored in the finite control of S, and it is noted if this symbol could be involved in the move of T.

Then S moves its input head to the left end, and simultaneously moves its stack head down the stack and its input head to the right, until $*$ is encountered on the stack. At this point, the number of cells between the input head and left end marker of the input will be equal to the number of symbols between the stack symbol selected by S and the $*$ that marks the left end of that symbol's block.

S raises its stack head to the top of stack without moving the input head and compares the number of cells to the left of the input head with j, the number of T's tape symbols above the topmost $*$ on the stack. If they agree, S has chosen the correct symbol to copy, and this symbol (or symbols if the move of T is involved) is printed on the top of stack. If they disagree, an erroneous choice was made. There is no next move of S in this situation. Of course, since S is nondeterministic, it always chooses correctly, so not all sequences of moves terminate.

If the new state of T is accepting, S accepts. Otherwise, S simulates the next move of T. The remaining details are left to the reader.

Theorem 13.5. If a language L is accepted by a deterministic Tm T of tape complexity class $n \log n$, then it is accepted by S, a deterministic nonerasing stack automaton.

Proof. The proof is similar to that of Theorems 13.1 and 13.4. We do not give the complete argument, but only briefly sketch the encoding of a configuration of T. A tape string of T and a state of T marking the position of T's tape head can be represented by a binary string of length at most $cn[\log_2 n]$ for some constant c. Divide the configuration into cn blocks each of length $[\log_2 n]$. The configuration is represented on the stack of S by cn blocks of 1's separated by $*$'s. The number of 1's in each block is equal to the value of the binary number in the corresponding block in the configuration of T. S can copy a configuration to the top of the stack by using the input to count cn blocks down the stack and then recording the number of 1's in the block on the input. S raises its stack head to the top of the stack without moving the input head, then copies the block on top of the stack. When S copies the block containing the state, S converts the string of 1's to binary by a process of repeated division, simulates the move of T, and then converts the new string back to a block of 1's.

The above explanation has ignored many details. Outstanding among these is the conversion from block length encoding to binary encoding and

back, and the method of handling the situation in which the storage head of
T moves out of the block it was in. All these details are found in the literature.

So far, we have been considering only nonerasing stack automata. We
should now add that deterministic erasing stack automata can accept whatever is accepted by a nondeterministic Tm of tape complexity class $n \log n$.
We first need the following lemma.

> **Lemma 13.1.** Let $L(n)$ be a tape bound such that there is a deterministic
> single-tape Tm which, given an input of length n, will use exactly $L(n)$
> cells of tape, then halt. If a language L is accepted by a single-tape
> nondeterministic Tm of tape complexity $L(n)$, then L is accepted by a
> similar Tm which always halts, no matter what sequence of moves is
> chosen.

Proof. Let T be such a Tm accepting L. Let T have s states and t tape
symbols. If the input is of length n, the number of configurations of T
accessible from the initial configuration is at most $sL(n)t^{L(n)}$. The factors s,
$L(n)$, and $t^{L(n)}$ represent the state, position of head, and tape contents, respectively. It is easy to show that there is an integer, b, such that for all $L(n)$,
$b^{L(n)} \geq sL(n)t^{L(n)}$. (Note that $L(n)$ is at least as great as n for a single-tape Tm.)

If T, with some input of length n, accepts after making a sequence of
more than $sL(n)t^{L(n)}$ moves, some configuration must have repeated. Hence,
there is a shorter sequence of moves leading to acceptance. We conclude
that if T accepts a given input of length n, then it is accepted by a sequence
of no more than $sL(n)t^{L(n)}$ moves.

We construct a new Tm T_1, which on one track of its tape simulates T.
On the other track of its tape T_1 counts in base b the number of moves of T
that have been simulated, up to $b^{L(n)}$. Clearly, T_1 must mark off a block of
length $L(n)$ on the second track. The statement of the theorem assumes that
$L(n)$ is of a nature such that this can be done. (Surely $L(n) = n[\log_2 n]$
satisfies this assumption.)

Each time T_1 simulates a move of T, it adds one to the counter. If the
counter "overflows," that is, exceeds $b^{L(n)}$, then T_1 halts without accepting
in this sequence of moves. Of course, T_1 simulates T nondeterministically,
so if any choice of less than $sL(n)t^{L(n)}$ moves of T leads to acceptance, T_1
will make this choice and accept.

> **Theorem 13.6.** If L is accepted by a nondeterministic Tm of tape com-
> plexity class $n \log n$, then it is accepted by a deterministic sa.

Proof. Let T_1 be a single-tape Tm accepting L. By Lemma 13.1, there is a
Tm T_2, equivalent to T_1, which always halts. If T_1 is of tape complexity
class $n \log n$, then T_2 will be also. Specifically, T_2 will never use more than
$cn[\log_2 n]$ storage cells, for some integer c.

We represent configurations of T_2 on the stack of S as in Theorem 13.5. Suppose that the maximum number of choices available to T_2 in any situation is r. In any situation, these choices may each be assigned a number between 1 and m, where $m \leq r$. We introduce a new track on the stack of S which, above each configuration, holds an integer between 1 and r. This number indicates which choice of move is made by T_2 in going from one configuration to the next configuration.

S places the initial configuration of T_2 on the stack followed by the number 1. Then S enters a routine which examines the number on the top of the stack. If this number is j, S examines the current top configuration to see if there are j different moves. If there are, a new configuration is created from the old, using the jth move. The method of adding this new configuration to the top of the stack is that described in Theorem 13.5. If there are not j distinct moves that can be made from the top configuration, the number j and the top configuration are erased and the new top number is incremented by one. Then S repeats the steps of the routine. Of course, if S creates on its stack a configuration with an accepting state, S halts and accepts. Until S creates an accepting configuration, it will systematically simulate all possible sequences of moves of T_2. (Note that there are no infinite sequences of moves of T_2.) If no sequence of moves of T_2 leads to an accepting state, then S will eventually empty its stack and halt without accepting.

13.4 THE POWER OF ONE-WAY STACK AUTOMATA

We have considered two-way stack automata and shown various relations between their power and the power of various tape-bounded Turing machines. Specifically:

1. A nonerasing sa is equivalent to a nondeterministic n^2 tape-bounded Tm.
2. A deterministic nonerasing sa is equivalent to a deterministic $n \log n$ tape-bounded Tm.
3. A deterministic sa can simulate a nondeterministic $n \log n$ tape-bounded Tm. Hence, among other languages, a deterministic sa can recognize all the context-sensitive languages.

We show, very briefly, that a one-way nondeterministic sa can be simulated by a deterministic n tape-bounded Turing machine (deterministic lba). Thus every one-way sa language is context sensitive.

We need to introduce a few lemmas. The first states that a one-way sa can accept by "empty store," like the pda can.

Lemma 13.2. If L is $T(S)$ for some one-way sa S, then $L = N(S_1)$ for another one-way sa S_1, where

$$N(S_1) = \{w | (q_0, Z_0, 0, 1) \mathop{\vdash}\limits^{*}_{S_1, w} (q, \epsilon, 0, n)\}.$$

Here q_0 and Z_0 are the start state and start symbol of S_1, respectively, and n is the length of w.

Proof. As in Theorem 5.1, S_1 simulates S. If S enters an accepting state, S_1 then moves its stack head to the top of stack, the input head to the right end marker, and erases the stack.

From here on we think of sa's as accepting by empty store.

Lemma 13.3. If $L = N(S)$ for some one-way sa S, then $L = N(S_1)$ for some one-way sa S_1 such that: If w is accepted by S_1, then there is a sequence of moves leading to acceptance, such that if the stack head leaves the top of stack, it does not return until it has moved its input head. This sequence of moves is said to have *property A*.

Proof. For every stack string y of S, we can find a *rebound table* which indicates, for each input symbol a, what state transitions S can make without moving its input head, starting at the rightmost symbol of y and ending with a move to the right from y, never having previously left y. There are only a finite number of rebound tables for S, since there are a finite number of input symbols and states.†

S_1 will simulate S, but on each stack cell S_1 will print, in addition to the symbol S prints, the rebound table for that symbol and the string below it on the stack. The technique of carrying a table on each cell of the stack is similar to that used in the "predicting machine" of Section 12.3.

To print the correct rebound table on each cell, S_1 must compute the rebound table for yZ from Z and the rebound table for y, where Z is any stack symbol of S. It is, in fact, true that the rebound table for yZ depends not upon all of y, but only upon the rebound table for y, which S_1 has available to it on the rightmost symbol of y. The details are left to the reader.

It should be clear that if S_1 has the correct rebound table incorporated into its rightmost nonblank stack symbol, it need not leave the top of stack to know what stack scans it can make without moving its input head. A stack scan in which the input head never moves results only in a change of state. This state transition can be accomplished by S_1 at the top of stack.

Lemma 13.4. If $L = N(S)$, for some one-way sa S, then $L = N(S_2)$ for some one-way sa S_2 for which: If w is accepted by S_2, then w is accepted by a sequence of moves such that, between two moves of the input head, all erasing moves precede all writing moves (hereafter called *property B*), and in addition, that the sequence has property A.

---

† Note that the rebound table is similar to the transition table used for the two-way sa. However, the input head position is not part of the information provided by the rebound table.

Proof. Let S_1 be the sa constructed in Lemma 13.3. Consider a sequence of moves of S_1 having property A and leading to acceptance of w. Between moves of the input head, S_1 can, since it has property A, only:

1. Raise the stack head to the top of stack.
2. Make erasing, writing, and stationary moves at the top of stack.
3. Move the stack head into the stack.

Of course, S_1 need not do all three, but what is done must be in that order.

For any states p and q, stack symbol Z, and input symbol a, either it is true that $(q, Z, 0, 1) \vdash^{*}_{S_1, \not{c}a\$} (p, Z, 0, 2)$ (although many symbols may be written and erased on the stack) or it is false.† If true, we can allow S_2, when scanning a on the input with Z as the rightmost nonblank on the stack, to go directly from state q to p. In addition, S_2 can do whatever S_1 can do.

Surely S_2 accepts only words accepted by S_1. Suppose that, between two moves of S_1's input head, the length of stack as a function of the number of moves is the solid line of Fig. 13.3. S_2 can imitate this motion, but can also use its additional rules to make the "jumps" indicated by the dashed lines. Note that S_2 first erases only, then prints only.

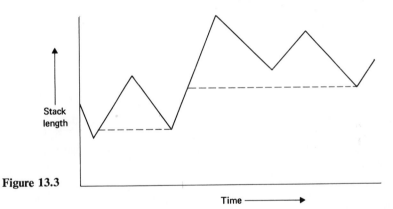

Figure 13.3

Time ⟶

We have now introduced two properties of sequences of moves, A and B, which we can assume without loss of generality. We must further modify the sa such that, if it accepts its input, it does so by a sequence of moves in which the stack length is at most a constant multiple of the input length. Then, we at least have simulation of a one-way sa by a nondeterministic lba. With a more sophisticated argument, we can show simulation by a deterministic lba.

---

† It may be comforting to know that there is an algorithm to decide whether this is true or false, but the existence of such an algorithm is not important to the argument. If the algorithm did not exist, some sa would still be S_2. We could not, however, tell which sa this was.

Observe that in any sequence of moves, of all the symbols ever written on the stack with an input of length n, at most $n - 1$ of them ever influence the sa's choice when the input head moves. We attempt to shorten stacks by combining long strings of symbols that in some particular sequence of moves are only scanned when moves keeping the input head in a fixed position are made. These strings can be replaced by a single symbol that will supply all the information needed to simulate the action of the stack head on the string.

Specifically, let $y = X_1 X_2 \ldots X_k$ be a stack string of some one-way sa, S. A *transmission table* (tt) for y is a symbol which gives the following information about y.

1. What is X_k?
2. For each input symbol a, and states q and p, can S erase y from its stack, while continuously scanning a, starting in state q and ending in state p?
3. While continuously scanning a on its input, starting in state q and scanning X_1 on the stack, can S be in state p when it first leaves y if it moves off y to the left? To the right? If S is started at X_k in state q, continuously scanning a, can it be in state p when it first leaves y going left? going right?

Note that, for a given S, there are a finite number of input symbols, stack symbols, and states, so there are only a finite number of tt's.

Let us consider a one-way sa S such that every word accepted is accepted by a sequence having properties A and B. We construct from S a *summary machine*, denoted by $\sigma(S)$. $\sigma(S)$ will simulate S, but has the privilege of combining any string of adjacent stack symbols into a tt or not combining them. Of course, $\sigma(S)$, being nondeterministic, always does both.

Specifically, let $S = (K, \Sigma, \Gamma, \delta, \delta_b, q_0, Z_0, \varphi)$. $\sigma(S)$ has as stack symbols the elements of Γ plus all possible tt's for S. $\sigma(S)$ keeps track of the state of S in $\sigma(S)$'s finite control. Suppose that $\sigma(S)$ has its stack head at the top of stack, and a symbol of Γ is the rightmost blank. Then $\sigma(S)$ can do whatever S could do. In addition, if S could print a Z, $\sigma(S)$ may either do that or print a tt for the string consisting of Z alone.

If a tt is the rightmost nonblank, it tells what the rightmost symbol is in the string it represents. So $\sigma(S)$ knows what symbol is the rightmost nonblank of the stack of S represented. If S can make a move which leaves the stack head fixed, $\sigma(S)$ can do the same. If S can print a symbol, $\sigma(S)$ can:

1. Print that symbol.
2. Print a tt representing that symbol.
3. Change the tt at the top of $\sigma(S)$'s stack to include the symbol printed.

The reader can show that if α is a tt for string y and Z is a stack symbol, then the tt for yZ is a function of α and Z only. The exact value of the string y is not needed.

Finally, $\sigma(S)$ may erase the tt, without moving its input head, executing a state transition of S that the tt says is possible.

Within the stack, scanning a symbol in Γ, $\sigma(S)$ can do exactly what S can do. If scanning a tt, $\sigma(S)$ must remember from which direction it moved to the tt. $\sigma(S)$ must then leave the tt without moving its input head. It may simulate any state transition S could make had S moved into and out of the string represented by tt. There is, of course, the requirement that S be able to make that same transition entering and leaving the string in the same directions as $\sigma(S)$ enters and leaves the tt.

It should be clear that anything $\sigma(S)$ does is, in a sense, a representation of what S does. Therefore, $N(\sigma(S)) \subseteq N(S)$. However, we must show that whatever S accepts is accepted by $\sigma(S)$, and that $\sigma(S)$ accepts it by a sequence of configurations in which the stack length is linearly bounded. We show this in the proof of the next theorem.

Theorem 13.7. If L is accepted by a one-way, nondeterministic stack automaton, then L is context sensitive.

Proof. Let $L = N(S)$. By Lemmas 13.3 and 13.4, we can construct S_2 with $L = N(S_2)$, where, if w is in L, then w is accepted by S_2 by a sequence of moves having properties A and B.

Let us consider what can happen between input head moves in a sequence of moves having properties A and B. First, it is possible that the stack head will never reach the top of stack. If it does reach the top of stack, it may erase some symbols, then print some symbols (property B). It may then leave the top of stack, but if it does it may not return until the input head has moved (property A).

Let P be such a sequence of moves of S_2 leading to acceptance of input w. P is modeled by many sequences of moves of $\sigma(S_2)$, as described in the previous discussion. We are interested in a particular sequence of moves of $\sigma(S_2)$, P_1, which has the following properties:

1. If in sequence P a stack symbol is printed, in sequence P_1, that symbol is printed only if S_2 either prints, erases, or scans it on a move which causes the input head to move. Otherwise, in sequence P_1, that symbol is incorporated into a tt. (Thus the tt may represent that symbol alone or that symbol in addition to others.)

2. If in sequence P_1 two tt's are ever adjacent on the stack of $\sigma(S_2)$, then, between two input head moves, S_2 erases all the symbols represented by the upper tt, but none of those represented by the lower tt.

We leave it to the reader to assure himself that such a sequence P_1 exists. The argument is essentially that $\sigma(S_2)$ always has the option of printing symbols or tt's and of starting new tt's or changing the one at the top of stack. The only time $\sigma(S_2)$ must print a stack symbol of S_2 is when that symbol will be involved in a move with input head motion, as required by Condition 1 above. The only time a string of symbols not involved in a motion of the input head needs to form two or more tt's is when, between two input moves, some symbols of the string are erased and others are not.

How long can the sequence P_1 cause the stack to grow? Any stack of $\sigma(S_2)$ can hold at most $n - 1$ stack symbols of S_2 (not counting the end of stack marker), since S_2 can make only $n - 1$ input head moves if $|w| = n$. Also, there can be at most $n - 1$ tt's that are immediately to the right of other tt's. This condition is due to property B. Between two input moves, some symbols may be erased, but once S_2 starts to print, no more symbols are erased. Two adjacent tt's on the stack of $\sigma(S_2)$ thus mark the boundary between the erased symbols and remaining symbols for some subsequent moves in sequence P_1.

Thus, no stack of $\sigma(S_2)$ in sequence P_1 can have more than $3n$ symbols of all types. We can easily construct a nondeterministic on-line Tm T, which simulates $\sigma(S_2)$. If, for some choices, T finds that $\sigma(S_2)$'s stack has grown longer than $3n$ symbols, T discontinues computation. We have already argued that if w, of length n, is in $N(\sigma(S_2))$, then there will be some sequence of moves P_1 which T can simulate without using more than $3n$ storage tape cells. The reader can easily show that $\sigma(S_2)$ can be simulated by an lba. Thus, we conclude that L is a csl.

We can prove more than Theorem 13.7, namely that a deterministic lba can simulate a one-way nondeterministic sa. We do not give even an informal proof of the latter result, but merely provide some hints as to how it is proved. We need to present one more lemma.

Lemma 13.5. Given a one-way nondeterministic sa S, we can find an sa S_3, with $N(S_3) = N(S)$, such that if S_3 accepts an input w, it does so by a sequence of moves having properties A and B and *property C*. Property C being that, on every move, S_3 moves either its input head or its stack head, but not both.

Proof. Consider S_2 constructed from S as in Lemma 13.4. S_2 introduces properties A and B. One can easily modify S_2 so that it moves at most one of its heads at a time. Suppose that S_2 makes a sequence of moves in which the two heads remain stationary. The net effect is a change of state. This change can be incorporated into the next move of S_2 which does not leave the heads fixed. Note that since S_2 accepts by empty stack, the last move cannot be one which leaves both heads fixed.

Define a *composite move* to be either a move to the left from the top of stack followed by a stack scan (sequence of moves returning the stack head to the top of stack) or a single move at the top of stack (print, erase, or stationary). The former type of composite move will informally be referred to as a "stack scan."

Theorem 13.8. If $L = N(S)$ for some one-way nondeterministic sa S, then L is recognized by a deterministic lba.

Proof. Consider $\sigma(S_2)$, constructed from S as in the proof of Theorem 13.7. Apply the constructions of Lemmas 13.4 and 13.5 to $\sigma(S_2)$ to get a new sa, S_3. We claim that, if w is in $N(S_3)$, then w is accepted by a sequence of moves P, which has properties A, B, and C and for which the length of the stack is bounded by $3|w|$. Moreover, P has the two properties of P_1 in Theorem 13.7.

Using the above properties, one can show that in sequence P the number of moves at the top of stack is at most $9|w|$ for any w. There is some constant r such that S_3 has no more than r choices in any configuration. We represent each of the moves in P at the top of stack by an integer between 1 and r according to some encoding.

The stack scans in sequence P number at most $|w|$. A particular stack scan can be represented by a pair of states, the states at the beginning and end of the scan, followed by as many 0's as there are input moves during the stack scan. All the stack scans can thus be represented by at most $2|w|$ states of S_3, and $|w|$ 0's. The entire sequence P may be represented by at most $12|w|$ symbols chosen from 0 through r and the states of S_3.

A deterministic lba T can generate all such sequences in a systematic manner and test each in turn to see if it represents a sequence which leads to acceptance of w and for which the stack is bounded in length by $3|w|$. Surely w is in $N(S_3)$ if and only if a sequence of this nature exists. We leave it to the reader to show the hard part—that T can determine if, for a given stack of length at most $3|w|$, a stack scan starting in state q, ending in state p, and moving the input head from position i to j on w is possible.

13.5   RECURSIVENESS OF STACK AUTOMATA

We have shown that two-way stack automata can recognize all the csl's. A diagonalization argument can be constructed (using the techniques of Section 13.3) to show that the deterministic sa can accept non-context-sensitive languages. One might ask if a two-way sa can recognize all type 0 languages. Such is not the case, as we shall immediately show.

Lemma 13.6. If L is accepted by a one-way nondeterministic sa, then L is recursive.

Proof. L is context sensitive by Theorem 13.7. Moreover, we can effectively find a csg generating L by Theorem 8.2. Thus, L is recursive by Theorem 2.2.

Theorem 13.9. If L is accepted by a two-way nondeterministic sa, then L is recursive.

Proof. Let $L = N(S)$, and let w be a particular input to S. We can construct a one-way nondeterministic sa S_w, with w and the position of S's input

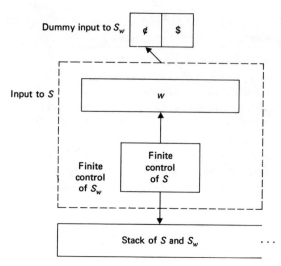

Fig. 13.4. Simulation of S by S_w.

Two-way stack automata   One-way stack automata

Closed under	Non-deterministic	Deterministic	Non-deterministic	Deterministic
Union	Yes	Yes	Yes	No
Concatenation	Yes	Yes	Yes	No
Closure	Yes	Yes	Yes	No
Reversal	Yes	Yes	Yes	No
Intersection	Yes	Yes	No	No
Complement	?	Yes	No	Yes
Intersection with regular set	Yes	Yes	Yes	Yes
Substitution	No	No	No	No
ϵ-free substitution	Yes	Yes	No	No
gsm mappings	No	No	Yes	No
ϵ-free gsm	Yes	Yes	Yes	No
Inverse deterministic gsm mappings	Yes	Yes	Yes	Yes
k-limited erasing	Yes	Yes	Yes	No
Quotient with regular set	No	No	Yes	Yes

Fig. 13.5. Closure properties of stack automata.

head incorporated into the finite control of S_w. S_w has "dummy" input $\not\!c\$$. See Fig. 13.4. S_w simulates S with input w, first moving to $\$$ on its dummy input. It is straightforward to show that S_w can be constructed so that S_w accepts if and only if S accepts w.

13.6 CLOSURE PROPERTIES

Many closure properties for stack automata can be established by methods similar to those used in Chapter 9. Some other closure results appear in the literature. For completeness, we summarize the results in Fig. 13.5.

PROBLEMS

13.1 Give two-way stack automata accepting the following:
   a) $\{w_1 c w_2 c \ldots c w_k | k$ arbitrary, w_i in $\{0, 1\}^*$ for each i, and for no m and n is $w_m = w_n\}$.
   b) The set of words consisting of an equal number of a's, b's, and c's.
   c) $\{ww | w$ in $\{a, b\}^*\}$.
   d) $\{0^i | i$ is prime$\}$.

13.2 Give one-way nondeterministic stack automata accepting:
   a) $\{0^i | i$ is a perfect square$\}$.
   b) The complement of the set given in Problem 13.1(a).
   c) $\{0^n 1^n 0^n | n \geq 0\}$.

13.3 The language $L = \{0^i | i$ is a perfect cube$\}$ is not accepted by any one-way nondeterministic sa. Can you prove this? If not, can you prove a simpler result such as:
   a) L is accepted by no one-way deterministic sa?
   b) L is accepted by no one-way nondeterministic nonerasing sa?

13.4 In Section 6.6, a pushdown automaton was defined as a Turing machine of a restricted type. Can you do the same for stack automata?

13.5 Show some of the closure properties indicated in Fig. 13.5.

REFERENCES

The notion of a stack automaton is from Ginsburg, Greibach, and Harrison [1967(a) and (b)]. Theorems 13.1, 13.9, and a weaker version of Theorem 13.6 were proved in the above references. Theorems 13.2, 13.3, 13.4, and 13.5 are from Hopcroft and Ullman [1967a]. Theorem 13.7 was first noted by Ginsburg, Greibach, and Harrison, although a proof has not appeared in print. Theorem 13.8 is from Hopcroft and Ullman [1968c]. Most of the closure properties of one-way stack automata were shown in Ginsburg, Greibach, and Harrison [1967b]. Some of those for two-way stack automata follow directly from results in Hopcroft and Ullman [1967b], Ullman [1968], and Ginsburg and Hopcroft [1968].

Theorems on stack automata which we have not covered in this chapter appear in the literature. In Hopcroft and Ullman [1968b] the closure of one-way deterministic sa under quotient with a regular set is shown. In Knuth and Bigelow [1967] it is shown that two-way deterministic sa can recognize languages which are not context sensitive. Ullman [1968] contains a proof that every two-way sa can be modified so that it halts in any sequence of moves (i.e., there are no infinite valid sequences of moves), without changing the language recognized, and keeping the sa deterministic if it was originally so.

CHAPTER 14

DECIDABILITY

14.1 SOLVABLE AND UNSOLVABLE QUESTIONS

In this book we have exhibited algorithms to answer various "questions" about languages and grammars. An example of such a question is Q_1: Given a cfg G, is $L(G)$ empty? In Theorem 4.1, we gave an algorithm to answer Q_1. Consider also Q_2: Given a type 0 grammar G and string w, is w in $L(G)$? One can easily show that Q_2 is essentially the halting problem for Turing machines. Thus, by Theorem 7.1, there is no algorithm to solve Q_2.

We attempt to give a reasonably precise indication of what a question is. We do not, however, define the term formally. Actually, we do not prove any results about solvability of questions in general, so no definition of the term is necessary. We try to provide a good understanding of what it means to say that a question is unsolvable, and to show certain questions to be solvable or unsolvable.

The questions Q_1 and Q_2 have two common characteristics, both of which we require of questions generally.

1. A question consists of an infinity of *instances*.
2. In each instance, the answer to the question is either yes or no.

In Q_1, the instances correspond to the individual cfg's. There is an infinity of cfg's, of course. In Q_2, each grammar-string pair is an instance of the question. Note that we are not attempting to define an instance, except to say that it must have a yes or no answer.

We say that a question is *solvable* if there is an algorithm which, given a "suitable" encoding of any instance of the question, will return the answer for that instance. If no such algorithm exists, the question is *unsolvable*.

We must be careful to say what a "suitable" encoding is. Suppose that we wished to "solve" the halting problem for Turing machines.† We could encode Turing machines and input strings as binary numbers, one number for each pair of Tm and string. So far so good. But suppose that we added the proviso that, if the Tm T halted on input w, then (T, w) was to receive an even number, and (T, w) was to receive an odd number otherwise. Then we could "solve" the halting problem by looking at the last bit of the encoding of the instance.

---

† This problem is, of course, unsolvable.

Something is wrong. The problem clearly lies with the hypothetical encoding. A concept such as a Turing machine has a "standard" definition. In Chapter 6, it was defined as a "6-tuple" $(K, \Sigma, \Gamma, \delta, q_0, F)$, where K is a set of states, etc. It is not surprising that we get strange results if we allow encodings of Turing machines that bear no relation to the "standard" definition. We therefore define an encoding as *suitable* if there are algorithms to translate from the encoding to the "standard" definition and back again. This is clearly not the case for the Turing machine encoding mentioned in the paragraph above.

Of course, one is free to make "nonstandard" definitions of models. But then any theorem he gets will be for his models, not the ones found in this book.

14.2 POST'S CORRESPONDENCE PROBLEM

We know of one unsolvable question—the halting problem for Turing machines. To show that other problems are unsolvable, one shows that, if they were solvable, then the halting problem for Tm's would be solvable also. One can do this directly, but it is easier to show first the unsolvability of Post's Correspondence Problem (PCP). *Post's Correspondence Problem* is the following:

Let Σ be a finite alphabet, and let A and B be two lists of strings in Σ^+, with the same number of strings in each list. Say

$$A = w_1, w_2, \ldots, w_k \qquad \text{and} \qquad B = x_1, x_2, \ldots, x_k.$$

We say this instance of PCP *has a solution*† if there is any sequence of integers $i_1, i_2, \ldots, i_m$, with $m \geq 1$ such that

$$w_{i_1} w_{i_2} \ldots w_{i_m} = x_{i_1} x_{i_2} \ldots x_{i_m}.$$

We say that $i_1, i_2, \ldots, i_m$ is a *solution* to this instance of PCP.

Example 14.1. Let $\Sigma = \{0, 1\}$. Let A and B be lists of three strings each, defined as follows.

	List A	List B
i	w_i	x_i
1	1	111
2	10111	10
3	10	0

† Do not confuse the unsolvability of PCP with the fact that a given instance may "have a solution."

PCP has a solution in this case. Let $m = 4$, $i_1 = 2$, $i_2 = 1$, $i_3 = 1$, and $i_4 = 3$. Then $w_2 w_1 w_1 w_3 = x_2 x_1 x_1 x_3 = 101111110$.

Example 14.2. Let $\Sigma = \{0, 1\}$. Let A and B be lists of three strings:

i	List A w_i	List B x_i
1	10	101
2	011	11
3	101	011

Suppose that this instance of PCP has a solution $i_1, i_2, \ldots, i_m$. Clearly, $i_1 = 1$, since no string beginning with $w_2 = 011$ can equal a string beginning with $x_2 = 11$; no string beginning with $w_3 = 101$ can equal a string beginning with $x_3 = 011$.

We write the string from list A above the corresponding string from B. So far we have

$$10$$
$$101.$$

The next selection from A must begin with a 1. Thus $i_2 = 1$ or $i_2 = 3$. But $i_2 = 1$ will not do, since no string beginning with $w_1 w_1 = 1010$ can equal a string beginning with $x_1 x_1 = 101101$. With $i_2 = 3$, we have

$$10101$$
$$101011.$$

A similar argument shows that $i_3 = 3$, leaving

$$10101101$$
$$101011011.$$

It is clear that this argument can go on forever. There is no choice of indices that will allow the length of the string from A to "catch up" with the string from B, making both strings identical.

We show that PCP is unsolvable by showing that, if it were solvable, we could solve the halting problem for Turing machines. First, we show that, if PCP were solvable, a modified version of PCP would also be solvable.

The *modified Post's correspondence problem* (MPCP) is the following: Given lists A and B, of k strings each in Σ^+, say

$$A = w_1, w_2, \ldots, w_k \quad \text{and} \quad B = x_1, x_2, \ldots, x_k,$$

does there exist a sequence of integers, $i_1, i_2, \ldots, i_r$, such that

$$w_1 w_{i_1} w_{i_2} \ldots w_{i_r} = x_1 x_{i_1} x_{i_2} \ldots x_{i_r}.$$

The difference between the MPCP and PCP is that, in the MPCP, a solution is required to start with the first string on each list.

Lemma 14.1. If PCP were solvable, then MPCP would be solvable.

Proof. Let

$$A = w_1, w_2, \ldots, w_k \qquad \text{and} \qquad B = x_1, x_2, \ldots, x_k$$

be an instance of the MPCP. We convert this instance of MPCP to an instance of PCP which has a solution if and only if our MPCP instance has a solution. If PCP were solvable, we would then be able to solve the MPCP, hence proving the lemma.

Let Σ be the smallest alphabet containing all the symbols in lists A and B, and let $\cent$ and $\$$ not be in Σ. Define two homomorphisms, h_L and h_R, on Σ^* by $h_L(a) = \cent a$ and $h_R(a) = a\cent$ for all a in Σ. That is, h_L inserts $\cent$ to the left of each symbol and h_R inserts $\cent$ to the right. Define

$$y_1 = \cent h_R(w_1) \qquad \text{and} \qquad y_{i+1} = h_R(w_i)$$

for $1 \le i \le k$. Let

$$z_1 = h_L(x_1) \qquad \text{and} \qquad z_{i+1} = h_L(x_i)$$

for $1 \le i \le k$. Let

$$y_{k+2} = \$ \qquad \text{and} \qquad z_{k+2} = \cent\$.$$

Define

$$C = y_1, y_2, \ldots, y_{k+2} \qquad \text{and} \qquad D = z_1, z_2, \ldots, z_{k+2}.$$

The lists C and D constructed from the lists A and B of Example 14.1 are:

	List A	List B		List C	List D
i	w_i	x_i	i	y_i	z_i
1	1	111	1	$\cent 1\cent$	$\cent 1\cent 1\cent 1$
2	10111	10	2	$1\cent$	$\cent 1\cent 1\cent 1$
3	10	0	3	$1\cent 0\cent 1\cent 1\cent 1\cent$	$\cent 1\cent 0$
			4	$1\cent 0\cent$	$\cent 0$
			5	$\$$	$\cent\$$
	MPCP			PCP	

The lists C and D represent an instance of PCP. The claim is made that this instance of PCP has a solution if and only if the instance of MPCP represented by lists A and B has a solution. To see this, note that if

$1, i_1, i_2, \ldots, i_r$ is a solution to MCPC with lists A and B, then

$$1, i_1 + 1, i_2 + 1, \ldots, i_r + 1, k + 2$$

is a solution to PCP with lists C and D. Likewise, if $i_1, i_2, \ldots, i_r$ is a solution to PCP with lists C and D, then $i_1 = 1$ and $i_r = k + 2$ since y_1 and z_1 are the only words with the same index that begin with the same symbol and y_{k+2} and z_{k+2} are the only words with the same index that end with the same symbol. Let j be the smallest integer such that $i_j = k + 2$. Then $i_1, i_2, \ldots, i_j$ is also a solution (since the symbol $ occurs only as the last symbol of y_{k+2} and z_{k+2}) and, for no l, where $1 \leq l < j$, is $i_l = k + 2$. Clearly $1, i_2 - 1, i_3 - 1, \ldots, i_{j-1} - 1$ is a solution to MCPC for lists A and B.

If there is an algorithm to solve PCP, we can construct an algorithm to solve MCPC by converting any instance of MCPC to PCP as above.

Theorem 14.1. PCP is unsolvable.

Proof. With Lemma 14.1, it is sufficient to show that, if MCPC were solvable, then the halting problem for Turing machines would be solvable. Given a Tm M and input w to M, we construct an instance of MCPC that has a solution if and only if M halts and accepts input w.

Let $M = (K, \Gamma, \Sigma, \delta, q_0, F)$ and let B be the blank symbol. Without loss of generality, we assume that for each q in F and a in Σ, $\delta(q, a)$ is undefined. We can represent the configuration (q, α, i) of M by the string $\alpha_1 q \alpha_2$, where $\alpha_1 \alpha_2 = \alpha$ and $|\alpha_1| = i - 1$. That is, q appears immediately to the left of the symbol scanned by M's tape head. If $q_0 w, \alpha_1 q_1 \beta_1, \alpha_2 q_2 \beta_2, \ldots, \alpha_k q_k \beta_k$ are the representations of a possible sequence of configurations of M, and q_k is in F, then there will be a solution to the MCPC where the strings of the solution each begin with $\#q_0 w\#\alpha_1 q_1 \beta_1 \#\ldots\#\alpha_k q_k \beta_k\#$. Here $\#$ is a new symbol not in K or Γ.

Formally, the pairs of strings forming lists A and B of the instance of MCPC are given below. Since, except for the first pair, which must be used first, the numbers of the pairs are irrelevant to the existence of a solution, the pairs will be given without indexing numbers.

The first pair is:

List A	List B
#	$\#q_0 w\#$

The remaining pair are grouped as follows:

Group I

List A	List B
X	X for each X in $\Gamma - \{B\}$.
#	#

Group II. For each q in $K - F$, p in K, and X, Y, and Z in $\Gamma - \{B\}$.

List A	List B		
qX	Yp	if	$\delta(q, X) = (p, Y, R)$
ZqX	pZY	if	$\delta(q, X) = (p, Y, L)$
$q\#$	$Yp\#$	if	$\delta(q, B) = (p, Y, R)$
$Zq\#$	$pZY\#$	if	$\delta(q, B) = (p, Y, L)$

Group III. For each q in F, and X and Y in $\Gamma - \{B\}$.

List A	List B
XqY	q
$Xq\#$	$q\#$
$\#qY$	$\#q$

Group IV

List A	List B
$q\#\#$	$\#$ for each q in F.

Let us say that (x, y) is a *partial solution* to MPCP with lists A and B if x is a prefix of y, and x and y are the concatenation of corresponding strings of lists A and B respectively. If $xz = y$, then call z the *remainder* of (x, y).

Suppose, from configuration q_0w, that there is a valid sequence of configurations $\alpha_1 q_1 \beta_1, \alpha_2 q_2 \beta_2, \ldots, \alpha_k q_k \beta_k$, where none of $q_1, q_2, \ldots, q_{k-1}$ are in F. We claim that there is a partial solution

$$(x, y) = (\#q_0w\#\alpha_1q_1\beta_1\#\ldots\#\alpha_{k-1}q_{k-1}\beta_{k-1}\#, \#q_0w\#\alpha_1q_1\beta_1\#\ldots\#\alpha_kq_k\beta_k\#).$$

Moreover, this is the only partial solution whose larger string is as long as $|y|$.

The above statement is easy to prove by induction on k. It is trivial for $k = 0$, since the pair $(\#, \#q_0w\#)$ must be chosen first.

Suppose that the statement is true for some k and that q_k is not in F. We can easily show that it is true for $k + 1$. The remainder of the pair (x, y) is $z = \alpha_k q_k \beta_k \#$. The next pairs must be chosen so that their strings from list A form z. No matter what symbols appear to the right and left of q_k, there is at most one pair in Group II that will enable the partial solution to be continued past q_k. This pair represents, in a natural way, the move of M from configuration $\alpha_k q_k \beta_k$. The other symbols of z force choices from Group I. No other choices will enable z to be composed of elements in list A.

We can thus obtain a new partial solution, $(y, y\alpha_{k+1}q_{k+1}\beta_{k+1}\#)$. It is straightforward to see that $\alpha_{k+1}q_{k+1}\beta_{k+1}$ is the one configuration which M can reach on one move from $\alpha_k q_k \beta_k$. Also, there is no other partial solution whose length of the second string equals $|y\alpha_{k+1}q_{k+1}\beta_{k+1}|$.

In addition, if q_k is in F, it is easy to find pairs from Groups I and III which, when preceded by the partial solution (x, y) and followed by the pair in Group IV, provide a solution to MPCP with lists A and B.

Thus if M, started in configuration q_0w, reaches an accepting state, the instance of MPCP with lists A and B has a solution. If M does not reach an accepting state, there may be partial solutions, but the string from B must exceed the string from A in length, so no solution is possible.

We conclude that the instance of MPCP has a solution if and only if M with input w halts in an accepting state. Since the above construction can be carried out for arbitrary M and w, it follows that if there were an algorithm to solve MPCP, then there would be an algorithm to solve the halting problem for Turing machines. But the halting problem for Turing machines is unsolvable. Therefore MPCP is unsolvable and by Lemma 14.1, PCP is unsolvable.

Example 14.3. Let

$$M = (\{q_1, q_2, q_3\}, \{0, 1, B\}, \{0, 1\}, \delta, q_1, \{q_3\}).$$

δ is defined by:

q_i	$\delta(q_i, 0)$	$\delta(q_i, 1)$	$\delta(q_i, B)$
q_1	$(q_2, 1, R)$	$(q_2, 0, L)$	$(q_2, 1, L)$
q_2	$(q_3, 0, L)$	$(q_1, 0, R)$	$(q_2, 0, R)$
q_3	—	—	—

Let $w = 01$. We construct an instance of MPCP, having lists A and B. The first pair is $\#$ for list A and $\#q_101\#$ for list B. The remaining pairs are:

Group I

List A	List B
0	0
1	1
$\#$	$\#$

Group II

List A	List B		
q_10	$1q_2$	from	$\delta(q_1, 0) = (q_2, 1, R)$
$0q_11$	q_200	from	$\delta(q_1, 1) = (q_2, 0, L)$
$1q_11$	q_210		
$0q_1\#$	$q_201\#$	from	$\delta(q_1, B) = (q_2, 1, L)$
$1q_1\#$	$q_211\#$		
$0q_20$	q_300	from	$\delta(q_2, 0) = (q_3, 0, L)$
$1q_20$	q_310		
q_21	$0q_1$	from	$\delta(q_2, 1) = (q_1, 0, R)$
$q_2\#$	$0q_2\#$	from	$\delta(q_2, B) = (q_2, 0, R)$

Group III

List A	List B
$0q_30$	q_3
$0q_31$	q_3
$1q_30$	q_3
$1q_31$	q_3
$0q_3\#$	$q_3\#$
$1q_3\#$	$q_3\#$
$\#q_30$	$\#q_3$
$\#q_31$	$\#q_3$

Group IV

List A	List B
$q_3\#\#$	$\#$

Note that M accepts input $w = 01$ by the sequence of configurations: q_101, $1q_21$, $10q_1$, $1q_201$, q_3101. Let us see if there is a solution to the MPCP we have constructed. The first pair gives a partial solution $(\#, \#q_101\#)$. Inspection of the pairs indicates that the only way to get a longer partial solution is to use the pair $(q_10, 1q_2)$ next. The resulting partial solution is $(\#q_10, \#q_101\#1q_2)$. The remainder is now $1\#1q_2$. The next three pairs chosen must be $(1, 1)$, $(\#, \#)$, and $(1, 1)$. The partial solution becomes $(\#q_101\#1, \#q_101\#1q_21\#1)$. The remainder is now $q_21\#1$. Continuing the argument, we see that the only partial solution, the length of whose second string is 14, is $(x, x0q_1\#1)$, where $x = \#q_101\#1q_21\#1$.

Here, we seemingly have a choice, because the next pair used could be $(0, 0)$ or $(0q_1\#, q_201\#)$. In the former case, we have $(x0, x0q_1\#10)$ as a partial solution. But this partial solution is a "dead end." No pair can be added to it to make another partial solution, so, surely, it cannot lead to a solution.

In a similar manner, we continue to be forced by our desire to reach a solution to choose one particular pair to continue each partial solution. Finally, we reach the partial solution $(y, y1\#q_310)$, where

$$y = \#q_101\#1q_21\#10q_1\#1q_20.$$

Since q_3 is a final state, we can now use pairs in Groups I, III, and IV to find a solution to the instance of MPCP. The choice of pairs is

$$(1, 1), (\#q_31, \#q_3), (0, 0), (1, 1), (\#q_30, \#q_3), (1, 1), (\#q_31, \#q_3), (\#, \#), (q_3\#\#, \#).$$

Thus, the shortest word which can be composed of corresponding strings from lists A and B, starting with pair 1, is:

$$\#q_101\#1q_21\#10q_1\#1q_201\#q_3101\#q_301\#q_31\#q_3\#\#.$$

14.3 A QUESTION CONCERNING CONTEXT-SENSITIVE LANGUAGES

By Theorem 2.2, it is a solvable problem to determine if a string w is in the language generated by the csg G. This question is called the *membership problem*. A more difficult question is: Given a grammar G, is $L(G) = \varphi$? This question is called the *emptiness problem*.

Theorem 14.2. The emptiness problem for context-sensitive grammars is unsolvable.

Proof. Let

$$A = w_1, w_2, \ldots, w_k \quad \text{and} \quad B = x_1, x_2, \ldots, x_k$$

be the lists in an instance of PCP. We can easily construct an lba M which, when given a string y, generates sequences of integers $i_1, i_2, \ldots, i_m$, with $1 \leq m \leq |y|$ and $1 \leq i_j \leq k$ for all j. Then M tests each sequence of integers in turn to see if $w_{i_1} w_{i_2} \ldots w_{i_m} = x_{i_1} x_{i_2} \ldots x_{i_m} = y$. If so, M accepts y. It is straightforward to see that there is a solution to PCP with lists A and B if and only if M accepts some input y. Now, by Theorem 8.2, we can construct a csg G such that $L(G)$ is the language accepted by M. Thus, if we could solve the emptiness problem for csg's, we could solve PCP.

There are a number of other questions concerning context-sensitive languages whose unsolvability follows immediately from the unsolvability of the emptiness problem. Many of these questions are also unsolvable for context-free languages. Thus we defer these questions to the next section.

14.4 UNSOLVABLE QUESTIONS FOR CONTEXT-FREE LANGUAGES

From Theorem 4.1, we see that the emptiness problem is solvable for context-free languages. However, there are other questions for cfl's that are unsolvable. Our plan is to give a method for constructing certain cfg's for each instance of PCP. The cfg's will form an instance of a question Q about cfg's which we wish to show is unsolvable. The answer to this instance of Q will be yes if and only if the given instance of PCP has a solution. Now, if Q were solvable, then we could solve PCP by converting each instance of PCP to an instance of Q. Thus we may conclude that Q is unsolvable.

Let

$$A = w_1, w_2, \ldots, w_k \quad \text{and} \quad B = x_1, x_2, \ldots, x_k$$

be two lists of strings in Σ^+. Let $K = \{a_1, a_2, \ldots, a_k\}$ be a set of k distinct symbols not in Σ. Define

$$G_A = (\{S_A\}, V_T, P_A, S_A) \quad \text{and} \quad G_B = (\{S_B\}, V_T, P_B, S_B),$$

where $V_T = \Sigma \cup K$, and P_A and P_B are defined as follows. For each i

between 1 and k, P_A contains productions of the form

$$S_A \to w_i S_A a_i \quad \text{and} \quad S_A \to w_i a_i,$$

and P_B contains productions of the form

$$S_B \to x_i S_B a_i \quad \text{and} \quad S_B \to x_i a_i.$$

Let $L_A = L(G_A)$ and $L_B = L(G_B)$. It is straightforward to show that

$$L_A = \{w_{i_1} w_{i_2} \ldots w_{i_m} a_{i_m} a_{i_{m-1}} \ldots a_{i_1} | m \geq 1\}$$

and

$$L_B = \{x_{i_1} x_{i_2} \ldots x_{i_m} a_{i_m} a_{i_{m-1}} \ldots a_{i_1} | m \geq 1\}.$$

The cfl's, L_A and L_B, shall be used extensively in what follows.

Theorem 14.3. It is unsolvable whether the intersection of the languages generated by two arbitrary cfg's is empty.

Proof. $L_A \cap L_B = \varphi$ if and only if PCP with lists A and B has no solution. Thus if there were an algorithm to determine if the intersection of the languages generated by two cfg's was empty, then there would be an algorithm to solve PCP. Therefore, the emptiness of intersection problem for cfg's must be unsolvable.

Next we will prove a lemma from which many of the unsolvability results for cfg's follow immediately. Let A and B be lists of words over Σ and $K = \{a_1, a_2, \ldots, a_k\}$ as before. Let c be a symbol not in K or Σ. Let R_{AB} be the language $\{ycy^R | y \text{ is in } \Sigma^* K^*\}$. Let

$$S_{AB} = \{ycz^R | y \text{ is in } L_A, z \text{ is in } L_B\}.$$

R_{AB} and S_{AB} are deterministic cfl's. Thus there is an algorithm (Theorems 5.3, 9.1, and 12.1) to find a cfg generating the language $L_{AB} = \bar{R}_{AB} \cup \bar{S}_{AB}$.

Lemma 14.2. $L_{AB} = (\Sigma \cup K \cup \{c\})^*$ if and only if PCP with lists A and B has no solution.

Proof. $L_{AB} = (\Sigma \cup K \cup \{c\})^*$ if and only if $R_{AB} \cap S_{AB} = \varphi$. Now, suppose that PCP with lists A and B has a solution. Then there exists a string y in both L_A and L_B and thus ycy^R is in S_{AB}. Now ycy^R is also in R_{AB} and thus in $S_{AB} \cap R_{AB}$. Conversely, suppose that x is in $S_{AB} \cap R_{AB}$. Then x must be of the form ycy^R where y is in both L_A and L_B. Thus PCP with lists A and B has a solution.

Theorem 14.4. It is unsolvable whether a cfg generates the set of all strings over its terminal vocabulary.

Proof. Let G_{AB} be a cfg generating L_{AB}. If it were solvable whether G_{AB} generated $(\Sigma \cup K \cup \{c\})^*$, we could solve PCP for lists A and B.

Theorem 14.5. It is unsolvable whether for a cfg G and regular set R:

1. $L(G) = R$
2. $L(G) \supseteq R$
3. $\overline{L(G)} = \varphi$.

Proof. Let G be the cfg G_{AB} generating L_{AB}, which is constructed from lists A and B. Let $R = (\Sigma \cup K \cup \{c\})^*$. Then (1), (2), and (3) are true exactly when PCP with lists A and B has no solution.

Corollary 14.1. It is unsolvable whether two cfg's generate the same language, or whether the language generated by one cfg is contained in the language generated by another cfg.

Proof. These questions are unsolvable for a cfg and a regular grammar by Theorem 14.5.

We now examine the cfl $L_{AB} = \overline{R}_{AB} \cup \overline{S}_{AB}$ more closely. In particular, consider the complement $\overline{L}_{AB} = R_{AB} \cap S_{AB}$. Now

$$\overline{L}_{AB} = \{w_{j_1}w_{j_2}\ldots w_{j_m}a_{j_m}a_{j_{m-1}}\ldots a_{j_1}ca_{j_1}a_{j_2}\ldots a_{j_m}x^R_{j_m}x^R_{j_{m-1}}\ldots$$
$$x^R_{j_1}|w_{j_1}w_{j_2}\ldots w_{j_m} = x_{j_1}x_{j_2}\ldots x_{j_m}\}.$$

The claim is made that $\overline{L}_{AB}$ is a cfl if and only if it is empty. Assume that $\overline{L}_{AB}$ is not empty. Let $uvcv^Ru^R$ be a shortest sentence in $\overline{L}_{AB}$, where u is in Σ^* and v in K^*. Note that, given a solution to an instance of PCP, we can repeat that solution to get additional solutions. Therefore, consider the intersection of $\overline{L}_{AB}$ with the regular set $u^*v^*c(v^R)^*(u^R)^*$. This intersection is $\{u^nv^nc(v^R)^n(u^R)^n|n \geq 1\}$. It is easily seen that there exists a gsm which maps the intersection onto the language $\{0^n1^n0^n|n \geq 1\}$. Now, if $\overline{L}_{AB}$ were a cfl, then, since the class of cfl's is closed under intersection with a regular set and under gsm mappings (Theorems 9.4 and 9.10), $\{0^n1^n0^n|n \geq 1\}$ must be a cfl. But $\{0^n1^n0^n|n \geq 1\}$ is not a cfl. (See Exercise 4.15.) Thus we conclude that $\overline{L}_{AB}$ is not a cfl unless it is empty. We are led to the following theorem.

Theorem 14.6. It is unsolvable whether for arbitrary cfg's G_1 and G_2:

1. $L(G_1) \cap L(G_2)$ is a cfl.
2. $\overline{L(G_1)}$ is a cfl.
3. $L(G_1)$ is a regular set.

Proof

1. Let G_1 and G_2 be cfg's generating R_{AB} and S_{AB}, respectively. Now, $\overline{L}_{AB} = R_{AB} \cap S_{AB}$ is empty if and only if the instance of PCP with lists A and B has no solution. Since $R_{AB} \cap S_{AB}$ is a cfl if and only if it is empty, we conclude that it is unsolvable to determine if $R_{AB} \cap S_{AB}$ is a cfl for arbitrary lists A and B.

2. Let G_1 be a cfg generating L_{AB}. $\bar{L}_{AB}$ is a cfl if and only if $L_{AB} = \Sigma^*$, i.e., the instance of PCP with lists A and B has no solution.

3. Let G_1 be a cfg generating L_{AB}. L_{AB} is regular if and only if $L_{AB} = \Sigma^*$.

14.5 AMBIGUITY IN CONTEXT-FREE LANGUAGES

Recall from Chapter 4 that a cfg is said to be ambiguous if there are two distinct leftmost derivations for some word. A pda is said to be *ambiguous* if some word is accepted by two distinct sequences of moves. One sees from the constructions of Chapter 5 that, from an unambiguous cfg G, one can construct an unambiguous pda M, such that $T(M) = L(G)$. Similarly, one sees that, from an unambiguous pda M, one can construct an unambiguous cfg G, such that $L(G) = T(M)$. We state without proof the following lemma.

Lemma 14.3. L is generated by an unambiguous context-free grammar if and only if L is accepted by an unambiguous pushdown automaton.

Thus, ambiguity in cfl's can be approached from either the grammar or the machine point of view. We use the machine approach to show that, if L is a cfl generated by an unambiguous cfg G, and A is a deterministic gsm, then there exists an unambiguous cfg generating $A^{-1}(L)$.

A cfl L is said to be inherently ambiguous if every cfg generating L is ambiguous. Otherwise L is said to be unambiguous. Inherent ambiguity is a property of a language, whereas ambiguity is a property of a grammar. We show that there exist inherently ambiguous cfl's and that it is recursively unsolvable to determine if an arbitrary cfg is ambiguous or if it generates an inherently ambiguous cfl.

Theorem 14.7. It is unsolvable whether an arbitrary cfg is ambiguous.

Proof. Let

$$A = w_1, w_2, \ldots, w_n \qquad \text{and} \qquad B = x_1, x_2, \ldots, x_n$$

be two lists of words over a finite alphabet Σ. Assume that $\Sigma \cap \{a_1, a_2, \ldots, a_n\} = \varphi$. Let G be the cfg

$$(\{S, S_1, S_2\}, \Sigma \cup \{a_1, a_2, \ldots, a_n\}, P, S),$$

where P contains the productions $S \rightarrow S_1$, $S \rightarrow S_2$, and, for $1 \leq i \leq n$, $S_1 \rightarrow w_i S_1 a_i$, $S_1 \rightarrow w_i a_i$, $S_2 \rightarrow x_i S_2 a_i$, and $S_2 \rightarrow x_i a_i$. The grammar G generates the language $L_A \cup L_B$. It is easily shown that G is ambiguous if and only if $L_A \cap L_B \neq \varphi$. Since it is recursively unsolvable to determine if $L_A \cap L_B \neq \varphi$, for L_A and L_B constructed from arbitrary lists of words, it is recursively unsolvable to determine if an arbitrary cfg is ambiguous.

We now establish a result which is useful in the study of inherent ambiguity.

We shall prove that the inverse of a deterministic gsm mapping preserves unambiguity. First, we need to introduce the following lemma.

Lemma 14.4. Every unambiguous language L is accepted by an unambiguous pushdown automaton which makes no move in a final state.

Proof. Let L be accepted by unambiguous pda $P = (K, \Sigma, \Gamma, \delta, q_0, Z_0, F)$. We create a new pda P_1, which will have extra copies of P's final states. These will be P_1's final states, and P_1 will have no allowable moves in those states.

Formally, let
$$P_1 = (K_1, \Sigma, \Gamma, \delta_1, q_0, Z_0, F_1),$$
where $K_1 = K \cup \{q'|q \text{ is in } F\}$ and $F_1 = \{q'|q \text{ is in } F\}$. We define δ_1 for all a in $\Sigma \cup \{\epsilon\}$ and Z in Γ, by:

1. If q is in $K - F$, then $\delta_1(q, a, Z) = \delta(q, a, Z)$.
2. If q is in F, then $\delta_1(q, a, Z) = \delta(q, a, Z) \cup \{(q', Z)\}$.
3. For all q' in F_1, $\delta_1(q', a, Z) = \varphi$.

It is easy to see that $T(P_1) = T(P)$ and that, if P is unambiguous, P_1 is also unambiguous.

Theorem 14.8. Let $A = (K_A, \Sigma, \Delta, \delta_A, q_0, F_A)$ be a deterministic gsm. Let L be unambiguous. Then $A^{-1}(L)$ is unambiguous.

Proof. Let $P = (K_P, \Delta, \Gamma, \delta_P, p_0, Z_0, F_P)$ be an unambiguous pda with $T(P) = L$. We may assume, by Lemma 14.4, that P makes no moves when in a final state. For each x in L, P accepts x by a unique sequence of moves. We now construct P_1 from P such that $T(P_1) = A^{-1}(T(P))$, and for x in $T(P_1)$, P_1 accepts x by a unique sequence of moves. Observe Fig. 14.1. The finite control of P_1 consists of the gsm A, the finite control of P, and a "storage buffer" of sufficient length to hold any w such that $(p, w) = \delta_A(q, a)$

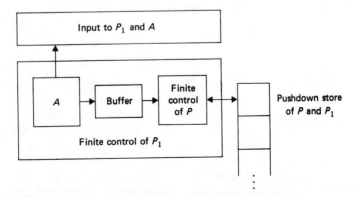

Fig. 14.1. Construction of P_1 from P and A.

for some q in K_A and a in Σ. P_1 operates by passing the input through A and simulating P on the output of A. Since x is accepted by P_1 if and only if $A(x)$ is accepted by P, P_1 accepts $A^{-1}(L)$. By being careful not to introduce unnecessary nondeterminism into P_1, P_1 will accept x by a unique sequence of moves if P accepts x by a unique sequence of moves.

Formally let

$$r = \max \{|w|\,|\,\delta(q, a) = (p, w) \text{ for some } q \text{ and } p \text{ in } K_A \text{ and } a \text{ in } \Sigma\}.$$

Then

$$P_1 = (K, \Sigma, \Gamma, \delta, [q_0, \epsilon, p_0], Z_0, F_1),$$

where K consists of all objects of the form $[q, x, p]$ and $[q, x, \bar{p}]$ such that q is in K_A, p is in K_P, x is in Δ^* with $|x| \leq r$, F_1 contains $[q, \epsilon, p]$ and $[q, \epsilon, \bar{p}]$ for all q in F_A and p in F_P, and δ is defined as follows:

1. For a in Σ, $\delta([q, \epsilon, p], a, Z)$ and $\delta([q, \epsilon, \bar{p}], a, Z)$ each contain $([q_1, x, \bar{p}], Z)$ if $\delta_A(q, a) = (q_1, x)$.
2. For a in Σ, $\delta([q, aw, \bar{p}], \epsilon, Z)$ and $\delta([q, aw, p], \epsilon, Z)$ contain $([q, w, p_1], \gamma)$ when $\delta_P(p, a, Z)$ contains (p_1, γ).
3. $\delta([q, w, p], \epsilon, Z)$ contains $([q, w, p_1], \gamma)$ when $\delta_P(p, \epsilon, Z)$ contains (p_1, γ).

Rule 1 allows P_1 to pass an input symbol through the gsm. The reason for the bar above p in the third component of the next state is to prevent P_1 from next simulating an ϵ move of P. Had we allowed P_1 the possibility of simulating an ϵ move of P immediately after passing a symbol through the gsm, P_1 might be ambiguous, since it could also simulate the ϵ move of P before passing the symbol through the gsm. Rule 2 allows P_1 to take the leftmost symbol from the storage buffer and use it as an input to P. Rule 3 allows P_1 to simulate an ϵ move of P.

It is easily shown that

$$x : ([q_0, \epsilon, p_0], Z_0) \,\Big|\overset{*}{\underset{P_1}{}}\, ([q, \epsilon, p'], \gamma),$$

where $p' = p$ or $\bar{p}$, if and only if

$$\delta_A(q_0, x) = (q, y)$$

for some y in Δ^* such that

$$y : (p_0, Z_0) \,\Big|\overset{*}{\underset{P}{}}\, (p, \gamma).$$

Furthermore, if the sequence of moves by which y takes configuration (p_0, Z_0) to (p, γ) is unique, then the sequence of moves by which x takes configuration $([q_0, \epsilon, p_0], Z_0)$ to $([q, \epsilon, p], \gamma)$ is unique. Thus $T(P_1) = A^{-1}(T(P))$, and P_1 is an unambiguous pda for $A^{-1}(T(P))$.

Before showing that there exist inherently ambiguous cfl's, we prove the following technical lemmas.

Lemma 14.5. Let (N_i, M_i), $1 \leq i \leq r$, be pairs of sets of integers. (The sets may be infinite or finite.) Let

$$S_i = \{(n, m) | n \text{ in } N_i, m \text{ in } M_i\}$$

and let

$$S = S_1 \cup S_2 \cup \cdots \cup S_r.$$

If each pair of integers (n, m) is in S for all n and m, where $n \neq m$, then $\{(n, n) | (n, n) \text{ is not in } S\}$ is finite.

Proof. Assume that for all n and m, where $n \neq m$, each (n, m) is in S, and that $\{(n, n) | (n, n) \text{ not in } S\}$ is infinite. Let J be the set of all n such that (n, n) is not in S. We construct a sequence of sets $J_r, J_{r-1}, \ldots, J_1$ such that $J \supseteq J_r \supseteq J_{r-1} \supseteq \cdots \supseteq J_1$, J_1 will be infinite, and for each n and m in J_i, (n, m) will not be in $S_i \cup S_{i+1} \cup \cdots \cup S_r$.

For n in J, either n is not in N_r or n is not in M_r; otherwise (n, n) would be in S_r. Thus there is an infinite subset of J, call it J_r, such that either, for all n in J_r, n is not in N_r or, for all n in J_r, n is not in M_r. Now for n and m in J_r, (n, m) is not in S_r.

Assume that $J_r, J_{r-1}, \ldots, J_{i+1}$ have been constructed. Then J_i is constructed as follows. For each n in J_{i+1}, either n is not in N_i or not in M_i; otherwise (n, n) would be in S_i. Thus, either an infinite subset of J_{i+1} is not in N_i or an infinite subset of J_{i+1} is not in M_i. In either case, let the infinite subset be J_i. Now for all n and m in J_i, (n, m) is not in S_i and hence not in $S_i \cup S_{i+1} \cup \cdots \cup S_r$.

Since J_1 contains at least two elements, there exist n and m in J_1, $n \neq m$. Now (n, m) is not in $S_1 \cup S_2 \cup \cdots \cup S_r = S$, contradicting the assumption that all (n, m), where $n \neq m$, are in S. Thus $\{(n, n) | (n, n) \text{ not in } S\}$ is finite.

Lemma 14.6. If G is an unambiguous cfg, then we can effectively find an equivalent unambiguous cfg, $G_1 = (V_N, V_T, P, S)$ such that

1. Each variable and each production is used in the derivation of some terminal string.

2. For each A in $V_N - \{S\}$, $A \overset{*}{\Rightarrow} z$ for infinitely many terminal strings z.

3. No production $A \rightarrow B$ is in P, for A and B in V_N.

4. For each A in $V_N - \{S\}$, $A \overset{*}{\Rightarrow} \alpha_1 A \alpha_2$ for some α_1 and α_2, not both ϵ.

Proof. The constructions of Theorems 4.3, 4.4, and 4.9 all produce unambiguous grammars, provided that the original grammars are unambiguous. To obtain a grammar satisfying Condition 4, proceed as follows. If A is in $V_N - \{S\}$ and there is no derivation $A \overset{*}{\Rightarrow} \alpha_1 A \alpha_2$ for any α_1 and α_2, then remove all productions of the form $A \rightarrow \alpha$ and replace those productions with A on the right by all possible productions that can be obtained by substituting, for each occurrence of A in an arbitrary production, any β such that $A \to \beta$ was a production. A is then deleted from the variables. It is easily shown that this procedure preserves unambiguity in the grammar.

Theorem 14.9. The cfl,

$$L = \{a^n b^n c^m d^m | n \geq 1, m \geq 1\} \cup \{a^n b^m c^m d^n | n \geq 1, m \geq 1\},$$

is inherently ambiguous.

Proof. Assume that there is an unambiguous grammar generating L. By Lemma 14.6 we can construct an unambiguous grammar $G = (V_N, V_T, P, S)$ generating L, which has the property that every variable is used in the derivation of some terminal string, and where, for each A in $V_N - \{S\}$, $A \overset{*}{\Rightarrow} x_1 A x_2$ where x_1 and x_2 are in V_T^*, and either x_1 or x_2 is not ϵ.

We note that the grammar G has the following properties:

1. If $A \overset{*}{\Rightarrow} x_1 A x_2$, then x_1 and x_2 each consist of only one type of symbol $(a, b, c, \text{ or } d)$; otherwise

$$S \overset{*}{\Rightarrow} t_1 A t_3 \overset{*}{\Rightarrow} t_1 x_1 x_1 A x_2 x_2 t_3 \overset{*}{\Rightarrow} t_1 x_1 x_1 t_2 x_2 x_2 t_3,$$

for some t_1, t_2, and t_3. This last terminal string is not in L.

2. If $A \overset{*}{\Rightarrow} x_1 A x_2$, then x_1 and x_2 consist of different symbols. Otherwise, in a derivation involving A, we could increase the number of one type of symbol in a sentence of L without increasing the number of any other type of symbol, thereby generating a sentence not in L.

3. If $A \overset{*}{\Rightarrow} x_1 A x_2$, then $|x_1| = |x_2|$. Otherwise we could find words in L having more of one symbol than any other.

4. If $A \overset{*}{\Rightarrow} x_1 A x_2$ and $A \overset{*}{\Rightarrow} x_3 A x_4$, then x_1 and x_3 consist of the same type of symbol. Likewise x_2 and x_4. Otherwise Property 1 above would be violated.

5. If $A \overset{*}{\Rightarrow} x_1 A x_2$, then either:

   a) x_1 consists solely of a's and x_2 solely of b's or of d's,
   b) x_1 consists solely of b's and x_2 solely of c's, or
   c) x_1 consists solely of c's and x_2 solely of d's.

   Thus, the variables other than S can be divided into four classes, C_{ab}, C_{ad}, C_{bc}, and C_{cd}. C_{ab} is the set of all A in V_N such that $A \overset{*}{\Rightarrow} x_1 A x_2$, with x_1 in a^* and x_2 in b^*, C_{ad}, C_{bc}, and C_{cd} are defined analogously.

6. A derivation containing a symbol in C_{ab} or C_{cd} cannot contain a symbol in C_{ad} or C_{bc}, or vice versa. Otherwise, we could increase the number of three types of symbols of a sentence in L without increasing the number of the fourth type of symbol. In that case, there would be a sentence in L for which the number of occurrences of one type of symbol is smaller than that of any other.

We now note that if a derivation contains a variable in C_{ab} or C_{cd}, then the terminal string generated must be in $\{a^n b^n c^m d^m | n \geq 1, m \geq 1\}$. For assume that A in C_{ab} appears in a derivation of a sentence x not in $\{a^n b^n c^m d^m | n \geq 1, m \geq 1\}$. Then x must be of the form $a^n b^m c^m d^n$, $m \neq n$. Since A is in C_{ab}, a sentence $a^{n+p} b^{m+p} c^m d^n$, $m \neq n$ for some $p > 0$, could be generated. Such a sentence is not in L. A similar argument holds for A in C_{cd}. We also note that similar reasoning implies that, if a derivation contains a variable in C_{ad} or C_{bc}, then the sentence generated must be in $\{a^n b^m c^m d^n | n \geq 1, m \geq 1\}$.

We divide G into two grammars:

$$G_1 = (\{S\} \cup C_{ab} \cup C_{cd}, V_T, P_1, S) \quad \text{and} \quad G_2 = (\{S\} \cup C_{ad} \cup C_{bc}, V_T, P_2, S),$$

where P_1 contains all productions of P with a variable from C_{ab} or C_{cd} on either the right or left and P_2 contains all productions of P with a variable from C_{ad} or C_{bc} on either the right or left. In addition, P_1 contains all productions from P of the form $S \to a^n b^n c^m d^m$, $n \neq m$, and P_2 contains all productions from P of the form $S \to a^n b^m c^m d^n$, $n \neq m$. Productions of P of the form $S \to a^n b^n c^n d^n$ are not in either P_1 or P_2.

Since G generates

$$\{a^n b^n c^m d^m | n \geq 1, m \geq 1\} \cup \{a^n b^m c^m d^n | n \geq 1, m \geq 1\},$$

G_1 must generate all sentences in

$$\{a^n b^n c^m d^m | n \geq 1, m \geq 1, n \neq m\}$$

plus possibly some sentences in $\{a^n b^n c^n d^n | n \geq 1\}$, and G_2 must generate all sentences in

$$\{a^n b^m c^m d^n | n \geq 1, m \geq 1, n \neq m\}$$

plus possibly some sentences in $\{a^n b^n c^n d^n | n \geq 1\}$. We now show that this cannot be the case unless G_1 and G_2 both generate all but a finite number of sentences in $\{a^n b^n c^n d^n | n \geq 1\}$. Thus all but a finite number of sentences in $\{a^n b^n c^n d^n | n \geq 1\}$ are generated by both G_1 and G_2 and hence by two distinct derivations in G. This contradicts the assumption that G was unambiguous.

To see that G_1 and G_2 generate all but a finite number of sentences in $\{a^n b^n c^n d^n | n \geq 0\}$, number the productions in P_1 of the form $S \to \alpha$ from 1 to r. For $1 \leq i \leq r$, if $S \to \alpha$ is the ith production, let N_i be the set of all n such that

$$S \underset{G_1}{\Rightarrow} \alpha \underset{G_1}{\overset{*}{\Rightarrow}} a^n b^n c^m d^m$$

for some m, and let M_i be the set of all m such that

$$S \underset{G_1}{\Rightarrow} \alpha \underset{G_1}{\overset{*}{\Rightarrow}} a^n b^n c^m d^m$$

for some n.

We leave it to the reader to show that, for any n in N_i and any m in M_i,

$$S \underset{G_1}{\Rightarrow} \alpha \underset{G_1}{\overset{*}{\Rightarrow}} a^n b^n c^m d^m.$$

(*Hint.* Recall that the variables of α are in C_{ab} or C_{cd}.) It follows immediately from Lemma 14.5 that G_1 must generate all but a finite number of sentences in $\{a^n b^n c^n d^n | n \geq 1\}$.

A similar argument applies to G_2. The reader can easily show that G_2 is a linear grammar. We number certain productions and pairs of productions in a single ordering. Productions of the form $S \rightarrow \alpha_1 B \alpha_2$, where B is in C_{bc}, will receive a number, and, if this number is i, let N_i be the set of all n such that, for some m,

$$S \Rightarrow \alpha_1 B \alpha_2 \overset{*}{\Rightarrow} a^n b^m c^m d^n.$$

Also let M_i be the set of m such that, for some n,

$$S \Rightarrow \alpha_1 B \alpha_2 \overset{*}{\Rightarrow} a^n b^m c^m d^n.$$

The pair of productions $S \rightarrow \alpha$ and $A \rightarrow \alpha_1 B \alpha_2$ will receive a number if α contains a variable in C_{ad}, A is in C_{ad}, and B is in C_{bc}. If this pair is assigned the number i, then define N_i to be the set of n such that, for some m,

$$S \Rightarrow \alpha \overset{*}{\Rightarrow} x_1 A x_2 \Rightarrow x_1 \alpha_1 B \alpha_2 x_2 \overset{*}{\Rightarrow} a^n b^m c^m d^n.$$

Also define M_i to be the set of m such that for some n,

$$S \Rightarrow \alpha \overset{*}{\Rightarrow} x_1 A x_2 \Rightarrow x_1 \alpha_1 B \alpha_2 x_2 \overset{*}{\Rightarrow} a^n b^m c^m d^n.$$

Once again, for any n in N_i and m in M_i,

$$S \underset{G_2}{\overset{*}{\Rightarrow}} a^n b^m c^m d^n,$$

and thus it follows from Lemma 14.5 that G_2 generates all but a finite number of sentences in $\{a^n b^n c^n d^n | n \geq 1\}$. We conclude that, for some n, $a^n b^n c^n d^n$ is in both $L(G_1)$ and $L(G_2)$. This sentence has two leftmost derivations in G.

Combining Theorems 14.8 and 14.9, we now show that it is recursively unsolvable to determine if an arbitrary cfg generates an inherently ambiguous cfl.

Theorem 14.10. It is unsolvable whether a cfg G generates an inherently ambiguous context-free language.

Proof. Let $w_1, w_2, \ldots, w_k$ and $x_1, x_2, \ldots, x_k$ be two lists of words over some alphabet Σ. Let $a_1, a_2, \ldots, a_k$ and c be new symbols. Let

$$S_{AB} = \{ w_{j_1} w_{j_2} \ldots w_{j_m} a_{j_m} a_{j_{m-1}} \ldots a_{j_1} c a_{i_1} a_{i_2} \ldots a_{i_n} x_{i_n}^R x_{i_{n-1}}^R \ldots x_{i_1}^R \}$$

and let

$$R_{AB} = \{wcw^R | w \text{ is in } \Sigma^* \{a_1, a_2, \ldots, a_k\}^*\},$$

as before. S_{AB} and R_{AB} can be generated by unambiguous cfg's and thus, $S_{AB} \cup R_{AB}$ can be generated by an unambiguous cfg, provided that $S_{AB} \cap R_{AB}$ is empty. We show that $S_{AB} \cup R_{AB}$ in an inherently ambiguous cfl whenever $S_{AB} \cap R_{AB}$ is not empty. Since it is unsolvable (for S_{AB} and R_{AB} obtained from arbitrary lists) whether $S_{AB} \cap R_{AB}$ is empty, it is unsolvable whether $S_{AB} \cup R_{AB}$ is inherently ambiguous.

Assume that $S_{AB} \cap R_{AB}$ is nonempty. Let

$$w_{j_1}w_{j_2}\ldots w_{j_m}a_{j_m}a_{j_m-1}\ldots a_{j_1}ca_{j_1}a_{j_2}\ldots a_{j_m}x^R_{j_m}x^R_{j_m-1}\ldots x^R_{j_1}$$

be in $S_{AB} \cap R_{AB}$. Let

$$u = w_{j_1}w_{j_2}\ldots w_{j_m} = x_{j_1}x_{j_2}\ldots x_{j_m}$$

and

$$v = a_{j_m}a_{j_m-1}\ldots a_{j_1}.$$

Now

$$(S_{AB} \cup R_{AB}) \cap u^*v^*c(u^R)^*(v^R)^* = \{u^nv^mc(v^R)^m(u^R)^n | n, m \geq 1\} \cup$$
$$\{u^nv^nc(v^R)^m(u^R)^m | n, m \geq 1\}.$$

Let this language be L_1. It is easy to construct a deterministic gsm A mapping a to u, b to v, c to v^R, d to u^R, and inserting one c before the first v^R. Then

$$A^{-1}(S_{AB} \cup R_{AB}) = A^{-1}(L_1) = \{a^nb^nc^md^m | n, m \geq 1\} \cup \{a^nb^mc^md^n | n, m \geq 1\}.$$

If $S_{AB} \cup R_{AB}$ were generated by an unambiguous cfg, then (by Theorem 14.8)

$$\{a^nb^nc^md^m | n, m \geq 1\} \cup \{a^nb^mc^md^n | n, m \geq 1\}$$

could be generated by an unambiguous cfg, contradicting Theorem 14.9. Thus, $S_{AB} \cup R_{AB}$ must be inherently ambiguous whenever $S_{AB} \cap R_{AB} \neq \varphi$. Since it is unsolvable whether $S_{AB} \cap R_{AB} = \varphi$, it is unsolvable whether an arbitrary cfg generates an inherently ambiguous language.

14.6 UNSOLVABLE QUESTIONS CONCERNING DETERMINISTIC CONTEXT-FREE LANGUAGES

Several questions that are unsolvable for context-free languages in general are solvable for deterministic languages. Among them are: (where L is a deterministic language and R is a regular set.)

1. Is L inherently ambiguous? (By Theorems 12.6 and 12.9, L is not inherently ambiguous.)
2. Is $L = R$? ($L = R$ if and only if $L_1 = (L \cap \bar{R}) \cup (\bar{L} \cap R)$ is empty. L_1 is context free by Theorems 9.1, 12.1, and 12.2.)

3. Is L regular? (This is a difficult theorem. A proof can be found in the literature.)
4. Is $\bar{L} = \varphi$?
5. Is $\bar{L}$ context free? (It always is, by Theorem 12.1.)
6. Is $L \supseteq R$? ($L \supseteq R$ if and only if $R \cap \bar{L} = \varphi$. $R \cap \bar{L}$ is a deterministic cfl.)

In addition, it is an unresolved question whether it is solvable to determine if two deterministic pda accept the same language.

Note that, for lists A and B, the languages L_A, L_B, R_{AB}, and S_{AB} are deterministic cfl's. Thus, we immediately have the following:

Theorem 14.11. It is unsolvable to determine, for languages L_1 and L_2 accepted by dpda, whether:

1. $L_1 \cap L_2 = \varphi$.   2. $L_1 \cap L_2$ is context free.
3. $L_1 \cup L_2$ is deterministic.   4. $L_1 \subseteq L_2$.

Question	Regular	LR(k) (deterministic)	Context free	Context sensitive	Type 0
Is $L(G)$ empty? finite? infinite?	S	S	S	U	U
Does $L(G) = \Sigma^*$?	S	S	U	U	U
Is $L(G_1) = L(G_2)$?	S	?	U	U	U
Is $L(G_1) \subseteq L(G_2)$?	S	U	U	U	U
Is $L(G_1) \cap L(G_2)$ empty? finite? infinite?	S	U	U	U	U
Does $L(G) = R$, R a specific regular set?	S	S	U	U	U
Is $L(G)$ a regular set?	T	S	U	U	U
Is the intersection of two languages a language of the same type?	T	U	U	T	T
Is the complement of a language a language of the same type?	T	T	U	?	U
Is the concatenation of two languages a language of the same type?	T	U	T	T	T
Is the union of two languages a language of the same type?	T	U	T	T	T

Fig. 14.2. Summary of decision problems for regular, $LR(k)$, context-free, context-sensitive, and type 0 grammars. S means solvable, U means unsolvable, T means that the question is trivial, and ? means that the answer is unknown.

Proof. (1) and (2) follow as Theorems 14.3 and 14.6.

3. Let $L_1 = \bar{R}_{AB}$ and $L_2 = \bar{S}_{AB}$. Then $L_1 \cup L_2 = L_{AB}$. Now L_{AB} is deterministic if and only if it consists of all strings in its terminal vocabulary. Thus L_{AB} is deterministic if and only if PCP with lists A and B has no solution.

4. Let $L_1 = S_{AB}$ and $L_2 = \bar{R}_{AB}$. $L_1 \subseteq L_2$ if and only if $L_1 \cap \bar{L}_2 = \varphi$. But $L_1 \cap \bar{L}_2 = S_{AB} \cap R_{AB}$ and $S_{AB} \cap R_{AB} = \varphi$ if and only if PCP with lists A and B has no solution.

14.7 SUMMARY OF UNSOLVABILITY RESULTS FOR REGULAR, *LR(k)*, CONTEXT-FREE, CONTEXT-SENSITIVE, AND TYPE 0 GRAMMARS

We summarize the unsolvability results for the different classes of grammars in Fig. 14.2.

PROBLEMS

14.1 Does PCP with lists:

i	A	B
1	10	101
2	10	010
3	011	11
4	101	011

have a solution?

14.2 Is PCP solvable if the strings of each list are over a one-symbol alphabet?

14.3 Show that it is solvable whether an instance of PCP with lists of exactly k strings has a solution for:

a) $k = 1$
b) $k = 2$
c) $k = 3$

14.4 Show that, for some k_0, it is unsolvable whether an instance of PCP with exactly k_0 strings in each list has a solution.

14.5 Show that it is unsolvable whether a given context-sensitive language is context free.

14.6 Show that it is unsolvable whether L_1L_2 is a deterministic cfl for deterministic cfl's L_1 and L_2.

14.7 A pda is *simple* if it is deterministic, has one state, and never makes a move on ϵ input. Show that it is solvable whether $N(P_1) = N(P_2)$, for simple pda's, P_1 and P_2.

14.8 Show that the emptiness problem is solvable for one-way nondeterministic stack automata.

14.9 Show that the emptiness problem is unsolvable for:

a) Deterministic Turing machines of tape complexity log log n.

b) Deterministic Turing machines of time complexity n.

14.10 For arbitrary cfg G and regular set R, show that it is solvable whether $L(G) \subseteq R$.

14.11 For arbitrary csg G, show that the following questions are unsolvable:

a) Is a given production of G ever used in the derivation of a terminal string?

b) Given strings β_1 and β_2, do there exist strings α_1 and α_2 such that $\beta_1 \xrightarrow[G]{*} \alpha_1\beta_2\alpha_2$.

14.12 Show that it is unsolvable whether a given cfg generates a deterministic language.

REFERENCES

The unsolvability of Post's correspondence problem was shown in Post [1946]. For an easy, alternative proof of PCP see Floyd [1964b]. Most of the unsolvability results can also be obtained from the fact that calculations of a given Turing machine can be identified with the intersection of two context-free languages (Hartmanis [1967a]).   The elementary unsolvable questions for context-free languages appeared in Bar-Hillel, Perles, and Shamir [1961].   Additional results concerning context-free languages appear in Ginsburg and Rose [1963a]. Theorem 14.7, which concerns the unsolvability of ambiguity of a cfg, was shown independently in Cantor [1962], Floyd [1962a], and Chomsky and Schutzenberger [1963]. Theorem 14.10, dealing with the unsolvability of inherent ambiguity, was shown in Ginsburg and Ullian [1966].   Theorem 14.11 is from Ginsburg and Greibach [1966a].

Many of the fundamental works on particular classes of languages include information as to whether certain common questions are solvable or unsolvable. Material on solvability for subfamilies of the context-free languages is abundant. For unsolvability of questions concerning linear languages, see Greibach [1963], Gross [1964], and Greibach [1966]. For sequential languages, see Ginsburg and Rose [1963a].   Many questions that are unsolvable for cfl's are solvable for bounded languages (Ginsburg and Spanier [1964]). In particular, it is solvable if $L(G_1) = L(G_2)$ if $L(G_1)$ is bounded and G_2 is an arbitrary cfg. The equivalence question has also been shown to be solvable for the simple deterministic languages by Korenjak and Hopcroft [1966], and, for parenthesis languages, by McNaughton [1967], Knuth [1967], and Paull and Unger [1967].

Recently, some results have appeared, relating the solvability and unsolvability of questions concerning any given class of languages. See Greibach [1967], Hartmanis [1967b], and Hopcroft and Ullman [1968a].

BIBLIOGRAPHY

AHO, A. V., J. E. HOPCROFT, and J. D. ULLMAN, [1968]. "On the computational power of pushdown store systems," *Inf. and Control*, to appear.

AXT, P., [1959]. "On a subrecursive hierarchy and primitive recursive degrees," *Transactions of American Mathematical Society*, **92**, 85–105.

BAR-HILLEL, Y., Y. GAIFMAN, and E. SHAMIR, [1960]. "On categorical and phrase structure grammars," *Bull. Res. Council Israel*, **9F**, 1–16.

BAR-HILLEL, Y., M. PERLES, and E. SHAMIR, [1961]. "On formal properties of simple phrase structure grammars," *Z. Phonetik, Sprachwiss. Kommunikationsforsch.*, **14**, 143–172.

BLUM, M., [1964]. *A machine-independent theory of recursive functions*, Doctoral Thesis, MIT, Cambridge, Mass. Also see *JACM*, **14**:2, 322–336.

BOOTH, T. L., [1967]. *Sequential Machines and Automata Theory*, Wiley, New York.

BRZOZOWSKI, J., [1962]. "A survey of regular expressions and their applications," *PGEC*, **11**:3, 324–335.

CANTOR, D. C., [1962]. "On the ambiguity problem of Backus systems," *JACM*, **9**:4, 477–479.

CHOMSKY, N., [1956]. "Three models for the description of language," *PGIT*, **2**:3, 113–124.

———, [1959]. "On certain formal properties of grammars," *Inf. and Control*, **2**:2, 137–167.

———, [1962]. "Context-free grammars and pushdown storage," *Quart. Prog. Dept. No. 65*, MIT Res. Lab. Elect., 187–194.

———, [1963]. "Formal properties of grammars," *Handbook of Math. Psych.*, **2**, Wiley, New York, pp. 323–418.

CHOMSKY, N., and G. A. MILLER, [1958]. "Finite state languages," *Inf. and Control*, **1**:2, 91–112.

CHOMSKY, N., and M. P. SCHUTZENBERGER, [1963]. "The algebraic theory of context-free languages," *Computer Programming and Formal Systems*, North Holland, Amsterdam, pp. 118–161.

COLE, S. N., [1964]. *Real-time computation by iterative arrays of finite-state machines*, Doctoral Thesis, Harvard University, Cambridge, Mass. Also see *IEEE Conference Record of Seventh Annual Symposium on Switching and Automata Theory*, Berkeley, Calif., pp. 53–77.

CHURCH, A., [1936]. "An unsolvable problem of elementary number theory," *Amer. J. Math.*, **58**, 345–363.

DAVIS, M., [1958]. *Computability and Unsolvability*, McGraw-Hill, New York.

EVEY, J., [1963]. *The theory and application of pushdown store machines*, Doctoral Thesis, Harvard University, Cambridge, Mass.

FISCHER, P. C., [1963]. "On computability by certain classes of restricted Turing machines," *Proceedings Fourth Annual Symposium on Switching Circuit Theory and Logical Design*, Chicago, Ill. 23–32.

———, [1965]. "Multitape and infinite state automata—a survey," *CACM*, **8**:12, 799–805.

———, [1966]. "Turing machines with restricted memory access," *Inf. and Control*, **9**:4, 364–379.

FLOYD, R. W., [1962a]. "On ambiguity in phrase structure languages," *CACM*, **5**:10, 526–534.

———, [1962b]. "On the nonexistence of a phrase structure grammar for ALGOL 60," *CACM*, **5**:9, 483–484.

———, [1963]. "Syntactic analysis and operator precedence," *JACM*, **10**:3, 316–333.

———, [1964a]. "Bounded context syntactic analysis," *CACM*, **7**:2, 62–67.

———, [1964b]. "New proofs and old theorems in logic and formal linguistics," Computer Associates Inc., Wakefield, Mass.

———, [1964c]. "The syntax of programming languages—a survey," *PGEC*, **13**:4, 346–353.

GILL, A., [1962]. *Introduction to the Theory of Finite-state Machines*, McGraw-Hill, New York.

GINSBURG, S., [1962]. *An Introduction to Mathematical Machine Theory*, Addison-Wesley, Reading, Mass.

———, [1966]. *The Mathematical Theory of Context-Free Languages*, McGraw-Hill, New York.

GINSBURG, S., and S. A. GREIBACH, [1966a]. "Deterministic context-free languages," *Inf. and Control*, **9**:6, 620–648.

———, [1966b]. "Mappings which preserve context-sensitive languages," *Inf. and Control*, **9**:6, 563–582.

———, [1967]. "Abstract families of languages," *IEEE Conference Record of Eighth Annual Symposium on Switching and Automata Theory*, Austin, Texas.

GINSBURG, S., S. A. GREIBACH, and M. A. HARRISON, [1967a]. "Stack automata and compiling," *JACM*, **14**:1, 172–201.

———, [1967b]. "One-way stack automata," *JACM*, **14**:2, 389–418.

GINSBURG, S., S. A. GREIBACH, and J. E. HOPCROFT, [1967]. *Pre-AFL*, SDC Document TM 738/037/00.

GINSBURG, S., and J. E. HOPCROFT, [1968]. *Two-way balloon automata and AFL's*, SDC Document TM 738/042/00.

GINSBURG, S., and H. G. RICE, [1962]. "Two families of languages related to ALGOL," *JACM*, **9**:3, 350–371.

GINSBURG, S., and G. F. ROSE, [1963a]. "Some recursively unsolvable problems in ALGOL-like languages," *JACM*, **10**:1, 29–47.

——, [1963b]. "Operations which preserve definability in languages," *JACM*, **10**:2, 175–195.

——, [1966]. "Preservation of languages by transducers, *Inf. and Control*, **9**, 153–176.

GINSBURG, S., and E. H. SPANIER, [1963]. "Quotients of context-free languages," *JACM*, **10**:4, 487–492.

——, [1964]. "Bounded ALGOL-like languages," *Trans. Amer. Math. Soc.*, **113**, 333–368.

——, [1967]. *Control sets on grammars*, SDC Document 738/036/00.

GINSBURG, S., and J. ULLIAN, [1966]. "Ambiguity in context-free languages," *JACM*, **13**:1, 62–88.

GRAY, J. N., M. A. HARRISON, and O. IBARRA, [1967]. "Two-way pushdown automata," *Inf. and Control*, **11**:1–2, 30–70.

GREIBACH, S. A., [1963]. "The undecidability of the ambiguity problem for minimal linear grammars," *Inf. and Control*, **6**:2, 117–125.

——, [1965]. "A new normal form theorem for context-free phrase structure grammars," *JACM*, **12**:1, 42–52.

——, [1966]. "The unsolvability of the recognition of linear context-free languages," *JACM*, **13**:4, 582–587.

——, [1967]. *A note on undecidable properties of formal languages*, SDC Document TM 738/038/00.

——, [1968]. *Checking Automata and One-Way Stack Languages*, SDC Document TM 738/045/00.

GREIBACH, S. A., and J. E. HOPCROFT, [1967]. *Independence of AFL operations*, SDC Document TM 738/034/00.

GROSS, M., [1964]. "Inherent ambiguity of minimal linear grammars," *Inf. and Control*, **7**:3, 366–368.

GRZEGORCZYK, A., [1953]. "Some classes of recursive functions," *Rosprawy matematyczne*, **4**, Instytut Matematyczne Polskiej Akademie Nauk, Warsaw.

HAINES, L. H., [1964]. "Note on the complement of a (minimal) linear language," *Inf. and Control*, **7**:3, 307–314.

——, [1965]. *Generation and recognition of formal languages*, Doctoral Thesis, MIT, Cambridge, Massachusetts.

HARRISON, M. A., [1965]. *Introduction to Switching and Automata Theory*, McGraw-Hill, New York.

HARTMANIS, J., [1967a]. "Context-free languages and Turing machine computations," *Proceedings of Symposia in Applied Mathematics*, **19**, American Mathematical Society, Providence, Rhode Island.

———, [1967b]. "On the complexity of undecidable problems in automata theory," *IEEE Conference Record of Eighth Annual Symposium on Switching and Automata Theory*, Austin, Texas, 112–116.

HARTMANIS, J., P. M. LEWIS II, and R. E. STEARNS, [1965]. "Hierarchies of memory limited computations," *IEEE Conference Record on Switching Circuit Theory and Logical Design*, Ann Arbor, Michigan, 179–190.

HARTMANIS, J., and R. E. STEARNS, [1964]. "Computational complexity of recursive sequences," *Proceedings of the Fifth Annual Symposium on Switching Circuit Theory and Logical Design*, Princeton, New Jersey, 82–90.

———, [1965]. "On the computational complexity of algorithms," *Trans. Amer. Math. Soc.*, **117**, 285–306.

HENNIE, F. C., [1965]. "One-tape, off-line Turing machine computations," *Inf. and Control*, **8**:6, 553–578.

HENNIE, F. C., and R. E. STEARNS, [1966]. "Two-tape simulation of multitape Turing machines," *JACM*, **13**:4, 533–546.

HOPCROFT, J. E., and J. D. ULLMAN, [1967a]. "Nonerasing stack automata," *JCSS*, **1**:2, 166–186.

———, [1967b]. "An approach to a unified theory of automata," *Bell System Technical Journal*, **46**:8, 1763–1829.

———, [1968a]. "Decidable and undecidable questions about automata," *JACM*, **15**:2, 317–324.

———, [1968b]. "Deterministic stack automata and the quotient operator," *JCSS*, **2**:1, 1–12.

———, [1968c]. "Sets accepted by one-way stack automata are context sensitive," *Inf. and Control*, to appear. Also, "Two results on one-way stack automata," *IEEE Conference Record of Eighth Annual Symposium on Switching and Automata Theory*, Austin, Texas.

———, [1968d]. "Some results on tape bounded Turing machines," *JACM*, to appear.

HUFFMAN, D. A., [1954]. "The synthesis of sequential switching circuits," *Journal of the Franklin Institute*, **257**:3–4, 161–190 and 275–303.

IRONS, E. T., [1961]. "A syntax directed compiler for ALGOL 60," *CACM*, **4**:1, 51–55.

KLEENE, S. C., [1936]. "General recursive functions of natural numbers," *Mathematische Annalen*, **112**, 727–742.

———, [1952]. *Introduction to Metamathematics*, D. Van Nostrand, Princeton, New Jersey.

———, [1956]. "Representation of events in nerve nets and finite automata," *Automata Studies*, Princeton Univ. Press, Princeton, New Jersey, pp. 3–42.

KNUTH, D. E., [1965]. "On the translation of languages from left to right," *Inf. and Control*, **8**:6, 607–639.

———, [1967]. "A characterization of parenthesis languages," *Inf. and Control*, **11**:3, 269–289.

KNUTH, D. E., and R. BIGELOW, [1967]. "Programming languages for automata," *JACM*, **14**:4, 615–635.

KORENJAK, A. J., and J. E. HOPCROFT, [1966]. "Simple deterministic languages," *IEEE Conference Record of Seventh Annual Symposium on Switching and Automata Theory*, Berkeley, California, 36–46.

KURODA, S. Y., [1964]. "Classes of languages and linear-bounded automata," *Inf. and Control*, **7**:2, 207–223.

LANDWEBER, P. S., [1963]. "Three theorems on phrase structure grammars of type 1," *Inf. and Control*, **6**:2, 131–136.

———, [1964]. "Decision problems of phrase structure grammars," *PGEC*, **13**:4, 354–362.

LEWIS, P. M., and R. E. STEARNS, [1966]. "Syntax directed transduction," *IEEE Conference Record of Seventh Annual Symposium on Switching and Automata Theory*, Berkeley,California, 21–35.

LEWIS, P. M., R. E. STEARNS, and J. HARTMANIS, [1965]. "Memory bounds for recognition of context-free and context-sensitive languages," *IEEE Conference Record on Switching Circuit Theory and Logical Design*, Ann Arbor, Michigan, 191–202.

MCCULLOCH, W. S., and W. PITTS, [1943]. "A logical calculus of the ideas immanent in nervous activity," *Bull. Math. Biophysics*, **5**, 115–133.

MCNAUGHTON, R., [1967]. "Parenthesis grammars," *JACM*, **14**:3, 490–500.

MCNAUGHTON, R., and H. YAMADA, [1960]. "Regular expressions and state graphs for automata," *PGEC*, **9**:1, 39–47.

MINSKY, M. L., [1961]. "Recursive unsolvability of Post's problem of 'Tag' and other topics in the theory of Turing machines," *Annals of Math.*, **74**:3, 437–455.

———, [1967]. *Computation: Finite and Infinite Machines*, Prentice-Hall, Englewood Cliffs, New Jersey.

MOORE, E. F., [1956]. "Gedanken experiments on sequential machines," *Automata Studies*, Princeton Univ. Press, Princeton, New Jersey, pp. 129–153.

MYHILL, J., [1960]. "Linear bounded automata," *WADD Tech. Note*, 60–165, Wright Patterson Air Force Base, Ohio.

NERODE, A., [1958]. "Linear automaton transformations," *Proc. Amer. Math. Soc.*, **9**, 541–544.

OETTINGER, A. G., [1961]. "Automatic syntactic analysis and the pushdown store," *Proc. Symp. Applied Math.*, **12**, American Mathematical Society, Providence, Rhode Island.

PARIKH, R. J., [1961]. "Language generating devices," *Quart. Prog. Rept.*, **60**, MIT Res. Lab. Elect., 199–212. Reprinted as "On context-free languages," *JACM*, **13**:4, 570–581.

PAULL, M., and S. H. UNGER, [1967]. "Structural equivalence of context-free grammars," *IEEE Conference Record of Eighth Annual Symposium on Switching and Automata Theory*, Austin, Texas, 7–13.

POST, E., [1936]. "Finite combinatory processes—formulation, I," *The Journal of Symbolic Logic*, **1**, 103–105.

———, [1946]. A variant of a recursively unsolvable problem, *Bull. Am. Math. Soc.*, **52**, 264–268.

RABIN, M. O., [1963]. "Real-time computation," *Israel J. Math.*, **1**:4, 203–211.

RABIN, M. O., and D. SCOTT, [1959]. "Finite automata and their decision problems," *IBM. J. Res.*, **3**:2, 115–125. Also in *Sequential Machines: Selected Papers*, E. F. Moore, ed., Addison-Wesley, Reading, Mass., 1964, pp. 63–91.

RITCHIE, R. W., [1963]. "Classes of predictably computable functions," *Transactions of the American Mathematical Society*, **106**, 139–173.

ROGERS, H., [1967]. *The Theory of Recursive Functions and Effective Computability*, McGraw-Hill, New York.

ROSENKRANTZ, D. J., [1967]. "Matrix equations and normal forms for context-free grammars," *JACM*, **14**:3, 501–507.

SAMELSON, K., and F. L. BAUER, [1960]. "Sequential formula translation," *CACM*, **3**:2, 76–82.

SCHEINBERG, S., [1960]. "Note on the Boolean properties of context-free languages," *Inf. and Control*, **3**:4, 372–375.

SCHUTZENBERGER, M. P., [1963]. "On context-free languages and pushdown automata," *Inf. and Control*, **6**:3, 246–264.

SHAMIR, E., [1965]. "On sequential languages," *Z. Phonetik, Sprachwiss. Kommunikationsforsch.*, **18**, 61–69.

SHANNON, C. E., [1956]. "A universal Turing machine with two internal states," *Automata Studies*, Princeton Univ. Press, Princeton, N.J., pp. 129–153.

SHEPHERDSON, J. C., [1959]. "The reduction of two-way automata to one-way automata," *IBM. J. Res.*, **3**, 198–200.

STANLEY, R. J., [1965]. "Finite state representations of context-free languages," *Quart. Prog. Rept.*, **76**, MIT Res. Lab. Elect., 276–279.

STEARNS, R. E., [1967]. "A regularity test for pushdown machines," *Inf. and Control*, **11**:3, 323–340.

TURING, A. M., [1936]. "On computable numbers with an application to the Entscheidungsproblem," *Proc. London Math. Soc.*, **2**–**42**, 230–265. A correction, *ibid.*, **43**, 544–546.

ULLMAN, J. D., [1968]. *Halting stack automata*, unpublished manuscript.

WANG, H., [1957]. "A variant to Turing's theory of computing machines," *JACM*, **4**:1, 63–92.

YAMADA, H., [1962]. "Real-time computation and recursive functions not real-time computable," *PGEC*, **11**:6, 753–760.

YOUNGER, D. H., [1967]. "Recognition and parsing of context-free languages in time n^3," *Inf. and Control*, **10**:2, 189–208.

INDEX